The Birds
of
Hungary

DAVE!
HOPE YOU
ENJOYED
YOUR MAGYAR
BIRDS.

GERARD
AUG. 2004.

The Birds
of
Hungary

Gerard Gorman

CHRISTOPHER HELM

A & C Black • London

For Dominic and Martin,

to whom even birds take second place

© Text and maps 1996 Gerard Gorman
Line drawings by John Davis

Christopher Helm (Publishers) Ltd, a subsidiary of A & C Black
(Publishers) Ltd, 35 Bedford Row, London WC1R 4JH

0-7136-4235-1

A CIP catalogue record for this book is available
from the British Library

Printed and bound by Biddles Ltd, Guildford, Surrey in Great Britain

CONTENTS

INTRODUCTION

Whichever way one looks at it, Hungary is an important place for birds. The country's populations of Great White Egret, Spoonbill, Imperial Eagle, Red-footed Falcon, Saker, Great Bustard and Aquatic Warbler, to name just a few species, are some of the most important in Europe. My aim in writing this book was quite simply to present and review the birdlife of the country which has been my home for the last ten years. Not only the rare, enigmatic or typical birds, but all the species which have ever occurred in the territory covered by today's Hungary are included. The book is aimed at both the ornithologist and the birdwatcher, and it is hoped that the information included and way it is presented satisfies both.

As I write, 363 bird species have been officially recorded in Hungary. Of these, around 200 can be regarded as regular breeders, that is, they breed every year. Approximately 75 species are regular non-breeding visitors, which for the purposes of this book I define as those species which occur on passage or in winter every year. As one would expect, the complete list of Hungarian birds is growing. New species are recorded every year and this is in part owing to a recent increase in birdwatching as a hobby among young people, many of whom now use quality optical equipment and read international ornithological and birding literature. There are now more local - and foreign - birders in the field in Hungary than ever before.

There are many outstanding bird habitats in Hungary. Perhaps the most famous is the Hortobágy, one of Europe's most important ornithological areas. Here, in summer, a phenomenal range of breeding birds is present; in autumn over 50,000 Common Cranes regularly stop over, and parties of Lesser White-fronted geese are annual. And there are, of course, other places. The Kiskunság is a vast region with wooded sandy grassland, dry alkaline *puszta* and salt lakes, with breeding Red-footed Falcons, Rollers, Lesser Grey Shrikes and thousands of waders and geese on passage. Alhough it lacks high mountains, Hungary has various hill ranges which all host rich avifaunas including rare birds of prey.

High profile bird species such as Imperial Eagle, Saker, Great Bustard and White Stork have been extensively studied and surveyed in Hungary. Other species are monitored in certain areas by local ornithologists but remain unstudied elsewhere in the country. Many species have been little studied, however, and thus, despite a rich ornithological tradition, large gaps in the overall knowledge of Hungary's birds remain. This has presented problems in producing nationwide status accounts and maps for some of the species in this book. I have endeavoured to be as comprehensive as possible, basing population estimates and the range maps on the available literature, on conversations and consultations with local ornithologists, and on my own observations over the last ten years. One only has to glance at the distribution maps in most of the popular European field-guides to see that for some species whole areas at the heart of Europe appear blank; yet these are species which do actually occur in the region. Winter ranges in particular are often absent or insufficiently covered. Such birds as Black-throated Diver, Velvet and Common Scoters and Scaup all regularly pass along or winter on the Danube and other Hungarian wetlands, but are often not shown on distribution maps. This is partly owing to the relative lack of data and the fact that much of the data that does exist is out of reach to most non-Hungarian authors owing to the language barrier (naturally, most local literature is in Hungarian). Hopefully the range maps and other information in this book will contribute to a more complete placing of Hungary's avifauna on the European ornithological map. In particular, I will have succeeded in my aim if this book proves to be a useful reference for the authors of future European and Palearctic works to what is one of the continent's most ornithologically important countries.

Gerard Gorman, Budapest, June, 1995.

ACKNOWLEDGEMENTS

Many people have directly and indirectly contributed to the writing of this book. I would like to thank the following who kindly supplied me with their personal data and opinions on particular species.

Gábor Firmánszky (Eagle and Ural Owls), Balázs Forgách (Levant Sparrowhawk), Róbert Horváth (Rock Bunting, Red-breasted Flycatcher, Crested Tit, White-backed Woodpecker, Dipper, Corncrake), Dr Zsolt Kalotás (Barn, Scops and Long-eared Owls, corvids), Dr Gábor Kovács (Great Bustard, Baillon's Crake, Dotterel, White-winged Black Tern, Short-eared Owl, Short-toed Lark, Bluethroat, Aquatic Warbler), Dr Gábor Magyar (divers, skuas, gulls, Cirl and Ortolan Buntings), Dr Tamás Székely (Kentish Plover), Dr Tibor Szép (Corncrake, Sand Martin, Thrush Nightingale).

Special thanks go to József Büki who dug out numerous useful papers and regularly allowed me to disturb him in the library of the Ornithological Institute. Ferenc Márkus kindly supplied me with key data on land-use. For their computer skills, I am indebted to Ákos Janca, Csaba Csikai and Viktor Márta.

The following have also been helpful in various ways over the years: János Bagyura, János Balogh, László Bank, László Bécsy, Tibor Csörgő, László Demeter, Péter Dénes, Imre Fatér, László Fenyvesi, Tibor Fülöp, Jenő Győry, Tibor Hadarics, István Harangi, Béla Kalivoda, László Kárpáti, Levente Kőrösi, Katalin Madas, László Molnár, László Nagy, Gábor Nechay, Sándor Palkó, Attila Pellinger, István Sándor, Egon Schmidt, Ferenc Somogyi, András Soós, Mary and Graham Sparkes, Béla Streit, Antal Széll, György Szimuly, János Tar, László Tirják, Tibor Tömösváry, László Tóth, Lajos Varga, Zsolt Varga, Gábor Vasuta, Ferenc Winkler.

I would particularly like to mention four special friends: Zsolt Kalotás (head of the Hungarian Ornithological Institute) was enthusiastic, supportive and always found the time to answer my numerous queries; Zsolt also commented on drafts of the range maps. The legendary Gábor Kovács willingly imparted his extensive knowledge of the birds and habitats of the Hortobágy and was a steady source of anecdote on long walks across the *puszta*. Gábor Magyar (Secretary of the Hungarian Rarities Committee) was a companion on numerous field trips and a knowledgeable sounding board. Gábor also read a draft of the text on rarities, and was supportive and reliable in many other ways. András Schmidt was always a gentleman, kindly read a draft of the regular species text and made many pertinent comments.

Of course, a book like this can only be written after previously published material has been consulted. Thus, I would also like to acknowledge and thank all those authors whose papers and books appear in the bibliography. I am also grateful to Robert Kirk and the staff at Christopher Helm (Publishers) Ltd for realising the importance of producing such a book in English and taking the idea on board.

FORMAT OF THE BOOK

All the bird species which have been officially accepted as having occurred in Hungary as of 1 January, 1995, are dealt with in this book. The book can be divided into three parts. Firstly, a section of introductory and background information which aims to provide an overall picture of Hungary's avifauna and habitats. Secondly, a systematic section on all regularly occurring species. Thirdly, a systematic section on rare visitors and vagrants.

Species are regarded as regular, whether resident, summer or winter visitors or passage species, if they occur every year. Those species which do not occur in Hungary annually are included in the rare visitors and vagrants section. Some species, such as Lesser Kestrel, Arctic Skua, Great Black-headed Gull, Little Tern and Woodchat Shrike, to mention only a few, fall into a grey area between the above two strict definitions. These species may or may not occur annually or have only recently begun to occur annually. I placed such species in the section I considered most appropriate on the basis of recent trends. Races are usually mentioned only when the regularly occurring subspecies differs from the nominate.

In the individual species texts a short general section is followed by these headings.

Status in Hungary This section aims to condense the status of each species. Thus population size, trends, and protection status are summarised briefly.

Status Internationally A detailed description of the international status of each species is beyond the scope of this book. Other works deal in more depth with the global status of the birds included here. The aim of this section is to provide a brief comparison of the global situation of each species with that of its status in Hungary.

Distribution This refers to the range of the species within Hungary. This information, and the range maps which follow, have been based upon the available literature and actual sightings, and thus their accuracy has been dependent upon the number of reliable and active birders and ornithologists in the country. When relevant, certain regions or exact sites are mentioned. This section is not intended as a 'where to watch' guide, thus exact locations are not described.

Timing Indicates the most regular or likely periods of occurrence.

Range Map For the first time ever, every species which has occurred in Hungary has a range map. Although every effort has been made to make them as accurate as possible, the maps are intended only as a guide as they are small scale and there is a general lack of precise distribution data for many species. In most cases, only the dominant status range is marked to avoid over-complication. For example, in the cases of Wood and Willow Warblers the main summer (breeding) areas are marked with lowland *puszta* areas left blank, though these species do occur there on passage. Of course nomadic and migratory species occur outside and between the indicated ranges. Within the areas marked, a species may be widespread, scattered or locally distributed depending on various factors such as habitat and season. The reader is advised to refer to the text for more detail. Some areas are indicated with a question mark to denote that confirmation of status is required. For obvious reasons, the maps for certain rare and vulnerable species are deliberately general.

Abundancy

Throughout the book such terms as *common, fairly common, uncommon, rare, very rare* etc., have been used. These are general terms and intended only as a guide. They do not correspond to exact figures as there is insufficient population data for many species. A certain amount of reader knowledge is presumed in interpreting these terms. For example, though Robin and

Marsh Harrier are both described as common, this does not mean that the population sizes of these two species are similar. In the strictest sense no bird of prey species can be really regarded as common; being at the end of the food chain they are invariably less numerous than most other birds. When a Common Buzzard is described as 'common' it is in comparison to the numbers of other bird of prey species rather than to wildfowl or passerine species. For more specific information, readers should refer to the population size figures.

Key to the Maps

■	Resident	- - -	Usual invasion range
‖‖	Summer visitor	●	Single vagrant occurrence
≡	Winter/passage visitor	○	Several vagrant occurrences
?	Status unclear or very irregular		

NOMENCLATURE

With the exception of a few deviations made to take into account more recent publications, the sequence and scientific nomenclature used in this book follows that of Dr K.H.Voous' *List of Recent Holarctic Bird Species* (1977) .

English Vernacular Names

Nowadays, almost every ornithological book written in English includes a paragraph or more on the choice and use of vernacular names. Although the debate on the standardisation of English bird names is becoming somewhat tedious, the subject will not go away. Anyone writing a book on birds, or indeed travelling in search of birds, is embroiled. An 'official' list of English names for use in literature will probably come eventually, though traditional names will no doubt be still used regionally. At the end of the day, I believe, perhaps unusually for an Englishman, that the scientific name is the one that most easily facilitates cross referencing, though this is also occasionally complicated by differences in this usage.

The English names in this book largely follow those used in the *Birding World Complete List of the Birds of the Western Palearctic* (1995). The reasons for this choice are entirely subjective. Firstly, this list seems to me to be one of the most sensible of those on offer. Secondly, they are largely the names that I learned in childhood and thus still feel most comfortable with. Nevertheless, in certain cases I could not bring myself to include some qualifying adjectives, and Hooded Crow is preferred to Carrion Crow as the latter is a visitor to Hungary whilst the former is the regular breeding race.

My choice of English name is supplemented by the scientific, Hungarian, and often an alternative English name or two from the many on offer. I trust that these will be sufficient for any reader, of any nationality, to be able to cross-reference this work to any other.

Hungarian Names

Although not to the extent of the English debate, the vernacular name argument is also raising its head in Hungary. The Hungarian names in this book are based on Keve's *Magyarország Madarainak Névjegyzéke* (1984), which is the official nomenclature. I have been audacious enough to deviate from this standard work in some cases to take into account the vernacular names currently used by most contemporary Hungarian birdwatchers, and for some species alternative names are given.

GEOGRAPHICAL
BACKGROUND

Hungary lies in central Europe on latitude 45° 45' N to 48° 35' N, and longitude 16° 5' E to 22° 55' E. The country covers an area of 93,032 km² and is split roughly in two by the Danube. Hungary is traditionally said to have six geographical regions: the Great Plain, the Little Plain, the Alp Foothills, the Transdanubian Hills, the Transdanubian Uplands, and the Northern Hills.

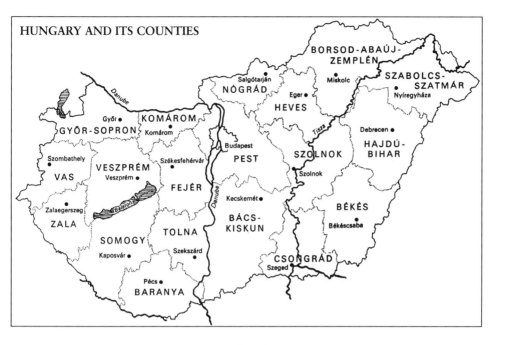

Geographical Zones

For the purposes of this book it has been convenient to divide Hungary into three larger main geographical zones. To the west of the Danube is Transdanubia and to the east the Great Plain. A series of hill ranges comprising the Northern Hills run to the north of the Great Plain.

Transdanubia is the country west of the Danube. The area comprises rolling low hills (Transdanubian Hills), the mainly forested hills of the Bakony and Vértes (Transdanubian Uplands), a series of hills on the Austrian border (Alp Foothills), a flat area in the northwest (Little Plain), numerous wooded fishpond systems and three large natural shallow lakes, Balaton, Velence and Fertő.

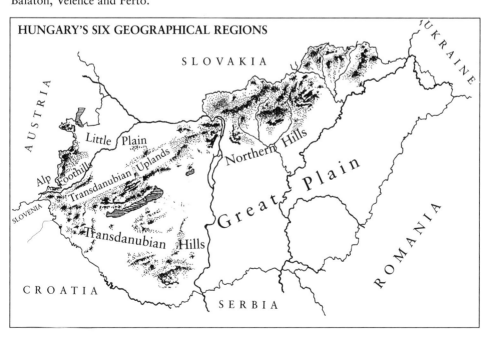

13

The Great Plain lies east of the Danube and south of the Northern Hills and comprises more than half the country. The most characteristic landscapes here are the *puszta* (grasslands) agricultural land, particularly vast crop monocultures such as sunflowers and maize, and large fishpond systems set in open landscapes. The Great Plain is divided by the River Tisza, which has been heavily regulated in the last 100 years but which still has some stretches of floodplain and riverine forest.

The Northern Hills run from the Danube Bend to the northeast corner of the country. The seven main ranges are covered in deciduous (especially beech) and conifer (mostly plantation) forest. The Aggtelek and Bükk ranges are typified by karst features. Many southern slopes are planted with vineyards. Hungary has no mountains proper, the highest peak being Kékes (1015 m) in the Mátra hills.

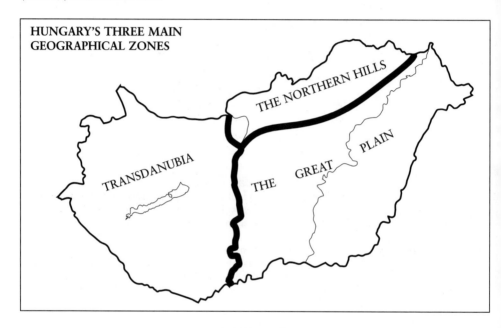

HUNGARY'S THREE MAIN
GEOGRAPHICAL ZONES

THE NORTHERN HILLS

TRANSDANUBIA

THE GREAT PLAIN

Land Use

Hungary is a predominantly agrarian country. Around 58% of the country's total area is farmed in some way or other. Low intensity agriculture, including both livestock and arable farming, accounts for between 15% and 20% of the country's area. From an ornithological standpoint, traditionally managed grassland is very important. Such grassland covers over 500,000 hectares, much of this being alkaline *puszta* grazed by cattle and sheep. Traditional pastoral farming is carried out around the Kiskunság salt lakes and in the Pusztaszer area. Here farming is practised with conservation in mind. Grass is cut for hay, and cattle grazed with the aim of providing optimal conditions for nesting birds such as Avocet, Redshank and Black-tailed Godwit. Much arable land is intensively farmed, with a low diversity of bird and other species. Small scale farms are often less intensive in their management, using less fertilisers and often horse-drawn ploughs rather than heavy machinery. Such areas provide habitat for birds of prey, Roller, Stone Curlew, larks, pipits and chats.

Forestry is concentrated in Transdanubia and the Northern Hills. Around 14% of the country's area is covered by woodland and forest of some type. Post-war forestry practices, particularly the planting of fast-growing monocultures, have reduced the amount of quality bird habitat, and several species, such as Hazel Grouse and White-backed Woodpecker, have declined in both number and range as a result.

Land Use in Hungary's Geographical Regions (Based on Márkus, 1994)

Region		Agriculture	Forestry	Other
1	Great Plain	81%	6%	13%
2	Little Plain	76%	11%	13%
3	Alp Foothills	66%	22%	12%
4	Transdanubian Hills	70%	18%	12%
5	Transdanubian Uplands	55%	30%	15%
6	Northern Hills	55%	30%	15%

Climate

A land-locked country, Hungary has a typical continental climate of harsh winters and hot summers. The climate is, however, as much influenced by the Atlantic and Mediterranean Sea as by the colder air of Eastern Europe and Central Asia.

Months	Jan	Feb	Mar	Apr	May	June	July	Aug	Sep	Oct	Nov	Dec
Average day temperatures (degrees centigrade)												
	2	4	11	17	22	26	28	27	23	16	8	3
Average night temperatures (degrees centigrade)												
	-3	-2	2	6	11	14	16	15	12	7	3	-1
Average hours of sunshine per day												
	2	3	4	6	8	8	9	9	7	5	2	1
Average number of days with rainfall												
	8	7	7	7	9	8	7	6	6	8	9	9

Bird Habitats

Lakes Hungary is dotted with shallow, often saline lakes. From west to east, the most significant include Fertő, Velence, Kelemen-szék, Kolon and Kardoskút. There are also many smaller, often temporary lakes such as Sárkány-tó in Fejér County, Nagyszék in Hajdú-Bihar County and Fülöp-szék and Müller-szék in Csongrád County. All are important for breeding and migratory birds. Typical breeding species include Little Bittern, Great White Egret, Purple and Squacco Herons, Spoonbill, Ferruginous Duck, Marsh Harrier, Little Crake, marsh terns and various warblers. Large numbers of grey geese use these lakes during migration and in winter. Lake Balaton is one of the largest lakes in Europe covering c. 55,000 hectares, and in summer is a major recreational area, though there are many spots around the lake where birds breed. In autumn and winter, Balaton is an important site for wildfowl.

Marshes Many of the country's marshes have been drained or converted to fish-farms. There are scattered remnant marshes throughout the Kiskunság, and large tracts remain on the Hortobágy at Angyalháza, Ágota, Pusztakócs, Kunmadaras, Pentezug, Zám and elsewhere. Much of the Kis-Balaton reserve is freshwater marsh. Smaller but ornithologically important marshes remain on the Hanság and at Ócsa, Dabas and Dinnyés. Red-necked and Black-necked Grebes, Greylag Goose, Gadwall, Ferruginous Duck, Little Crake, Whiskered Tern and occasionally White-winged Black Tern are just some of the birds which breed in Hungary's marshes. During migration, marshes are important stop-over sites for both White and Black Storks and large numbers of wildfowl, waders and passerines.

Fishponds Hungary has around 27,000 hectares of man-made fishponds (the most in Europe after the Czech Republic). Although artificially created and managed, many are among the most important wetland habitats for birds in the country. The word 'pond' may imply a relatively small body of water, whereas many fishponds in Hungary are, by any definition of size, 'lakes'. Many fishponds are set in semi-wild landscapes and are often surrounded by reedbeds. Ponds in Transdanubia are typically smaller than those on the Great Plain, and often set in rolling or wooded country. Some of the most important fishpond systems for birds in Transdanubia are Boronka, Balatonlelle, Pacsmag and Rétszilas. There are fewer fishponds on the Great Plain but they invariably include much larger single bodies of water. Important systems for birds are at Hortobágy, Szeged, Pusztaszer and Biharugra. The latter complex lies in 10,000 hectares of *puszta* and farmland on the Romanian border.

Birds which breed in the various habitats around fishponds include Pygmy Cormorant, Great White Egret, Glossy Ibis, Spoonbill, Garganey, Spotted and Little Crakes, Whiskered Tern, Penduline and Bearded Tits, Bluethroat and Savi's, Moustached and Great Reed Warblers.

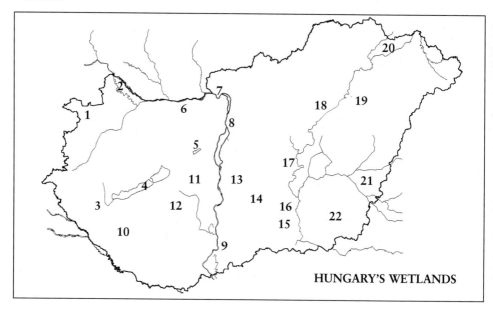

HUNGARY'S WETLANDS

1	Lake Fertő (Fertő-tó)	14	Lake Kolon (Kolon-tó)
2	Szigetköz	15	Szeged Lake Fehér-tó
3	Kis-Balaton	16	Csaj fishponds (Csaj-tó)
4	Lake Balaton	17	River Tisza
5	Lake Velence (Velencei-tó)	18	Lake Tisza (Tisza-tó)
6	Lake Tata (Tatai-Öreg-tó)	19	Hortobágy fishponds (Hortobágy-
7	Danube Bend		halastó)
8	River Danube	20	Bodrogzug floodplain
9	Gemenc floodplain forest	21	Biharugra fishponds (Biharugai halas-
10	Somogy fishponds		tavak)
11	Lake Sárkány (Sárkány-tó)	22	Kardoskút salt lake (Kardoskúti
12	Pacsmag fishponds (Pacsmagi-tavak)		Fehér-tó)
13	Kiskunság salt lakes (Kiskunsági szikes tavak)		

Rivers Although many natural waterways have been regulated, Hungary is in many ways still dominated by its two main rivers, the Danube and Tisza. The Rába, Dráva, Sió and Ipoly are tributaries of the Danube, with important bird habitats along their routes. The Szamos, Bodrog, Körös, Hernád and Maros flow into the Tisza and all have stretches of floodplain woodland along their banks. The open waters of the Danube and Tisza are important for wintering and migrating divers, grebes and wildfowl.

Floodplains   Floodplains are biologically diverse and are invariably rich in bird species. Although much of this important habitat has been lost, magnificent wooded stretches of poplar and willow remain at Szigetköz and Gemenc on the Danube and along the Tisza and Drava. Floodplain meadows at Bodrogzug, at the confluence of the Tisza and Bodrog, are important for Corncrake. Other typical floodplain birds include Black Stork, Black Kite and River Warbler.

Puszta   Hungary has 1,200,000 hectares of grasslands of various types, which are commonly and collectively referred to as the *puszta*. This uniquely Hungarian habitat is essentially lowland dry-grassland-steppe. *Puszta* is secondary steppe, i.e. it is not 'natural' but the result of a process which began with the felling of woodland, followed by burning and wind erosion, and which is largely maintained in its current state by grazing. Much *puszta* has been reclaimed or degraded. The largest remaining expanses lie east of the Danube, and particularly east of the Tisza. Notable areas include Apaj and Harta-Akasztó in the Kiskunság, Zám, Nagyiván, Angyalháza-Szelencés and Ágota on the Hortobágy, the Mezőség area, the Nagykunság region, Szabadkígyós in Békes County and Pitvaros in Csongrád County. Breeding birds of the *puszta* include Lapwing, Kentish Plover, Stone Curlew and Tawny Pipit. At various times of the year Long-legged, Common and Rough-legged Buzzards, Hen and Montagu's Harriers, Short-toed Eagle, Saker, Merlin and Red-footed Falcon all hunt over the *puszta*. Common Crane, Golden Plover, Dotterel, Curlew, Ruff and many other species stop here during migration. Flat open *puszta* is also often the lekking ground of Great Bustards.

Karst   The best examples of karst landscape in Hungary are in the Bükk, Gerecse, Pilis and Buda hills, and particularly Aggtelek National Park. Typical birds in such places are Red-backed Shrike, Barred Warbler, Nightjar, Woodlark and Rock Bunting. In Hungary karst landscapes are usually open areas of rocky limestone marked by sinks, crevices, ridges and typically covered by scrub, grassland and scattered woods.

Forest   Around 14% of Hungary's land surface is covered in forest or woodland. Some stretches of the Danube, Tisza and tributaries are lined by willow and poplar woods, though many stands of native trees have been replaced with faster growing introduced species. Oak woodland dominates in hilly areas between 200 and 700 m. Above this, beech takes over. Most conifer plantation is in Transdanubia. Although small in area, *acacia* copses and windbreaks are scattered across the Great Plain and provide nesting sites for birds.

Farmland   Around 58% of Hungary's land surface is farmed. Of this, around 58% is arable, 10% grazing and 5% meadows. Depending upon the type and intensity of land use, farmland can be important bird habitat. Great Bustards, for example, often feed and nest in cultivated areas, and passage Common Cranes and geese rely heavily upon stubble and harvest spillage for food.

HUNGARY'S IMPORTANCE FOR BIRDS

Hungary might be considered as lying at an ornithological crossroads. Species such as Collared Pratincole *Glareola pratincola* and Olivaceous Warbler *Hippolais pallida* are at the very north of their European breeding ranges, whilst Fieldfare *Turdus pilaris* and Willow Warbler *Phylloscopus trochilus* rarely nest south of Hungary. Red-footed Falcon *Falco vespertinus* and White-winged Black Tern *Chlidonias leucopterus* are at the westernmost limit of their ranges. Whilst Lesser Grey Shrikes *Lanius minor* are summer visitors and rare north of Hungary; Great Grey Shrikes *Lanius excubitor* on the other hand do not breed but move in from the north to replace the former in winter.

If one takes an international conservation stance and concentrates on those species which are threatened across their world ranges, then Hungary's ornithological significance is clear. According to the criteria of BirdLife International, 123 species of 'European Conservation Concern' breed in Hungary. Of these, five species - Ferruginous Duck *Aythya nyroca*, Imperial Eagle *Aquila heliaca*, Corncrake *Crex crex*, Great Bustard *Otis tarda*, Aquatic Warbler *Acrocephalus paludicola* - are regarded as being of 'Global Conservation Concern'. Another globally threatened species, Lesser White-fronted Goose *Anser erythropus*, occurs on passage.

There are currently around 1,000 Great Bustards in Hungary, which represents one of Europe's most important populations (others being in Iberia, Russia and the Ukraine). The Hungarian population is all the more crucial when one considers that these majestic birds are all but extinct in neighbouring Austria (50 birds), Slovakia (25-40) and Romania (10-20). Yet the current Hungarian figure is a fraction of the numbers which occurred in the country earlier this century, and despite many conservation efforts the population is far from secure having declined badly since the Second World War.

Hungary's Aquatic Warbler population is also internationally significant, the 1994 estimate of over 400 pairs being the third largest in the world after those in Poland and Russia. First found breeding as recently as 1971, numbers have fluctuated somewhat since, but overall the species has increased. Indeed the Hortobágy, where the population is concentrated, is the only area in Europe where this trend is known to have occurred. Although it has increased in size, this population is rather local, concentrated in Hortobágy National Park, in albeit strictly protected areas.

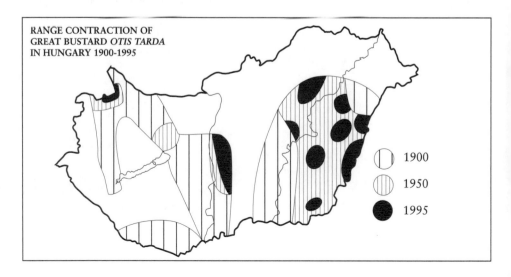

RANGE CONTRACTION OF
GREAT BUSTARD *OTIS TARDA*
IN HUNGARY 1900-1995

1900
1950
1995

Singing male Aquatic Warblers (*Acrocephalus paludicola*) in Hungary (Hortobágy National Park) 1977-1994. (Based on Kovács, 1994)

Year	Number of singing males	Trend
1977	89	Increase
1978	70-80	Decrease
1979	100-110	Increase
1980	110-120	Increase
1981	74	Decrease
1982	158	Increase
1983	113	Decrease
1984	160-170	Increase
1985	200-215	Increase
1986	130-150	Decrease
1987	190-206	Increase
1988	171	Decrease
1989	200-206	Increase
1990	207	Increase
1991	189-209	Stable
1992	223-234	Increase
1993	293-313	Increase
1994	400-425	Increase

The country's Imperial Eagles have steadily recovered from a post-war decline, and the current 35-40 pairs now constitute the core Central European population. Ferruginous Ducks are not as widespread as they once were, though the estimated 1,000-1,500 pairs again represents the most important population in central Europe. Corncrakes are doing less well. The number of calling males varies greatly each year, but, overall, numbers have fallen in Hungary as elsewhere in Europe. Hungary also supports the largest breeding population in Europe of Red-footed Falcon and some of the largest of wetland birds such as Little Bittern *Ixobrychus minutus*, Great White Egret *Egretta alba* and Spoonbill *Platalea leucorodia*. There are also unknown but certainly large numbers of woodpeckers (though White-backed Woodpecker *Dendrocopos leucotos* is rare and under pressure), and *Locustella* and *Acrocephalus* warblers.

Although not threatened globally, Eagle Owl *Bubo bubo* is a species which has declined in much of its European range. Over the last 50 years the Hungarian population has crashed. In 1950, pairs still bred in most hilly areas of the country, but today it is a rare breeding species down to, at most, a dozen pairs confined to the northeast of the country. Attempts have been made at strengthening the population with the introduction of birds from Germany, but

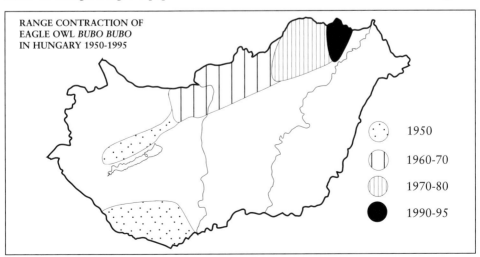

RANGE CONTRACTION OF
EAGLE OWL *BUBO BUBO*
IN HUNGARY 1950-1995

1950
1960-70
1970-80
1990-95

though well meant, the project was doomed as the causes for the initial decline had not been dealt with or indeed adequately researched.

Naturally, whilst some species have declined others have increased in both number and range. In November 1928 a Syrian Woodpecker *Dendrocopos syriacus* was observed and collected at Bácska (which today lies in Serbia). Syrian Woodpeckers were first observed in the area which is today's Hungary in the 1930s, with the first breeding confirmed in 1937 at Kiskunfélegyháza, Bács-Kiskun County. The range expansion of the species through Hungary was rapid, with, in less than 20 years, the species having passed through the country to reach Austria and Slovakia. By 1960, suitable habitats nationwide had been colonised.

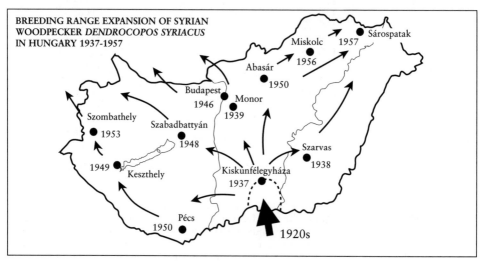

Another species which has only relatively recently expanded its range into Hungary is Olivaceous Warbler *Hippolais pallida*. Although this expansion has been less dynamic, and visible, than that of Syrian Woodpecker, a steady movement northwards along the country's two main rivers has been documented. In less than 40 years, Olivaceous Warblers have extended from the Balkans via the Tisza and Danube rivers with breeding even confirmed in Austria. Recent indications suggest that this movement has now slowed if not halted completely.

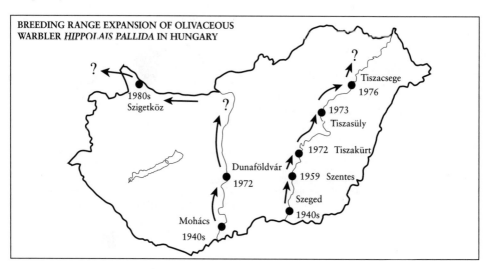

CONSERVATION

There are two main organisations in Hungary concerned with the protection of birds and their habitats. Firstly, there is the Hungarian Ornithological Institute, located at Költő utca 21, 1121, Budapest, which is a department of the Ministry For Environment and Regional Policy and deals with the administration of protected areas, international agreements, hunting regulations and other matters of a legal nature. The Institute also carries out ornithological research and publishes an annual journal *Aquila*. The Hungarian Ornithological and Nature Conservation Society (MME) is a non-governmental organisation with around 4,000 members. Its activities include bird protection projects, the organisation of bird ringing and educational work. Hungary has signed all the main international agreements and conventions which affect birds and bird habitats. There are currently four UNESCO Biosphere Reserves, 13 Ramsar wetlands, and BirdLife International has listed 59 sites in the country as Important Bird Areas.

Reserves and Parks

There are five National Parks in Hungary, all of which are important for birds, and almost 200 reserves or protected areas (Landscape Protection Areas, National Protection Areas, Bird Reserves and Nature Reserves) many of which are, or contain, important bird habitats.

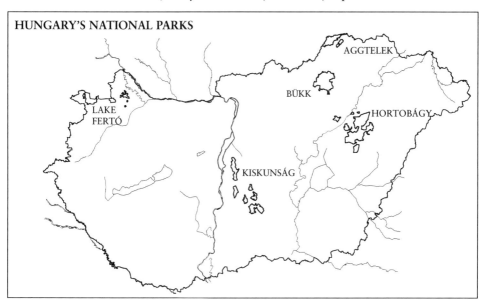

HUNGARY'S NATIONAL PARKS

AGGTELEK

BÜKK

LAKE FERTŐ

HORTOBÁGY

KISKUNSÁG

Hortobágy Size: 52,000 hectares. A Unesco Biosphere Reserve and includes Ramsar sites. Mosaic lowland area of grassland *puszta*, farmland, fishpond systems, marshes and woodland. Important for birds in all seasons. ***Selected bird species***: Night Heron (400-500 pairs), Great White Egret (250 pairs), White Stork (up to 200 pairs), Spoonbill (400-450 pairs), White-tailed Eagle (50-60 in winter), Red-footed Falcon (up to 400 pairs), Saker (3-5 pairs), Great Bustard (150-200 birds), Whiskered Tern (400-450 pairs), Aquatic Warbler (200 pairs), Lesser White-fronted Goose (100-250 in autumn), Ruff (200,000+ in spring), Common Crane (50,000+ in autumn).

Kiskunság Size: 31,529 hectares. Flat lowland region between the Danube and the Tisza.

Includes Ramsar sites and a Unesco Biosphere Reserve. The National Park comprises six scattered areas, each of particular habitat importance. Areas include saline *puszta,* salt lakes, marshes, sand dunes, backwaters, farmland and *acacia* woods. Important for birds in all seasons. *Selected bird species*: White Stork (common), Red-footed Falcon (200+ pairs), Great Bustard (300+ birds), Kentish Plover (100 pairs), Stone Curlew (50 pairs), Roller (locally common). Large numbers of wildfowl and waders on passage.

Bükk Size: 38,815 hectares. Hill range of volcanic origin covered particularly in oak and beech forest, pasture, karst plateau and areas of scrub. Very important for birds of prey and woodpeckers. *Selected bird species*: Black Stork (3-4 pairs), Honey Buzzard (30 pairs), Short-toed Eagle (6 pairs), Lesser Spotted Eagle (8-10 pairs), Imperial Eagle (3-4 pairs), Saker (4 pairs), Grey-headed, Middle Spotted and Black Woodpeckers (all common), White-backed Woodpecker (50 pairs). Birds such as Woodlark, Barred Warbler and Red-backed Shrike are common.

Aggtelek Size: 19,708 hectares. Unesco Biosphere Reserve. An attractive upland region of karst landscapes, meadows, craggy valleys and rolling hills covered mainly in broadleaved forest. The last viable numbers of Hazelhen in Hungary and the core Rock Bunting population are here. *Selected bird species*: White Stork (50 pairs), Honey Buzzard (10-15 pairs), Imperial Eagle (2-3 pairs), Hazel Grouse (50-70 pairs), Grey-headed, Black and Middle Spotted Woodpeckers (common), White-backed Woodpecker (10 pairs), Barred Warbler, Woodlark, Red-backed Shrike and Rock Bunting (all common).

Lake Fertő (Fertő-tó) Size: 12,542 hectares. A Unesco Biosphere Reserve and Ramsar site. Forms a cross-frontier National Park with the Austrian part of the lake (the Neusiedler See). A so-called 'steppe-lake', a lowland, shallow lake of high salinity. Fertő is the westernmost in a series of similar lakes scattered from central Asia to Europe. Reed covers over half the lake's surface, and in some places reedbeds are more than 6 kms wide. Important for birds in all seasons. *Selected bird species*: Bittern (20 pairs), Great White Egret (15-20 pairs) Purple Heron (20 pairs), Spoonbill (25 pairs) Red-crested Pochard (40 pairs), Savi's, Moustached and Great Reed Warblers (all common). In winter and on passage up to 30,000 Bean Geese occur.

Bird Protection

Of the 363 bird species which have occurred in Hungary 342 are currently protected by law. There are three categories of protection: Strictly Protected, Protected and Unprotected. A total of 65 species are categorised as 'Strictly Protected' (see table). Each protected species has a legal 'value' in financial terms which corresponds to a fine system. With the official Hungarian average annual wage in 1995 being around 30,000 Hungarian forints (HUF), the severity of the fine system can be illustrated by the examples of Imperial Eagle, Saker and Great Bustard, which each carry the maximum figure of 500,000 HUF. The lowest sum in the Strictly Protected category is 100,000 HUF.

Some species (see table) are totally unprotected and can be killed all year round. Certain species (Herring Gull, Yellow-legged Gull, Jay, Magpie, Hooded Crow, House Sparrow, Tree Sparrow) are considered pests and thus remain unprotected, though the traditional view that such species are common and therefore vermin no doubt plays a part in their classification. Other birds are game species which can be shot in certain areas at certain times of the year, with the appropriate licence. White-fronted Goose and Grey Partridge are both unprotected and classified as game, but for conservation reasons the hunting of these two species is suspended each year and thus, in practice, they are currently 'protected'. Although they are protected species, Grey Herons and Black-headed Gulls can be killed on fish-farms which lie outside reserves (from 1 August to 31 March). Goshawks are protected, but they can be shot on poultry and pheasant farms.

Strictly Protected Bird Species in Hungary

Species	'Value' (HUF)	Species	'Value' (HUF)
Pygmy Cormorant	250,000	Corncrake	100,000
White Pelican	250,000	Little Bustard	250,000
Dalmatian Pelican	250,000	Great Bustard	500,000
Squacco Heron	250,000	Black-winged Stilt	250,000
Little Egret	250,000	Stone Curlew	250,000
Great White Egret	250,000	Avocet	250,000
Black Stork	250,000	Collared Pratincole	250,000
White Stork	100,000	Black-winged Pratincole	250,000
Glossy Ibis	250,000	Kentish Plover	250,000
Spoonbill	250,000	Sociable Plover	250,000
Lesser White-fronted Goose	250,000	Great Snipe	250,000
Red-breasted Goose	250,000	Slender-billed Curlew	250,000
Marbled Duck	250,000	Curlew	100,000
Ferruginous Duck	100,000	Marsh Sandpiper	250,000
White-headed Duck	250,000	Whiskered Tern	100,000
Black Kite	100,000	White-winged Black Tern	250,000
Red Kite	250,000	Little Tern	100,000
White-tailed Eagle	500,000	Barn Owl	100,000
Black Vulture	250,000	Eagle Owl	250,000
Short-toed Eagle	250,000	Snowy Owl	250,000
Montagu's Harrier	250,000	Little Owl	100,000
Levant Sparrowhawk	250,000	Ural Owl	100,000
Lesser Spotted Eagle	250,000	Short-eared Owl	100,000
Imperial Eagle	500,000	Bee-eater	100,000
Golden Eagle	250,000	Roller	250,000
Booted Eagle	250,000	White-backed Woodpecker	100,000
Osprey	250,000	Short-toed Lark	250,000
Lesser Kestrel	250,000	Dipper	100,000
Eleonora's Falcon	250,000	Thrush Nightingale	100,000
Saker	500,000	Rock Thrush	250,000
Peregrine	250,000	Aquatic Warbler	250,000
Hazel Grouse	250,000	Ortolan Bunting	100,000
Baillon's Crake	100,000		

Unprotected Bird Species in Hungary

Species	Official Reason	Species	Official Reason
Cormorant	Damage to fish-farming	Yellow-legged Gull	Damage to fish-farming/pest
Bean Goose	Game species		
White-fronted Goose	Game species (Hunting suspended)	Woodpigeon	Game species/damage to farming
Teal	Game species	Collared Dove	Game species/damage to farming
Mallard	Game species		
Garganey	Game species	Jay	Songbird protection/pest
Pochard	Game species	Magpie	Songbird protection/pest
Goldeneye	Game species	Rook	Damage to farming/pest
Pheasant	Game species.	Hooded Crow	Damage to farming/pest
Grey Partridge	Game species (Hunting suspended)	Starling	Damage to farming/pest
		House Sparrow	Damage to farming/pest
Coot	Damage to fish-farming.	Tree Sparrow	Damage to farming/pest
Woodcock	Game species		
Herring Gull	Damage to fish-farming/pest		

Birds of Prey

Diurnal birds of prey have received particular attention from Hungarian ornithologists and conservationists. In the 1970s and 1980s the Hungarian Ornithological Society (as it was then named) focused much of its attention on the protection of birds of prey. Its work has since broadened somewhat. The important Hungarian populations of two enigmatic species, Imperial Eagle and Saker, have been monitored and assisted since 1975.

In the 1970s, cliff-nesting Saker pairs were almost extinct in Hungary owing to several factors including the theft of eggs and birds for the illegal falconry trade and accidental disturbance by rock climbers. Tree-nesting pairs were vulnerable to being shot-through by 'hunters', and a decline in a main prey species, the Suslik *Citellus citellus*, also affected the population. In the early 1970s the Saker population was estimated at 30 known pairs. The smuggling of eggs, young and adult birds has now been largely eradicated, and vulnerable nests guarded. A lack of safe and suitable nest sites has been addressed by the erection of artificial nests and platforms, and other problems such as electrocution on electricity pylons have also been tackled. Today the estimated Hungarian Saker population of 130-140 pairs is the largest in Europe.

In Hungary, the majestic Imperial Eagle has suffered from many of the problems which affected Saker: a lack of safe nesting sites, reduction in the Suslik population and disturbance. Susliks have been reintroduced to hunting areas, old nests reinforced and artificial ones erected in safe sites. From fewer than 20 pairs estimated in the mid 1980s, the population has now grown to around 35-40 pairs, again a key European population.

In 1987, an action plan for White-tailed Eagle was launched by conservationists in Somogy County in the south of Transdanubia. This ambitious project involved research into habitats and prey, and much hard lobbying for funds, media attention and international support. Forestry practices, hunting, fishing, poisoning and disturbance were identified as the main threats. Artificial nests were erected, vulnerable nesting sites guarded and winter food provided. All in all the project has been a success, with the first privately owned nature reserves in the former Socialist countries established, the project expanding to include other wetland bird and mammal species and the White-tailed Eagle population increasing from an estimated 15 pairs in 1987 to 41 pairs in 1994.

Status of Breeding Diurnal Birds of Prey in Hungary

Species	No. of Pairs 1995	10-Year Trend
Honey Buzzard	300-350	Stable
Black Kite	150-175	Increase
Red Kite	1-2	Stable
White-tailed Eagle	40-45	Increase
Short tocd Eagle	50-70	Stable
Marsh Harrier	1500-2000	Stable
Montagu's Harrier	200-250	Increase
Goshawk	2000-3000	Increase
Sparrowhawk	800-1000	Increase
Levant Sparrowhawk	2-6	Unknown
Common Buzzard	5000-6000	Increase
Long-legged Buzzard	0-1	Increase
Lesser Spotted Eagle	120-150	Stable
Imperial Eagle	35-40	Increase
Golden Eagle	2-4	Increase
Booted Eagle	10-20	Unknown
Lesser Kestrel	0-?	Unknown
Kestrel	3500-4000	Decrease
Red-footed Falcon	2000-2200	Decrease
Hobby	1000-1200	Decrease
Saker	130-140	Increase

Migration

There are no true migration bottlenecks in Hungary but the Carpathian Basin in which Hungary lies is an ornithological junction. Hungary's wetlands are very important as refueling and moulting stop-overs for migratory wildfowl and waders, and the River Tisza and the Danube are flyways for many species, particularly divers and sea ducks. In August and September an impressive selection of birds of prey move through on a broad front and loiter on the *puszta*.

In autumn, over 50,000 Bean Geese pass through the country and up to 200,000 White-fronted Geese occur in spring. Although both species occur together at almost all regular goose sites, the Danube is a demarcation line between the biggest flocks of the two species. The vast majority of Bean Geese roost in Transdanubia whilst White-fronts congregate mostly on Great Plain wetlands

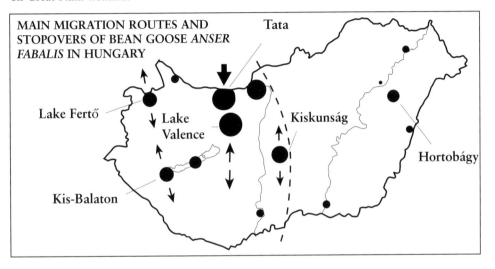

MAIN MIGRATION ROUTES AND STOPOVERS OF BEAN GOOSE *ANSER FABALIS* IN HUNGARY

Tata

Lake Fertő

Lake Valence

Kiskunság

Kis-Balaton

Hortobágy

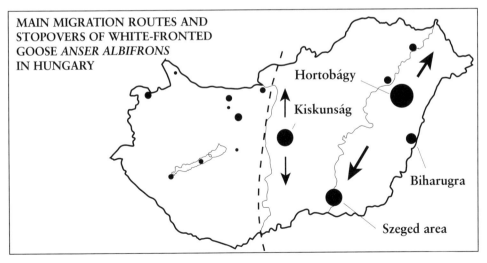

MAIN MIGRATION ROUTES AND STOPOVERS OF WHITE-FRONTED GOOSE *ANSER ALBIFRONS* IN HUNGARY

Hortobágy

Kiskunság

Biharugra

Szeged area

Since the 1980s, the number of Common Cranes *Grus grus* passing through the east of the country each autumn has steadily increased. Over 50,000 now regularly roost on the Hortobágy in October. In some years up to 70,000 have been counted in the country as a whole in peak periods. The route taken is largely restricted to a band east of the Tisza. Only some hundreds occur west of the Tisza and very few pass through Transdanubia.

Flooded *puszta,* marshes and particularly drained fishponds (which are traditionally emptied in autumn) attract large flocks of passage waders. In autumn, Dunlin, various sandpipers, Black-tailed Godwits and between 50,000 and 60,000 Ruff are estimated nationwide each year. In spring 250,000-300,000 Ruff pass through Hungary.

Areas of dry *puszta* are important hunting areas for nomadic and passage birds of prey. Harriers, eagles and falcons move through on a broad front, often lingering for some days at scattered sites. Up to 50 Long-legged Buzzards occur east of the Danube in late summer.

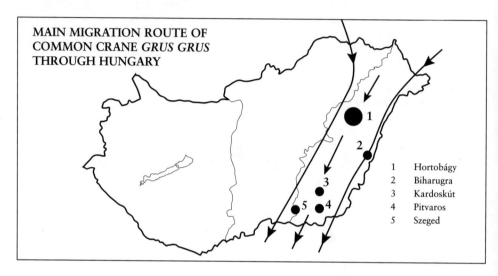

MAIN MIGRATION ROUTE OF
COMMON CRANE *GRUS GRUS*
THROUGH HUNGARY

1   Hortobágy
2   Biharugra
3   Kardoskút
4   Pitvaros
5   Szeged

Sites for Non-Passerine Migratory Birds

Lake Fertő	Storks, Bean Goose, ducks
Lake Tata	Bean Goose, ducks
Danube Bend	Divers, sea ducks
Lake Velence	Bean Goose, Ruff, Curlew
Kis-Balaton	Storks, Great White Egret, wildfowl
Lake Balaton	Wildfowl, Osprey
Kiskunság Salt lakes	White-fronted Goose, Ruff, Curlew
Hortobágy fishponds	Storks, wildfowl, Common Crane, waders, Slender-billed Curlew
Hortobágy *puszta*	Birds of prey, Ruff, Dotterel

Rarities

Reports and descriptions of unusual sightings and rarities seen by visiting birdwatchers should be sent to Dr G.Magyar, Secretary, Hungarian Rarities Committee, c/o MME, Költő u.21, 1121, Budapest, Hungary.

GLOSSARY OF SELECTED TERMS

Accidental A species which has been seen very few times in a given region and is far from its normal range.

Danube Bend Stretch of River Danube and adjacent habitats in northern Hungary between Esztergom and Szentendre.

Fishpond Man-made wetlands for fish production, usually carp. In Hungary often very large lakes in semi-natural habitats and quite unlike most western European fish-farms.

Great Plain The area east of the Danube to the Romanian border and south of the northern hill ranges.

Holarctic Faunal region of the Northern Hemisphere north of the tropics. Embraces both the Nearctic and Palearctic regions.

Influx Periodical movements of a species into an area.

Invasion Infrequent movement of a very large number of a species into an area.

Local Occurring in very defined, specialised and scattered locations.

Montane Relating to and of mountains.

Nationwide Throughout the country in suitable habitat.

Nearctic North American faunal region.

Nomadic Wandering rather than migrating along regular routes.

Northern Hills A belt of hill ranges running from the Börzsöny (to the north of Budapest) northeastwards to the Zemplén.

Palearctic Faunal region of Europe, Asia and part of North Africa.

Passage General term for spring and autumn migration periods.

Puszta Lowland, poor grazing grassland or semi-steppe.

Resident Implies a non-migratory species and usually presumes breeding.

Riparian Inhabiting rivers and adjacent habitats.

Transdanubia The area westwards from the Danube to the Austrian border.

Vagrant A rare and irregular species but not as unexpected as an accidental.

SYSTEMATIC LIST OF SPECIES

GAVIIDAE (Divers or Loons)

Red-throated Diver *Gavia stellata*   (Red-throated Loon)
Északi búvár

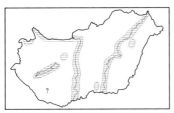

The rarest of the two divers occurring in Hungary annually. Small numbers regularly pass through every autumn, some staying for weeks at one site before moving on farther south. Mostly solitary birds, occasionally two or three, though parties of up to 12 have been recorded. It is not unknown for a few Red-throated Divers to overwinter on the Danube. The species is less commonly observed on spring passage.

STATUS IN HUNGARY: Uncommon autumn and winter visitor. Some in spring. Protected.
STATUS INTERNATIONALLY: Holarctic species. Considered vulnerable in Europe where there has been a general decline in the breeding population.
DISTRIBUTION: Wetlands nationwide, particularly rivers and Lakes Fertő, Velence and Balaton, larger fishponds such as Szeged Fehér-tó and those on the Hortobágy. Occasionally gravel pits. Over half of all records are from the Danube, many from the Danube Bend between Esztergom and Göd.
TIMING: Mainly October-December, with peak in November when can occur on the Danube within the city limits of Budapest. From January, records tail off with birds seen only occasionally from February to early May.

Black-throated Diver *Gavia arctica*   (Arctic Loon)
Sarki búvár

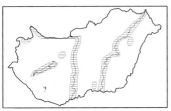

A regular autumn visitor to Hungary, and in contrast to Red-throated Diver also frequently occurs in spring, though never in the numbers seen in autumn. The ratio of observations between Red-throated and Black-throated Divers is almost 1:3, and Black-throated Divers are also more likely to overwinter. Most observations concern solitary birds, though small parties of up to six are not unknown and double figures have occurred, most notably on Lake Balaton. Some of the first autumn birds and those seen in spring can be in breeding plumage.

STATUS IN HUNGARY: Uncommon but regular on both autumn and spring passage. An almost annual winter visitor. Protected.
STATUS INTERNATIONALLY: Palearctic species. Considered vulnerable in Europe where population in decline.
DISTRIBUTION: Just about any large open water nationwide when on passage, particularly the Danube and Tisza rivers, Lakes Fertő, Balaton, Velence and Tisza. Also larger fishponds and reservoirs. The Danube Bend and river south of Budapest host a few birds most winters.
TIMING: From October through to May. Overall, November and December are peak months and the Danube Bend the most regular area.

Black-throated Diver

PODICIPEDIDAE (Grebes)

Little Grebe *Tachybaptus ruficollis* (Dabchick)
Kis vöcsök

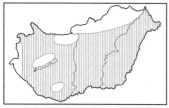

Probably the most common grebe species in Hungary, found on lakes, ox-bows, marshes, fishponds, canals, rivers, indeed just about any suitable wetland. In the usually hard Hungarian winter, most Little Grebes leave the country though some do remain, moving to waters fed by warm springs and fishponds where the water is kept free of ice. The invariably unfrozen Danube hosts such dispersed birds and no doubt some from populations further north and east. Small groups regularly winter on the river in the capital's Óbuda district.

STATUS IN HUNGARY: Common and widespread. Population size and trends unknown. Partial migrant, some remaining through milder winters. Protected.

STATUS INTERNATIONALLY:Old World species. Common and widespread in Europe where population probably stable.

DISTRIBUTION: Wetlands nationwide.

TIMING: In most years all year round though the majority of birds leave for the Mediterranean basin in November, returning in March.

Great Crested Grebe *Podiceps cristatus*
Búbos vöcsök

A familiar bird of Hungary's larger fishponds, reservoirs and lakes. Although Hungarian Great Crested Grebes regularly take the abundant fish of stocked ponds, their presence is generally tolerated by fish-farmers and anglers. However, the draining of ponds during the nesting period is a problem at some fish-farms, and despite being a protected species some illegal culling does occur. Most birds begin to display in April, with nesting usually commencing at the end of the month and into May.

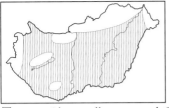

STATUS IN HUNGARY: Common and widespread. Population size and trends unknown. Mainly migratory, though a few stay through mild winters. Protected.
STATUS INTERNATIONALLY: Old World species. Common, widespread and considered to be increasing in Europe.
DISTRIBUTION: Wetlands nationwide. Significant breeding populations on larger Hortobágy fishponds, Lakes Velence and Tisza and at Kis-Balaton.
TIMING: Almost all year round. Some sedentary, others move short distances at the end of the breeding season. Migratory birds move southwards in November. Majority return in March.

Red-necked Grebe *Podiceps grisegena*
Vörösnyakú vöcsök

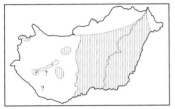

The rarest of the four grebe species breeding in Hungary. Red-necked Grebes have, however, increased over the last 20 years. They are also the last of the family to return from winter quarters, with the majority arriving back in early April. As do their congeners, a few Red-necked Grebes will occasionally stay in Hungary through mild winters on suitable ice-free wetlands.
STATUS IN HUNGARY: Uncommon breeder. Population size unknown but thought to be gradually increasing. Migrant. Protected.
STATUS INTERNATIONALLY: Holarctic species. Fairly common but rather scattered in Europe where most populations considered to be stable.
DISTRIBUTION: Very local. Nowhere common in Transdanubia. Fairly common locally east of the Danube, particularly in the Tisza floodplain. Hortobágy and Szeged areas remain the strongholds.
TIMING: Essentially migratory, with main period of occurrence from late March to early November. A few occasionally overwinter.

Slavonian Grebe *Podiceps auritus*   (Horned Grebe)
Füles vöcsök

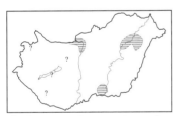

Although there are records from all four seasons, Slavonian Grebes mainly occur in Hungary in early or late winter. The most regular area is the Danube north of Budapest. Formally very seldom recorded, nowadays Budapest birdwatchers find one or two birds almost every year, and records from fishponds and lakes around the country are also on the increase. Usually single birds, with five the most seen together to date. With birds usually in the less conspicuous winter plumage the species is probably overlooked in some areas.
STATUS IN HUNGARY: Rare but annual passage and winter visitor. Protected.
STATUS INTERNATIONALLY: Holarctic species. European population considered stable.
DISTRIBUTION: Mainly the Danube. Annual on Hortobágy fishponds and probably Szeged area, but possible on any open water nationwide.
TIMING: Most likely in winter, November to January. Some pass through as late as April.

Black-necked Grebe *Podiceps nigricollis*   (Eared Grebe)
Feketenyakú vöcsök

Black-necked Grebes are the only true colonial breeders of the grebes nesting in Hungary. Colonies are often located alongside or within those of Whiskered and Black Terns and particularly Black-headed Gulls. Single colonies of over 50 pairs have and do appear, but smaller

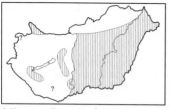

colonies of fewer than 20 nests each, established on marshes, deeper fishponds and salt lakes, ox-bows and reservoirs with emergent vegetation are the norm. Several small colonies can be located quite close to each other and exact sites often shift from year to year depending on water levels and amount of aquatic vegetation.
STATUS IN HUNGARY: Fairly common locally. Rather scattered nationally. Population size and trends unknown.
Migrant. Protected.
STATUS INTERNATIONALLY: Populations scattered globally. Fairly common in Europe and probably increasing.
DISTRIBUTION: Breeds on both man-made and natural wetlands across the Great Plain, especially those in the Tisza floodplain. Less common in Transdanubia, though regularly breeds at Kis-Balaton, Sárrét, Dinnyés and Boronka fishponds in Somogy County.
TIMING: Most arrive back from wintering areas in the Mediterranean and Black Sea at the end of March. The majority have left by November, though occasionally some through-passage, mainly along the Danube, continues into December.

Black-necked Grebe

PHALACROCORACIDAE (Cormorants)

Cormorant *Phalacrocorax carbo* (Great Cormorant)
Kárókatona

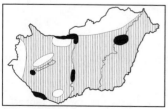

Hungary is populated by the *sinensis* race of the species, and adults in breeding plumage are very striking with their white heads and glossy, greenish plumage. But this is not enough to endear them to fish-farmers and seemingly even to most Hungarian ornithologists. As they consume considerable amounts of fish on fish-farms, the species is unprotected in Hungary. With their droppings they also destroy the very trees in which they and other birds nest.
Some 40 years ago the species bred at one site only, Kis-Balaton in Transdanubia. Since then a population explosion has seen colonies established nationwide.

STATUS IN HUNGARY: Common breeder. Population size unknown but increasing. Some resident, many nomadic, but most migratory moving with the onset of winter. Unprotected.

STATUS INTERNATIONALLY: Almost cosmopolitan range. Common and widespread in most of Europe and increasing.

DISTRIBUTION: Occurs nationwide on fishponds, reservoirs, rivers and lakes. Breeds in mixed colonies with herons and egrets at Lake Tisza, Hortobágy-halastó, Kis-Balaton, along the Danube and on the River Dráva. Some regularly winter on the Danube Bend. Outside the April-June nesting period can occur on almost any wetland. The winter of 1994-95 saw large numbers on the Danube in Budapest.

TIMING: Occurs all year round but mainly February to November.

Pygmy Cormorant *Phalacrocorax pygmeus*
Kis kárókatona

Pygmy Cormorants disappeared from Hungary as a breeding species around the turn of the century, before sporadically returning to breed in 1960s at various sites along the River Tisza. In the late 1980s, birds were regularly seen at Hortobágy-halastó, and in 1990 five pairs bred at Lake Tisza. Today about 12 pairs breed in mixed colonies with Cormorants, egrets and herons in trees, bushes and in reedbeds. Whilst the main European breeding populations in Romania and the former Yugoslavia have declined, Pygmy Cormorants have actually expanded their range via small scattered populations such as the one in Hungary. Despite being strictly protected, Pygmy Cormorants are still very vulnerable in Hungary. Their abundant larger relative can be legally shot, and a potential problem lies in the fact that few cullers are able to safely differentiate between the two species.

STATUS IN HUNGARY: Very rare breeder. 12 pairs nationwide. Migrant. Strictly protected.

STATUS INTERNATIONALLY: Palearctic species. Classified as globally threatened and vulnerable in Europe.

DISTRIBUTION:Rarely seen away from the Tisza floodplain. A few pairs at Hortobágy-halastó, Lake Tisza and Csaj-tó fishponds, otherwise accidental on wetlands around the country. Although only a few pairs breed at each site they are usually quite easy to locate as they move to and from nesting sites to feeding areas.

TIMING: Main period of occurrence from April to October.

Pygmy Cormorants

ARDEIDAE (Bitterns, Herons and Egrets)

Bittern *Botaurus stellaris* (Common Bittern, Great Bittern)
Bölömbika

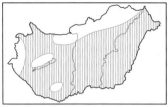

Bitterns in Hungary do not occur exclusively in large *Phragmites* reedbed habitat, but also breed in mosaic areas of marsh with reedmace *Typha*, rushes and willow *Salix* bushes. Booming begins in mid March and generally lasts till early June. It is not unusual in Hungary to see Bitterns sitting in open areas adjacent to wetlands, such as newly mown meadows and upon high dykes. In the Kiskunság, birds have been seen displaying together on open damp *puszta*. In winter, several may gather together at open water, especially spring-fed lakes, ice-free fishponds and flowing feeder canals.

STATUS IN HUNGARY: Uncommon to fairly common locally. A population of between 500 and 1,000 booming males estimated. No exact survey has ever been carried out. Mainly migratory. Some winter. Protected.

STATUS INTERNATIONALLY: Mainly Palearctic species. Vulnerable in Europe where declining, though in some countries populations are considered stable.

DISTRIBUTION: Suitable wetlands nationwide. Lakes and ponds with large reedbeds but also smaller marshes and backwaters. Particularly good locations are Kis-Balaton, Lakes Fertő, Velence and Péteri, Kiskunság salt lakes, Pusztaszer, Biharugra fishponds, Tápió marshes and most fish-pond systems on the Hortobágy.

TIMING: In most years possible all year round, though March to October is regular period of occurrence.

Little Bittern *Ixobrychus minutus*
Törpegém, Pocgém

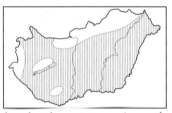

Although there has been an overall decline in Hungary as elsewhere in Europe, Little Bitterns are still widespread occurring in *Phragmites* reedbeds proper but also at the margins of fishponds, rivers, canals, marshes, reservoirs, ox-bows, village ponds, indeed almost anywhere with adequate cover. More often than not birds are first seen as they fly out of a reedbed and head across water, staying in view before entering cover again. Although not a colonial breeder, there are several records of Little Bitterns nesting beneath the nests of other Ardeidae such as Great White Egret and Purple Heron.

STATUS IN HUNGARY: Fairly common locally. Probably between 4,000 and 5,000 pairs. Hungary is an important country for the species, though the population is thought to have declined in recent decades. Migrant. Protected.

STATUS INTERNATIONALLY: Old World and Australasian species. Vulnerable in Europe and declining in most countries.

DISTRIBUTION: Wetlands nationwide. Areas with particularly good numbers in Transdanubia are Lake Velence and adjacent Dinnyés marsh, Pacsmag and Sumony fishponds. Across the Great Plain: Ócsa, Tápió marshes, Lake Péteri, Szeged fishponds, Biharugra and the Hortobágy.

TIMING: From mid April to early October, though most arrive back from winter quarters rather late, often only in May. The majority leave in September.

Little Bittern

Night Heron *Nycticorax nycticorax* (Black-crowned Night Heron)
Bakcsó

Night Herons are familiar birds of Hungary's wetlands, and though essentially crepuscular and nocturnal feeders, they are often also active and easily seen by day. They breed in colonies in riverine woodland, fishponds with thickets, feeder channels lined with willows, poplars or *acacias* and in backwaters, often in the company of Little Egrets. The 60-70 regular colonies, some of which consist of several hundred pairs, are scattered fairly evenly nation-wide. Although highly colonial, pairs will nest in isolation or in small loose groups when there is a lack of bushes and trees around favoured wetlands.

STATUS IN HUNGARY: Fairly common breeder. From 4,000-5,000 pairs estimated. Population probably stable. Migrant. Protected.

STATUS INTERNATIONALLY: Global distribution. A declining species across Europe, though improved monitoring in Eastern Europe is needed to clarify the population size.

DISTRIBUTION: Suitable wetlands nationwide but often rather local. Several important colonies lie along the River Tisza. Locally common in summer at wetlands in the Tisza flood-plain, the southern stretches of the Danube, Kis-Balaton and scattered fishponds in southern Transdanubia.

TIMING: April to September. Some birds arrive back at the end of March. Colonies are usually occupied by mid April. Most leave for West Africa in September. A few may remain into October.

Squacco Heron *Ardeola ralloides*
Üstökös gém, Selyemgém

The rarest of Hungary's breeding Ardeidae, Squacco Herons usually nest in loose colonies in trees and bushes among Night Herons and Little Egrets. The majority of the Hungarian breed-ing population is found in floodplain woodland, with the main colonies along the Tisza. Some also breed around fishponds, rice fields and in marshes with bush and tree cover. Birds will also nest in reedbeds among Purple Herons, Great White Egrets and Spoonbills. They rarely form autonomous colonies. The period of occurrence of the species in Hungary is shorter than for other herons, with nesting sites occupied later than their congeners, usually at the end of May, and most birds migrating to winter in West Africa in September.

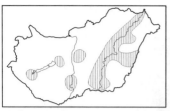

STATUS IN HUNGARY: Uncommon breeder. Around 300-400 pairs estimated. Has declined. Migrant. Protected.
STATUS INTERNATIONALLY: Old World species. Considered vulnerable in Europe where it continues to decline.
DISTRIBUTION: Rather uncommon in Transdanubia, though plenty of seemingly suitable wetlands exist. Traditional sites are Kis-Balaton, Lake Kolon in the Kiskunság, Pusztaszer, Lakes Péteri and Tisza, Tiszaalpár, fishponds and marshes on the Hortobágy and Bodrogköz.
TIMING: Arrives rather later in Hungary than other heron species, in late April. Most depart in September.

Little Egret *Egretta garzetta*
Kis kócsag

As is the case with Squacco Heron, this species is very much a bird of the Tisza floodplain. Indeed, these two species often breed together in mixed colonies in the Tisza's remnant woodland. Occasionally some Little Egrets will nest in marshes with willow and poplar bushes and on the tree-covered islands and dykes of fish-pond systems. In mixed heronries, the number of Little Egrets can vary from as few as 2-3 pairs to around 50. Colonies of around 200 pairs were recorded in the last century but those days have long gone. In contrast to the overall European trend, Little Egret numbers have fallen in Hungary throughout this century.
STATUS IN HUNGARY: Uncommon to locally fairly common. From 400-500 breeding pairs estimated. Has declined. Migrant. Strictly protected.
STATUS INTERNATIONALLY: Old World species. Overall European population increasing and expanding in range.
DISTRIBUTION: Mainly the south and east of the country. Uncommon in most of Transdanubia though there are colonies at Kis-Balaton, the Danube at Gemenc, in Tolna County, Sárrét and sometimes the Sárvíz valley. More common though rather local and never numerous on fishponds, marshes and riverine woodland along the Tisza and further east. Main colonies in floodplain woodland at Tiszadob, Ároktő-Tiszacsege and Tiszaalpár, and fishponds in the Hortobágy and Pusztaszer regions.
TIMING: First birds often seen at the end of March, though most arrive at the end of April. First birds leave for wintering areas at the end of August. By the end of September only stragglers remain.

Great White Egret *Egretta alba* (Great Egret)
Nagy kócsag

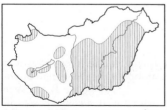

At the turn of the century, Great White Egrets were seriously endangered in Hungary owing to the plume trade. Today they are among the most conspicuous and familiar of Hungary's wetland birds thanks to decades of conservation work which began with protection status in 1912. In 1951 only one colony, of 33 pairs at Kis-Balaton, existed. Today there are around 30 colonies nationwide. Indeed, with an estimated breeding population of up to 800 pairs, Hungary is one of Europe's most important countries for this species. Great White Egret is also the emblem of Hungarian state nature conservation. The majority nest in mixed reedbed colonies with Purple Herons and Spoonbills, though some breed in marshes and floodplains. A few pairs may nest among other species or Great White Egrets can predominate with up to a 100 pairs together. By April, birds are already incubating and by July breeding is complete.

STATUS IN HUNGARY: Fairly common breeder. Between 700 and 800 pairs. Population stable. Most of population migratory though some overwinter. Strictly protected.

STATUS INTERNATIONALLY: Cosmopolitan species. After persecution and decline European population now increasing.

DISTRIBUTION: Nationwide. Fairly common locally. Significant colonies at Dinnyés (42 pairs 1994), Lakes Fertő, Kolon and Tisza, Pacsmag fishponds, Kis-Balaton, Hortobágy, Pusztaszer and Bodrogköz. Some pairs also on the Hanság and at Sárrét, Nagyberek, Ócsa, Tápió marshes, Péteri-tó, Tiszaalpár, Biharugra fishponds and elsewhere.

TIMING: Often all year round as small groups of birds stay in most winters. The majority migrate to the Mediterranean basin, returning to Hungary in March and leaving in September and October.

Great White Egret

Grey Heron *Ardea cinerea*
Szürke gém

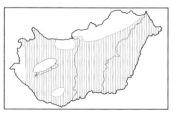

Despite being legally and regularly shot on Hungary's numerous fish-pond systems, Grey Herons continue to gradually increase in number. Mainly migratory, most have returned from the Mediterranean basin by early March and soon occupy nesting colonies. Large autonomous heronries of several hundred pairs no longer exist, rather small numbers nest among other heron species in noisy and colourful mixed colonies, often in trees but sometimes in reedbeds.

STATUS IN HUNGARY: Fairly common to common breeder. Increasing. Between 1,500 and 2,000 pairs. Mainly migratory. Protected, though can be shot on fish-farms outside protected areas from 1 August to 31 March.

STATUS INTERNATIONALLY: Old World species. Common, widespread and increasing in Europe.

DISTRIBUTION: Nationwide. Small colonies scattered mostly in the floodplain woodland of the Danube, Tisza, Dráva and other rivers, but also by fishponds and marshes.

TIMING: Migratory birds return at the end of February and leave at the end of September into October. Some can usually be found all year round. In hard winters groups congregate on the Danube, by other open water and also on farmland.

Purple Heron *Ardea purpurea*
Vörös gém

Of all the herons occurring in Hungary, this is the species most attached to large stands of *Phragmites* reed. Loose colonies or just a few pairs nest in the company of Spoonbills, Great White Egrets and other Ardeidae around lakes, fishponds, marshes and floodplain wetlands. When feeding it is not unusual to see several at a time spaced out in newly mown meadows, open marsh or stalking prey on raised dykes. There have been two recent cases of Purple Herons apparently interbreeding with Grey Herons and producing hybrid offspring, interestingly both at Dinnyés in Transdanubia in 1990 and 1991 respectively.

STATUS IN HUNGARY: Uncommon to fairly common locally. Fewer than 1,000 pairs estimated. Has probably declined. Migrant. Protected.

STATUS INTERNATIONALLY: Old World species. Considered to be vulnerable and declining in Europe.

DISTRIBUTION: Wetlands with extensive reedbeds nationwide. Traditional sites include: natural lakes such as Fertő, Velence and Kolon; marshes such as Dinnyés, Tápió, Pusztakócs, Bodrogzug and Kesznyéten; and fishpond systems at Sumony, Pacsmag, Hortobágy, Szeged, Csaj-tó and Biharugra.

TIMING: From April to August. Some birds, possibly through-migrants, in October.

CICONIIDAE (Storks)

Black Stork *Ciconia nigra*
Fekete gólya

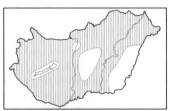

There are two sides to the Black Stork story in Hungary. In the breeding period they are secretive tree-nesters found in forest and woodland, feeding in stream valleys, backwaters and on secluded ponds. They are only usually seen at this time when soaring above their woodland breeding sites. Whilst on passage, however, Black Storks feed and roost communally on open fishponds, marshes, ox-bows and floodplain meadows and are almost confiding. Although thinly scattered, Black Storks breed in a variety of habitats in Hungary such as riverine forest, wooded hill ranges, old woodland dotted in lowlands and above all in the wooded fishpond systems of southern Transdanubia, particularly at Gemenc and the lower Danube where around 30 pairs nest.

STATUS IN HUNGARY: Rare breeder. Currently around 150 pairs but probably increasing. Migrant. More on passage. Strictly protected.

STATUS INTERNATIONALLY: Old World species. Rare but gradually increasing in Europe in both numbers and range.

DISTRIBUTION: Scattered nationwide. Traditional breeding areas include the Hanság, Szigetköz and Gemenc on the Danube, Szaporca on the Dráva, woodland along almost the whole length of the Tisza and numerous sites in Somogy County. A few pairs in the Börzsöny, Mátra, Zemplén and other hill ranges.

TIMING: April to September. Small migrating groups stop off on fishponds, floodplains and wet *puszta* in August and September.

Black Stork

White Stork *Ciconia ciconia*
Fehér gólya

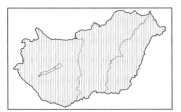

With the exception of Iberia, White Storks in Europe are today essentially birds of the east. In Hungary, as elsewhere, White Storks are entwined in folklore and legend. In country districts it is traditionally regarded as an honour to have a pair nest upon one's roof, though the mess that successive broods make over the years has modified this tradition somewhat, with home owners sometimes grateful when the birds move to a nearby telegraph pole to breed. A survey in 1984 found that from a total of 4,700 pairs, 52% nested on telegraph poles, 31% on buildings (usually chimneys) and 13% in trees. In 1989 the number of occupied nests on poles had risen to 65%. Successful cooperation between conservationists and the regional Hungarian electricity companies has resulted in the erection of nesting platforms atop telegraph poles nationwide and the insulation of potentially dangerous lines and conductors. Single White Stork pairs are widely scattered but loose colonies also exist, notably in villages such as Szalonna in Borsod County and Nagyiván on the Hortobágy where almost every telegraph pole along the highstreet is occupied.

STATUS IN HUNGARY: Fairly common. Around 5,000 pairs. Population now stable after a period of decline. Migrant. More on passage. Strictly protected.

STATUS INTERNATIONALLY: Old World species. Considered vulnerable in Europe, which holds almost 90% of the world population. Has declined and still under threat.

DISTRIBUTION: Nationwide. Fairly common locally in parts of Transdanubia (Vas, Somogy and Baranya Counties), in parts of the Great Plain (especially in the Tisza floodplain) and in Szabolcs-Szatmár-Bereg County. Up to 70% of pairs breed in and around human settlements.

TIMING: First birds arrive in March, with bulk of population in place from April. Migrating groups numbering up to several hundred gather in August, with stragglers seen as late as October.

THRESKIORNITHIDAE (Ibises and Spoonbills)

Glossy Ibis *Plegadis falcinellus*
Batla

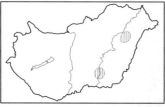

Once widespread, Glossy Ibis disappeared as a regular Hungarian breeding species after the draining and regulation of wetlands early this century. The days of 1,000 pairs at Kis-Balaton are long gone, with, since the Second World War, only small numbers occasionally breeding nationally, mainly in the Tisza floodplain. In the late 1980s, a few pairs began to regularly breed on fishponds on the Hortobágy and more recently at Csaj-tó fishponds in Csongrád County to the south. Pairs join mixed colonies of cormorants, egrets and herons, some years nesting in bushes and trees and in others reedbeds. Birds feed in marshes, on fishponds with emergent vegetation and in flooded meadows and backwaters. Recent conservation influenced water management at Kis-Balaton may encourage the species to return to this once important site.

STATUS IN HUNGARY: Rare breeder. Around ten pairs annually. Migrant. Recent small increase in Hungary runs against overall European trend. Strictly protected.

STATUS INTERNATIONALLY: Cosmopolitan species. Has declined across most of its European range.

DISTRIBUTION: Very rare in Transdanubia. Very local on Great Plain, with only regular breeding sites at Hortobágy-halastó and Csaj-tó.

TIMING: First birds arrive in mid April and leave in September.

Spoonbill *Platalea leucorodia* (Eurasian Spoonbill)
Kanalasgém

Hungary is an important country for this endangered species, with large colonies at Hortobágy-halastó, Csaj-tó and Lake Tisza. There are also several smaller colonies dotted around the country. Although Hungary has lost most of its natural wetlands, Spoonbills seem to have adapted well to man-made fishpond systems where they nest in safety from most predators on reed-covered islands. Owing to their specialised feeding method, adult birds often need to fly several miles from breeding colonies, which are invariably situated on ponds unsuitable for feeding, to other sites such as marshes, shallower fishponds, goose-farm ponds and even shallow feeder canals. This explains the seemingly constant overhead movements of Spoonbills on the Hortobágy and elsewhere.

STATUS IN HUNGARY: Uncommon to fairly common locally. 700-800 pairs and increasing. Migrant. Strictly protected.

STATUS INTERNATIONALLY: Old World species. Endangered in Europe where it has declined throughout the century.

DISTRIBUTION: On passage occurs on wetlands nationwide. From 200-300 pairs at Hortobágy-halastó and colonies of various sizes from 20 to 100 pairs at Lake Fertő, Lake Velence, Dinnyés (89 pairs 1994), Kis-Balaton, Lake Tisza, Pusztakócs, Csaj-tó and the Szeged area.

TIMING: Most birds arrive in late March and early April. Return migration, mainly to the Mediterranean area, is in September. In mild winters a few birds may remain.

Spoonbill

ANATIDAE (Wildfowl)

Mute Swan *Cygnus olor*
Bütykös hattyú

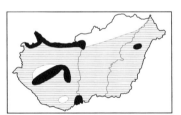

It is difficult to state just how many Hungarian Mute Swans are semi-domestic or truly wild specimens. Certainly those at Lake Balaton in summer are confiding and fail the 'bread test' miserably. In winter, some of the birds present no doubt originate from further afield and seem genuinely wild, if indeed any European birds can still be regarded as such. Certainly, few Hungarian ornithologists have a good word for the species because of the large territory pairs aggressively defend against other wildfowl. Despite local increases in breeding pairs at such places as Kis-Balaton, Mute Swans are still rather scarce in Hungary as a whole.

STATUS IN HUNGARY: Nationally uncommon but locally a common resident and increasing. More in winter. Protected.

STATUS INTERNATIONALLY: Originally a Eurasian species but now has cosmopolitan range owing to introductions. Common in Europe and increasing.

DISTRIBUTION: Very local. Regular sites being Lake Balaton, Szigetköz and Kis-Balaton where common. Feral populations scattered around the country.

TIMING: All year round.

Whooper Swan *Cygnus cygnus*
Énekes hattyú

Nowadays a rare but annual winter visitor, Whooper Swan was once a Hungarian breeding bird. Up to the middle of the last century scattered pairs nested in the then extensive marshes along the Tisza. Single birds, family groups and more rarely small herds are sighted every year on larger unfrozen wetlands. Some years see slight invasions, birds presumably originating from the Black Sea wintering population.

STATUS IN HUNGARY: Rare winter visitor. Protected.

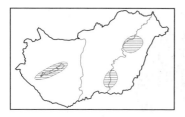

STATUS INTERNATIONALLY: Palearctic species. European population considered stable.

DISTRIBUTION: Wetlands nationwide, particularly on the Hortobágy, Kis-Balaton, Lake Balaton and the Szeged area.

TIMING: Winter. October to April but most regular in January and February.

Bean Goose *Anser fabalis*
Vetési lúd

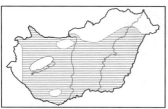

Hungary is one of the most important countries in Europe for wintering Bean Geese. Preferred roosts in Transdanubia, each with tens of thousands of birds, vary slightly from year to year but in total up to 100,000 birds can occur. In 1984, a synchronised count estimated almost 200,000 to be wintering nationwide. In some years over 50,000 have been estimated to pass through Lake Tata alone, with 10,000 sometimes wintering here. Recent counts have estimated 40,000 to pass through nationwide in spring and 50,000 in autumn. Many birds may now not reach Hungary, preferring to winter in the Czech Republic. It is not entirely clear which of two races predominate in Hungary. Some authorities mention the nominate race from the taiga as being more numerous, others the tundra breeding *rossicus*. A few of the *johanseni* race from western Siberia have also been recorded.

STATUS IN HUNGARY: Numerous on passage. Common locally in winter. 66,786 counted nationwide in November 1992 and 47,000 in January 1993. Unprotected. Game species.

STATUS INTERNATIONALLY: Palearctic species. Probably stable breeding population though under threat in European wintering areas.

DISTRIBUTION: Occurs nationwide, but largest numbers in Transdanubia. Smaller flocks in east of country with other geese at Hortobágy, Biharugra, salt lakes in the Kiskunság and other goose sites. Main Transdanubian roosts are Lake Fertő, Lake Tata, Balaton, Kis-Balaton, Sumony fishponds and Dinnyés. Usually some hundreds on Danube between Komárom and Szob, more if lakes totally freeze over.

TIMING: First flocks appear at the end of September. Majority arrive in October and November. Many birds stay through winter to March. A few straggling groups may be seen in April.

White-fronted Goose *Anser albifrons* (Greater White-fronted Goose)
Nagy lilik

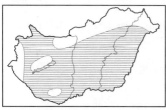

Although one of the highlights of the Hungarian winter is watching and hearing thousands of White-fronts flying in to roost, it is tempered by the thought that, according to the literature, as recently as the 1930s 'millions' visited Hungary. Migrating White-fronts pass through Hungary on a wide front from Lake Fertő on the Austrian border to the Biharugra fishponds far to the east on the frontier with Romania. Although all main goose sites in Hungary host the species, in contrast to Bean Goose, the vast majority of White-fronts occur east of the Danube. Around 200,000 pass through in spring and 25,000 in autumn. Up to 50,000 regularly winter on wetlands across the Great Plain. Although technically an unprotected species which can be shot in the wildfowl season, hunting of the species is at present suspended.

STATUS IN HUNGARY: Numerous on spring passage. Also autumn and winter. 36,473 counted nationwide in November 1992 and 33,715 in January 1993. Unprotected. Game species but shooting suspended.

STATUS INTERNATIONALLY: Holarctic species. Breeding population stable but under threat in European wintering areas.

DISTRIBUTION: Largest numbers on Great Plain at Hortobágy, Biharugra, Kardoskút, Pusztaszer and in the Kiskunság, particularly Kelemen-szék. In Transdanubia, smaller numbers occur among Bean Goose flocks at usual goose sites.

TIMING: First birds arrive in September, with peak numbers in November. The majority leave in March, though stragglers remain into April.

Lesser White-fronted Goose *Anser erythropus*
Kis lilik

Hungary is not a regular wintering area for Lesser White-fronted Goose as some literature suggests. There are rarely groups of any size after the first hard frosts in November. A few birds are seen after autumn passage but these are always among other geese. Lesser White-fronts linger in the east of Hungary for some weeks during autumn migration, less so in spring. Favoured roosts are shallow fishponds in the Hortobágy National Park. In March 1978, 400 were seen at Hortobágy-halastó. The largest number to occur in recent years was 240, again at Hortobágy-halastó, in October 1992. Singles and small numbers also occur with flocks of other geese around the country, feeding on agriculture land and drained fishponds. The species is strictly protected under Hungarian law whereas White-fronted Goose is a game species (but see above). Quite how wildfowlers are able to distinguish between the two species as they fly overhead is questionable.

STATUS IN HUNGARY: Uncommon on passage. Strictly protected.

STATUS INTERNATIONALLY: Palearctic species. Globally threatened and a vulnerable breeding species in Europe.

DISTRIBUTION: Great Plain, mainly east of the Tisza. Most observations now on the Hortobágy, with Kardoskút, Biharugra and Szeged Fehér-tó other sites. West of the Tisza sometimes occurs on the Kiskunság salt lakes. Very rare in Transdanubia but individuals possible at any goose site.

TIMING: The classic period is from mid September to November at the most reliable site, Hortobágy-halastó. Also end of February into March, with some records from April.

Lesser White-fronted Geese

Greylag Goose *Anser anser*
Nyári lúd

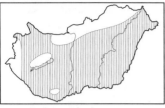

The only breeding goose species in Hungary. Pairs will commence nesting as soon as winter is over, usually in March, in marshes and around lakes and fishponds with reed cover. Some remain through milder winters. On passage, flocks of from 100 to 1,000 stop over at Lake Fertő, Kis-Balaton, Biharugra and wetlands in the Kiskunság and on the Hortobágy. Breeding birds are considered to be of the eastern race *rubrirostris,* though intergrades with the nominate no doubt occur. The nominate race is said to occur mainly on passage and in winter.

STATUS IN HUNGARY: Fairly common resident. Between 1,000 and 2,000 pairs. Population probably stable. More pass through on migration. Protected.

STATUS INTERNATIONALLY: Originally a Palearctic species, though has been introduced into other areas of the world. Fairly common and increasing in most of Europe.

DISTRIBUTION: Wetlands nationwide. Main breeding areas are Lake Fertő, Kis-Balaton, Lake Velence and Dinnyés, Hortobágy, Pusztaszer and Biharugra.

TIMING: Possible all year round. Most leave Hungary in November and early December, arriving back in February and March. Overwintering birds regular at Lake Fertő and elsewhere in mild years.

Barnacle Goose *Branta leucopsis*
Apácalúd

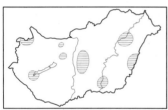

A few Barnacle Geese turn up each year in flocks of White-fronted and Bean Geese around the country. The largest recorded number seen together was 16 in March 1978 at Dunapataj in the Kiskunság. Birds are thought to originate from the Russian breeding population and usually occur with White-fronted Geese.

STATUS IN HUNGARY: Rare but annual winter visitor. Protected.

STATUS INTERNATIONALLY: North Atlantic-Arctic breeding species. European breeding population stable if not increasing. Under threat on wintering grounds.

DISTRIBUTION: Can occur at any major goose roost or feeding site. Annual at Lake Fertő where birds regularly seen from September to March.

TIMING: Mainly autumn and winter. Records spread from July to April.

Red-breasted Goose *Branta ruficollis*
Vörösnyakú lúd

A few of these stunning geese turn up each winter, often in the company of White-fronted Geese and mainly on the Great Plain. In some years small groups invade. The largest single flock on record is 52 at Kardoskút in the south of the Great Plain in November, 1980. The winter of 1993-94 saw a major influx, with birds dotted around the country among flocks of grey geese. Contrary to some literature, Red-breasted Geese do not regularly winter in significant numbers in Hungary.

STATUS IN HUNGARY: Rare but annual winter visitor. Strictly protected.

STATUS INTERNATIONALLY: Breeds in Arctic Siberia and winters mainly in Black Sea basin. Considered to be globally threatened. However, a reappraisal of the status of this species may be needed as a result of counts of wintering birds in the Balkans, currently thought to number

76,000 birds.

DISTRIBUTION: At main goose sites east of the Tisza such as Hortobágy, Kardoskút, Biharugra, Pusztaszer, Szeged area, and at other fishponds frequented by wildfowl, but also on the Kiskunság salt lakes. Rare in Transdanubia, though there are several records from Lake Tata and Lake Fertő.

TIMING: Winter. From October to March.

Shelduck *Tadorna tadorna* (Common Shelduck)
Bütykös ásólúd

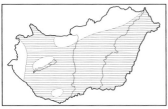

Although somewhat sporadically, Shelducks occur annually in Hungary. There are records from every month of the year though the main period of occurrence is late autumn. Usually small parties but sometimes single birds.

STATUS IN HUNGARY: Uncommon visitor. Protected.

STATUS INTERNATIONALLY: Palearctic species. Fairly common in Europe and probably increasing in number.

DISTRIBUTION: Wetlands nationwide. Regular on Great Plain at Szeged-Fehértó, Csaj-tó and fishponds on the Hortobágy.

TIMING: Possible all year round but most records from October to December.

Wigeon *Anas penelope* (Eurasian Wigeon)
Fütyülő réce

In a good spring up to 10,000 migrating Wigeon occur on shallow, vegetation-rich wetlands around Hungary. The main route through the country roughly follows the River Tisza but small flocks are often dotted nationwide. Some overwinter and a few stay through the summer but autumn is the classic time for this species.

STATUS IN HUNGARY: Fairly common on passage. Protected.

STATUS INTERNATIONALLY: Palearctic breeding species. Common in Europe where population considered stable.

DISTRIBUTION: Nationwide. Particularly the Great Plain with the Kiskunság, fishponds on the Hortobágy, Csaj-tó and Szeged-Fehértó being regular sites. In Transdanubia congregates at Dinnyés, Rétszilas, Kis-Balaton and Lake Fertő.

TIMING: Main flocks in spring from February to late April and in autumn from September to November.

Gadwall *Anas strepera*
Kendermagos réce

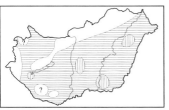

As elsewhere in Europe, Gadwall numbers have fallen in Hungary. The species was considered common before the war, both as a breeding and passage species, but today Gadwall is one of the country's rarest breeding ducks. Pairs typically breed on shallow fishponds with emergent vegetation, salt lakes, ox-bows and marshes. For unknown reasons, the species has disappeared from several formerly regular breeding areas along the Tisza. On passage, particularly in late September and October, parties of birds (dozens rather than hundreds) occur on more open waters and in wet meadows.

STATUS IN HUNGARY: Common on passage. Rare to uncommon breeder. From 150-200 nesting pairs, which represents a large post-war decline. Protected.

STATUS INTERNATIONALLY: Holarctic species. Considered vulnerable in Europe where declining.

DISTRIBUTION: Breeding birds scattered around the country but mainly east of the Danube, particularly the Hortobágy and Pusztaszer regions. On passage, wetlands nationwide.

TIMING: Spring passage peaks in March. More occur in autumn, from September to early November. Between passage periods at scattered breeding sites.

Teal *Anas crecca* (Green-winged Teal)
Csörgő réce

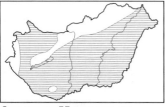

After Mallard this is the most commonly occurring duck species in Hungary. Some are present almost all year round, and a few pairs breed each year, though confirmed records are few. In 1994, one pair was confirmed breeding at Dinnyés in Transdanubia. Most Teal, however, occur in Hungary on passage when flocks of several thousand each congregate at scattered sites around the country. In milder winters some hundreds may stay on.

STATUS IN HUNGARY: Numerous on passage, with flocks of several thousand regular. Rare breeder with some nesting birds suspected around the country each year. Unprotected. Game species.

STATUS INTERNATIONALLY: Holarctic breeding species. Common and widespread in Europe. Population considered to be stable.

DISTRIBUTION: Wetlands nationwide. Largest numbers pass through Great Plain wetlands such as Kiskunság salt lakes, Hortobágy, Pusztaszer, fishponds around Szeged, Kardoskút and Biharugra. In Transdanubia, good numbers assemble at Lake Fertő, Szigetköz, Balaton, Sárrét, Lake Tata and Dinnyés.

TIMING: All year round. Peak passage periods are March-April and September-October.

Mallard *Anas platyrhynchos*
Tőkés réce

Perhaps not surprisingly the most common duck species in Hungary as it is in all of Europe. There are resident birds, thousands more on passage and many raised commercially and released for the profitable wildfowling business.

STATUS IN HUNGARY: Abundant resident. Large numbers (several thousands at numerous sites) on passage in spring and autumn. Almost 100,000 counted nationwide in January 1994. Unprotected. Game species.

STATUS INTERNATIONALLY: Originally a Holarctic breeding species. Populations introduced globally. Most common duck species in the world and most populations stable.

DISTRIBUTION: Breeds on just about any wetland nationwide, from park ponds to rivers to marshes. On passage, largest numbers on lowland fishponds, reservoirs and lakes.

TIMING: All year round.

Pintail *Anas acuta* (Northern Pintail)
Nyílfarkú réce

The number of Pintails nesting in Hungary varies from year to year and probably depends upon the prevailing weather and the numbers and condition of birds which stop over in spring. The species mainly breeds on salt lakes, open marshes and flooded alkaline *puszta*, such as those found in Kiskunság and Hortobágy National Parks, and at scattered sites in the southeast of Hungary. Fishponds are important roosting and moulting places.

STATUS IN HUNGARY: Rare breeder with probably fewer than 50 pairs annually. Fairly

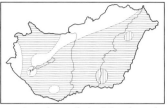

common on passage. Protected.

STATUS INTERNATIONALLY: Holarctic breeding species. Vulnerable in Europe where has declined badly.

DISTRIBUTION: Localised breeding pairs scattered nationwide, but mainly east of the Danube.

TIMING: Possible all year round. Besides breeding birds, some occasionally overwinter. Essentially a passage duck, with first birds arriving in February and peak numbers passing through in March and early April. Main autumn migration from late October into November.

Garganey *Anas querquedula*
Böjti réce

Despite having declined across much of Europe, Garganey are still familiar birds on

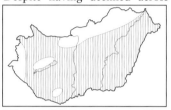

Hungary's wetlands, particularly fishponds, marshes, flooded meadows and salt lakes. The courtship flight of a female pursued by several drakes is arguably one of the most fascinating sights of a spring day at a Hungarian wetland. In addition to breeding birds, many more pass through the country, often stopping over to moult.

STATUS IN HUNGARY: Fairly common breeder. Stable population of between 1,300 and 1,500 pairs estimated. Migrant. More on passage. Unprotected. Game species.

STATUS INTERNATIONALLY: Palearctic breeding species. Although still widespread, has declined in Europe where regarded as vulnerable.

DISTRIBUTION: Breeding pairs scattered on wetlands nationwide but majority east of Danube. On migration, small parties stop off at same sites.

TIMING: First birds return from wintering areas in Africa often as early as the end of February, though peak passage falls in March. In autumn, return migration is in August and September when flocks of several hundred, though usually tens, may occur.

Garganey

Shoveler *Anas clypeata* (Northern Shoveler)
Kanalas réce

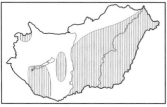

Traditionally a duck of wet meadows, salt lakes and marshes, this is another species which, though it has adapted fairly well to the relatively new habitats of fish-pond systems, has experienced an overall decline in numbers in Hungary. Never common as a breeding species, Shovelers are much more numerous in Hungary on passage when single flocks of over 1,000 birds are not unknown. Some years see scattered parties overwintering.

STATUS IN HUNGARY: Common to uncommon breeder. Population size unknown. Migrant. Numerous on passage. Protected.

STATUS INTERNATIONALLY: Holarctic breeding species. Widespread and fairly common in Europe.

DISTRIBUTION: Breeds nationwide but mainly wetlands east of the Danube, particularly along and east of the Tisza. Also found around the country on passage but largest numbers occur on sites in the east such as Hortobágy-halastó and other wetlands in Hortobágy National Park, Csaj-tó and the Szeged area.

TIMING: Possible almost all year round. First passage groups arrive in February, with peak soon after in mid March. Largest numbers occur in autumn in October-November.

Red-crested Pochard *Netta rufina*
Üstökösréce

This species is perhaps surprisingly uncommon in Hungary given the proximity of populations in the Czech Republic and neighbouring Romania and Austria. Indeed, most records are from Lake Fertő, the Hungarian side of the Neusiedlersee, and this is now the Hungarian breeding stronghold with around 40 pairs annually. Perhaps the reason for its scarcity as a breeder lies in the fact that Red-crested Pochards are loth to nest on fishpond systems, which are Hungary's main wetland habitat, unlike most other breeding duck species. A slow but noticeable eastward expansion of range in Hungary has occurred since the first confirmed breeding at Lake Fertő in 1986. The species first bred at Dinnyés in 1989.

STATUS IN HUNGARY: Rare breeder but increasing. Currently 50-75 pairs. Migrant. Uncommon on passage. Protected.

STATUS INTERNATIONALLY: Palearctic breeding species. Although still widespread in Asia, declining in Europe.

DISTRIBUTION: Scattered pairs breed in Transdanubia at Lake Fertő, Lake Velence (five pairs 1994), Dinnyés (seven pairs 1994) and Kis-Balaton. East of the Danube has bred at Szeged Fehér-tó. Most migration is also through western Hungary. Elsewhere rare on passage.

TIMING: From February to November. Passage birds occur from February to early May and from August to November.

Pochard *Aythya ferina* (Common Pochard)
Barátréce

After Mallard, the most widespread breeding duck in Hungary, occurring on wetlands of all kinds, including fishponds, reservoirs, lakes and even gravel pits as long as adequate cover for nesting exists. Besides breeding pairs, many thousands more move through Hungary in spring and autumn. In winter rafts of from 20 to 200 remain on the Danube and other open waters such as Lake Tata.

STATUS IN HUNGARY: Common breeder. Stable population of around 20,000-25,000 pairs estimated. Many more on passage. Unprotected. Game species.

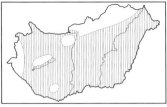

STATUS INTERNATIONALLY: Palearctic breeding species. Common and widespread in Europe.

DISTRIBUTION: Almost any wetland nationwide. Very common on reservoirs and the large fishpond systems of the Great Plain. Common in Transdanubia on both natural lakes and on the region's numerous fishponds.

TIMING: Usually all year round. Migratory birds return in February and March and leave as late as November. Largest numbers occur in September and October when flocks of several thousand birds each congregate around the country.

Ferruginous Duck *Aythya nyroca* (White-eyed Pochard)
Cigányréce

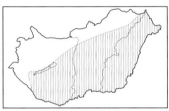

Although numbers have fallen, Ferruginous Ducks are still fairly widespread in Hungary, breeding on a range of wetlands including deeper fishponds, salt lakes, marshes, ox-bows and reservoirs. The common requirement is an abundance of emergent vegetation and thick reed cover for nesting. The species is often seen swimming in channels between islands or in and out of vegetation, rarely sitting out in large expanses of open water. Both man-made and natural wetlands throughout Hungary which have a patchwork appearance of open water, plant cover and reedy islands are invariably good sites for the species.

STATUS IN HUNGARY: Fairly common to uncommon locally. From 1,000-1,500 pairs, which represents a decline. Migrant. Strictly protected.

STATUS INTERNATIONALLY: Palearctic breeding species. Globally threatened and considered vulnerable in Europe where it has declined sharply.

DISTRIBUTION: Scattered nationwide. In Transdanubia, regular areas include Lake Velence, Dinnyés (six pairs 1994), Sárrét, Kis-Balaton, Pacsmag fishponds, Sumony fishponds and Szaporca. On the Great Plain: Lake Péteri, Tiszadob, Mártély, Csaj-tó fishponds, Biharugra, Lake Tisza, Pusztakócs marshes and the various wetlands of the Hortobágy.

TIMING: First birds return from wintering quarters in the Mediterranean in March. Return passage in October and November. A few occasionally overwinter.

Ferruginous Duck

Tufted Duck *Aythya fuligula*
Kontyos réce

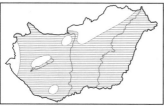

Although Tufted Duck can be seen all year round in Hungary, the species rarely nests. Two pairs bred at Dinnyés, Transdanubia, in 1994 and it may breed annually at Kis-Balaton. Rather the species is a common visitor on passage and in winter. Thousands stop off on reservoirs, deeper fishponds, lakes, particularly Balaton, and on the Danube in the autumn. In midwinter, numerous rafts of several hundred each congregate on the Danube and unfrozen wetlands dotted around the country such as Lake Tata.

STATUS IN HUNGARY: Common on passage and in winter. Very rare breeder with 0-10 pairs annually. Protected.

STATUS INTERNATIONALLY: Palearctic breeding species. Widespread in Europe where population stable.

DISTRIBUTION: On passage and in winter nationwide. The first three breeding records were from Győr-Sopron County in the northwest in 1965, from Hódmezővásárhely in the very southeast in 1973, and thirdly from Szabolcs-Szatmár County in the extreme northeast in 1980. It is difficult to imagine three sites in Hungary being more widely scattered than this. In winter, favoured areas along the Danube include Szigetköz, Süttő, Szob, Nagymaros, Vác and Óbuda.

TIMING: All year round as some non-breeders regularly oversummer. October-November and February-March for largest numbers.

Scaup *Aythya marila* (Greater Scaup)
Hegyi réce

Although rare, Scaup do occur every year in Hungary. Mostly females and juveniles are observed, with as few as 50 birds reported nationwide annually, often in the company of Pochards, Tufted Ducks and Velvet Scoters. Rarely more than ten together. Scaup are rather nomadic outside the breeding season and this probably accounts for their erratic occurrence in land-locked Hungary, though the Danube does seem to be a regular flyway.

STATUS IN HUNGARY: Rare passage and winter visitor. Protected.

STATUS INTERNATIONALLY: Holarctic species. Under threat in Europe where rather localised in both breeding and main wintering areas.

DISTRIBUTION: Mainly Transdanubia, especially the Danube, Lake Balaton and various reservoirs. East of the Danube, the River Tisza, Lake Tisza and larger fishponds.

TIMING: Has occurred from September to May but main period is from November to February and the Danube Bend the most regular area.

Long-tailed Duck *Clangula hyemalis* (Oldsquaw)
Jegesréce

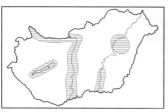

This is another northern duck, which though rare in Hungary, still finds its way into the heart of Europe annually. As with Scaup, it is often found in the midst of other more numerous winter visitors such as Tufted Duck and Goldeneye.

STATUS IN HUNGARY: Rare winter visitor. Protected.

STATUS INTERNATIONALLY: Holarctic species. Stable population in Europe.

DISTRIBUTION: Mostly the Danube though some occur on Lake Balaton and occasionally on larger, deeper fishponds such as those at Csaj-tó.

TIMING: Has occurred from October (earliest record the 13th) to early May. Main period November and December on the Danube.

Common Scoter *Melanitta nigra* (Black Scoter)
Fekete réce

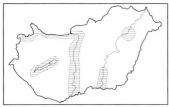

Historically a very rare visitor to Hungary, but closer watching of the Danube by Budapest birdwatchers in recent years has revealed the annual occurrence of Common Scoter. Mostly single birds or small groups are seen, double figures being very rare. Often one or two birds accompany Velvet Scoters.

STATUS IN HUNGARY: Rare winter visitor. Protected.

STATUS INTERNATIONALLY: Holarctic species. Stable population in Europe.

DISTRIBUTION: Mainly the Danube, especially at Pilismarót, Vác, Göd and Óbuda. Records also from Lake Balaton and a few from Lake Fertő, the River Tisza and very occasionally fishponds on the Great Plain.

TIMING: Possible from October through winter to April. Regular in November and December on the Danube north of Budapest.

Velvet Scoter *Melanitta fusca* (White-winged Scoter)
Füstös réce

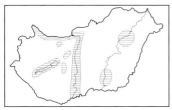

Much more frequent than Common Scoter, with small groups regular on the Danube every winter. Very occasionally, flocks of up to 100 occur on the Danube Bend in certain spots rich in freshwater molluscs. Records are on the increase, but this may well be owing to more observers rather than an actual increase in visiting birds.

STATUS IN HUNGARY: Uncommon winter visitor. Protected.

STATUS INTERNATIONALLY: Holarctic species. Populations stable in European breeding areas but considered to be under threat in wintering areas.

DISTRIBUTION: Almost exclusively the Danube, especially near Szob, Vác, Göd and Óbuda, but also on Balaton, Velence and other lakes. Occasionally occurs on the River Tisza and fishponds on the Great Plain.

TIMING: Records from September to May with December to March the most regular period.

Goldeneye *Bucephala clangula* (Common Goldeneye)
Kerceréce

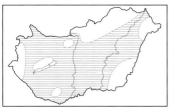

In most winters several thousand Goldeneye winter on the Danube from Szigetköz in the west to Budapest in the east, and in some years up to 10,000 have been estimated to winter on Lake Balaton alone. With such numbers it is perhaps not surprising that some stragglers have been recorded in summer though as yet there are no breeding records.

STATUS IN HUNGARY: Common winter visitor. Over 8,000 counted nationwide in January 1994. Unprotected. Game species.

STATUS INTERNATIONALLY: Holarctic species. European breeding population increasing.

DISTRIBUTION: Nationwide, but mainly the Danube and lakes in Transdanubia, particularly Fertő and Balaton. Also deeper fishponds in Transdanubia. Smaller numbers but regular on

Hortobágy and other fishpond systems in the east.

TIMING: End of October to mid April. Several thousand on Danube in January and February.

Smew *Mergus albellus*
Kis bukó

By far the most common of the three *Mergus* species which visit Hungary. In hard winters several hundred Smew concentrate on the open water of the Danube when other waters freeze over. In January, around the Danube Bend, conspicuous groups of up to a dozen males and the always more numerous 'redheads' can be seen together in favoured areas. At other times during winter, birds occur on deeper waters nationwide. Hungary is the most important country in Central Europe for the species. STATUS IN HUNGARY: Fairly common winter visitor. 248 counted nationwide in January 1994. Protected.

STATUS INTERNATIONALLY: Palearctic breeding species.

Considered vulnerable in Europe where population is thought to have declined sharply.

DISTRIBUTION: Wetlands nationwide. Mainly the Danube and lakes and ponds in Transdanubia. Fewer on the Great Plain.

TIMING: Records from September to June, with main period November to March.

Red-breasted Merganser *Mergus serrator*
Örvös bukó

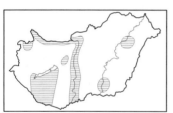

The rarest of the three *Mergus* species. Although never numerous, some Red-breasted Merganser are, however, recorded every year, usually single birds or twos and threes, with double figures very rare. Most pass through the country via the Danube in autumn, with a few very occasionally overwintering.

STATUS IN HUNGARY: Uncommon passage and winter visitor. Protected.

STATUS INTERNATIONALLY: Holarctic species. Stable European breeding population.

DISTRIBUTION: Mainly the Danube, and deeper wetlands in Transdanubia. Rather rare east of the Danube though some are seen on the River Tisza and various fishponds each year.

TIMING: Has occurred from September to May. Best month overall is November and, as with most other winter ducks, most records from the Danube.

Goosander *Mergus merganser* (Common Merganser)
Nagy bukó

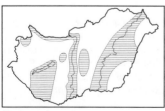

Goosander is a much more common visitor to Hungary than Red-breasted Merganser. Often in small groups of fewer than ten birds, but in January and February loose flocks of 50 and occasionally up to 100 are not unknown, particularly on the Danube Bend. Small parties also frequent the numerous fishponds of Transdanubia, and to a lesser extent the Great Plain, when waters remain open.

STATUS IN HUNGARY: Fairly common winter visitor.
Protected.

STATUS INTERNATIONALLY: Holarctic species. Stable European breeding population.

DISTRIBUTION: Possible on any wetland nationwide but mainly the Danube, especially the stretch between Szob and Vác. Also reservoirs and Lake Balaton. Fewer, but annual on Great Plain wetlands.

TIMING: Has occurred from September to June but November to March is main period and the Danube Bend the main area.

ACCIPITRIDAE (Hawks, Vultures and Eagles)

Honey Buzzard *Pernis apivorus*
Darázsölyv

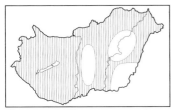

Honey Buzzards are scattered breeders in Hungary, with a strong preference for oak woods on the southern slopes of rolling hills such as those typical of Transdanubia. Thus, unlike most Hungarian breeding birds of prey, the species is more widespread in the west than east of the Danube. Some pairs also breed in lowland areas, particularly where bee-keeping is widespread and there are suitable copses or floodplain woodland for nesting.

STATUS IN HUNGARY: Fairly common breeder. Between 300 and 350 pairs. After a period of decline, numbers now probably stable. Migrant. Protected.
STATUS INTERNATIONALLY: Palearctic breeding species. Stable breeding population in Europe but considered threatened.
DISTRIBUTION: Scattered nationwide in wooded hilly areas, particularly in Zala and Vas Counties, and the Bakony and Vértes hills. Also the Börzsöny, Pilis, Mátra, Bükk, Aggtelek and Zemplén ranges, the Hajdúság region and along the Danube.
TIMING: Arrives at the end of April into May. Departs in late August and September.

Black Kite *Milvus migrans*
Barna kánya

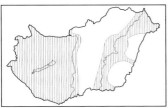

This species is not as common in Hungary as one might perhaps expect given the amount of seemingly suitable habitat. In common with Honey Buzzard, this is a bird of prey which is more abundant in the west of Hungary than the east. The fishponds of southern Transdanubia, which are mostly set in woodland, are preferred to those of the Great Plain, which are invariably set in more open landscapes. Rarely building their own nests, Black Kites in Hungary use those of Cormorants, Grey Herons, Common Buzzards and Rooks and sometimes breed within heronries.

STATUS IN HUNGARY: Uncommon breeder with 150-175 pairs. Probably a recent population increase after an overall decline. Migrant. Strictly protected.
STATUS INTERNATIONALLY: Old World and Australasian species. Vulnerable in Europe where there has been a steep decline, particularly in the east.
DISTRIBUTION: Thinly scattered nationwide, mainly by wetlands such as the wooded fishpond systems of Somogy County and elsewhere in Transdanubia. Also riverine forest along the Danube at Szigetköz, the Danube Bend and Gemenc. Some pairs along the River Dráva, the Hanság and Gerecse hills. Along the Tisza at Bodrogzug, Lake Tisza, Tiszadob, Tiszaalpár, Ároktő and Mártely.
TIMING: Occurs from late March through summer to early October.

Red Kite *Milvus milvus*
Vörös kánya

With only one regular pair each year, Red Kite is one of the rarest breeding birds in Hungary. It is not clear why the species is so rare, as suitable habitat and adequate protection exists and neighbouring countries have relatively large breeding populations. However, Red Kites have never been common in Hungary, with never more than 30 pairs found in any year since the Second World War. Most of the breeding pairs of the last 20 years have been recorded in the Hanság, Szabolcs-Szatmár-Bereg County, the Zemplén hills and Baranya County. Significantly, perhaps all these areas border neighbouring countries with breeding populations. Although the species used to nest in the Bakony, Vértes, Pilis, Bükk and other hill ranges, the heart of Hungary can no longer be regarded as Red Kite country.

STATUS IN HUNGARY: Very rare breeder. 1-2 pairs. Partial migrant, otherwise vagrant and occasional winter visitor. Strictly protected.

STATUS INTERNATIONALLY: Western Palearctic species. Categorised as globally threatened. European breeding population stable.

DISTRIBUTION: In recent years has only been recorded breeding in the very south-west of Hungary. Visiting nomadic birds can occur almost anywhere.

TIMING: Occupies nest site in March and leaves in early winter. One or two birds regular in lowlands in autumn. A few sometimes winter.

White-tailed Eagle *Haliaeetus albicilla*
Réti sas

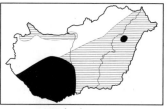

The recent history of this species is one of success for Hungarian conservation. After a period of decline there has been a population and range increase over the last 20 years. At the turn of the century the species was widespread, but egg collectors, hunters and later habitat loss, development and forestry practices reduced the population to a dozen pairs in the 1970s. The present 40-45 pairs is partly a result of conservation initiatives such as wardening, winter feeding, improving often flimsy nests and erection of artificial nests. Breeding White-tailed Eagles do best on wooded fishpond systems in Transdanubia, rather than the more exposed fishponds of the Great Plain. But in winter, visiting birds from northern Europe and dispersing young also gather at the latter sites, with over 25 regular at Hortobágy-halastó and 50-60 in the whole Hortobágy area. When carp or carrion have been put out on frozen ponds in hard winters up to 30 birds have congregated.

STATUS IN HUNGARY: Rare breeder, with 40-45 pairs. Increasing. Resident. Influxes in winter. Wintering population 140-150 birds. Strictly protected.

STATUS INTERNATIONALLY: Mainly Palearctic species. Globally threatened. Rare in Europe but increasing.

DISTRIBUTION: Lakes, reservoirs, fishponds and floodplains. Around 85% of pairs in Transdanubia, 15% on Great Plain. In winter 62% of birds in Transdanubia and 38% on Great Plain. Main wintering sites: Hortobágy, Szigetköz, Lake Balaton, Gemenc, with some at Pacsmag fishponds, Lake Tisza, Mártély, Csaj-tó and Biharugra. Core breeding populations at Gemenc and Mohács Island on the southern stretches of the Danube, and at Boronka and other areas in Somogy County.

TIMING: All year round as breeding pairs are mainly resident. From October to March on fishponds and lakes with wildfowl flocks.

Short-toed Eagle *Circaetus gallicus*
Kígyászölyv

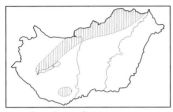

In common with many languages, the Hungarian name translates as 'Snake Buzzard' though this only partly reflects the diet of the species as insects, lizards, frogs, small mammals and birds are also taken. In Hungary, Short-toed Eagles breed on the southern slopes of hill ranges, especially those with Mediterranean-type habitats of dry scrub, grassland, stony pastures, karst and open areas with scattered trees. In short, warm habitats where reptiles abound. Most pairs nest in woodland proper, especially oakwoods, and hunt in adjacent open country. Birds move to and loiter in lowland areas at the end of summer, and a few pairs also breed here.

STATUS IN HUNGARY: Rare, but with a stable population of around 50-70 pairs. Migrant. Strictly protected.

STATUS INTERNATIONALLY: Mainly Palearctic breeding species. Rare in Europe and under threat.

DISTRIBUTION: As a breeding species scattered across the country but mostly the hill ranges of the north and northeast. Traditional areas include the Börzsöny, Pilis, Bükk, Aggtelek and Zemplén hill ranges.

TIMING: First birds arrive in late March and early April. Most leave in September though some, possibly late through-passage birds, linger into October.

Marsh Harrier *Circus aeruginosus*
Barna rétihéja

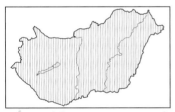

Today Marsh Harriers are one of Hungary's most widespread birds of prey and the vocal display flight of the species is a familiar sight over wetlands in April and May nationwide. First legally protected in 1982, the species has recovered from a decline linked to the effects of toxins in the food chain and direct persecution. The range of habitats in which Marsh Harriers now occur in Hungary is remarkable. Birds can be seen hunting over fishpond systems, lakes, reservoirs, marshes, meadows, *puszta*, arable land and even motorway verges, though reedbeds, not necessarily large ones, are almost essential for breeding.

STATUS IN HUNGARY: Common. Stable population of 1,500-2,000 pairs estimated. Mainly migratory but some do winter, numbers depending on weather. Numerous birds from northern Europe also pass through on migration. Protected.

STATUS INTERNATIONALLY: Old World and Australasian species. European population increasing.

DISTRIBUTION: Breeds on wetlands nationwide. Areas with particularly good numbers are Lake Fertő, Kis-Balaton, Sárrét, Pacsmag fishponds, Dinnyés, Lake Velence, Ócsa, Tápió marshes, Kiskunság, Pusztaszer, Biharugra, Hortobágy and Bodrogzug.

TIMING: Possible all year round as some occasionally overwinter. Main period of occurrence from March to October.

Hen Harrier *Circus cyaneus* (Northern Harrier)
Kékes rétihéja

It has been estimated that each winter more than 2,000 Hen Harriers quarter Hungary's lowlands. On an average winter day 'ring-tails' outnumber adult males by 4 to 1 in a given area. Roosts of over 50 birds are regular. Hen Harrier is at the very south of its European breeding range here and is thus a very rare occasional breeder. Nesting was confirmed in Transdanubia in 1922, 1925, 1935 and 1948. Recently, breeding was suspected at Dinnyés,

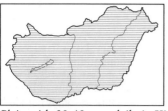

again in Transdanubia, but not confirmed.
STATUS IN HUNGARY: Common winter and passage visitor. Has bred. Protected.
STATUS INTERNATIONALLY: Holarctic species. Vulnerable and in decline in most of Europe.
DISTRIBUTION: Lowlands nationwide. The Hanság, Lake Fertő, Dinnyés, Sárrét and Zámoly basin are favoured areas in Transdanubia, but majority occur on the Great Plain with 30-40 seen daily in Kiskunság and Hortobágy National Parks.
TIMING: First visitors arrive in late August. Numbers build up in October and most stay till March. A few linger into April.

Pallid Harrier *Circus macrourus*
Fakó rétihéja

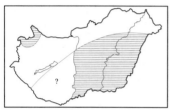

Most Pallid Harriers are seen in Hungary in early autumn over farmland and dry *puszta*, and the further east one goes the more likely one is to see this species. Owing to the difficulties in safely separating females and juveniles from Montagu's Harrier, most Hungarian records relate to males. Birds seem to be nomadic, wandering in the country rather than passing through on a particular route. Single birds have oversummered.
STATUS IN HUNGARY: Rare but annual on passage. Protected.
STATUS INTERNATIONALLY: Palearctic breeding species. Lack of data means exact status unknown but probably threatened across its world range. Very rare and considered to be endangered in Europe.
DISTRIBUTION: Can occur in lowland areas nationwide. Most observations from the Great Plain, particularly *puszta* in the Hortobágy and Kiskunság regions. Scattered records from Transdanubia.
TIMING: In spring, most regular in March and April. In autumn September and October.

Montagu's Harrier *Circus pygargus*
Hamvas rétihéja

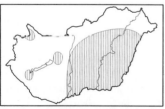

Once widespread, Montagu's Harrier declined badly in Hungary, as elsewhere in Europe, during the middle of this century. Recently, against the European trend, the species has made something of a comeback in Hungary. Although breeding populations are very localised, numbers are on the increase. Pairs breed across the country in a variety of habitats, including meadows, marshes, grassland and agricultural areas, especially those planted with lucerne.
STATUS IN HUNGARY: Uncommon breeder. Fairly common locally. The estimated 200-250 pairs represents a gradual population increase after a decline. Migrant. Strictly protected.
STATUS INTERNATIONALLY: Palearctic breeding species.
European population probably increasing.
DISTRIBUTION: Scattered in lowlands nationwide, nowhere common, but more frequent east of the Danube. On the Great Plain breeds throughout the Kiskunság, the Hortobágy and in the southeast. In Transdanubia, traditional areas include the Hanság, Kis-Balaton and Sárrét.
TIMING: From April to September.

Goshawk *Accipiter gentilis* (Northern Goshawk)
Héja

Goshawks are more common in Hungary's woodland and forest than actual sightings may initially suggest. All upland forest has breeding pairs, and though conifer plantations are the preferred nesting habitat, deciduous forest, copses, riverine woodland and even some lowland poplar plantations are also inhabited. Adult birds usually remain around their nesting sites all year, whilst young birds and visitors from further north are nomadic and can be seen over the *puszta* in winter. Goshawk is the only bird of prey species which can be legally killed in Hungary, but only on pheasant and poultry farms. It is also the only species which can be taken for falconry, though a permit is required. The Hungarian nomenclature divides breeding birds into two races, '*gallinarum*' in the west and north and '*marginatus*' in the south and east. Other authorities regard these as clines of the nominate *gentilis*. The northern race *buteoides* has also been recorded.

STATUS IN HUNGARY: Common resident. Between 2,000 and 3,000 pairs. Probably a recent population increase. Protected, except on poultry and pheasant farms.
STATUS INTERNATIONALLY: Holarctic species. European population increasing.
DISTRIBUTION: Mostly sedentary. Breeds in woodland nationwide but mainly in hill areas.
TIMING: All year round. In autumn and winter seen more often in lowlands.

Goshawk

Sparrowhawk *Accipiter nisus*
Karvaly

Hungary's healthy population of resident Sparrowhawks is supplemented in winter by an influx of birds from the north and east. Owing to this, and because they are less secretive outside the breeding season, Sparrowhawks are more often seen in winter when they move nearer to settlements and hunt in open country and over reedbeds. Classic breeding habitat in Hungary, as elsewhere, is conifer plantation with adjacent clearings. Some also nest in mixed woodland, floodplain forest, colonnades and lowland copses.

STATUS IN HUNGARY: Fairly common resident. Around 1,000 pairs estimated. This represents a population increase after decades of decline for unclear reasons. More in winter. Protected.

STATUS INTERNATIONALLY: Palearctic breeding species. European population stable if not increasing.

DISTRIBUTION: Breeds in wooded areas nationwide. In winter more often in open country and urban areas.

TIMING: All year round.

Levant Sparrowhawk *Accipiter brevipes*
Kis héja

Whether it has simply been overlooked or is just an occasional visitor with no regular pattern of occurrence, this species remains something of a mystery bird in Hungary as indeed it is across most of its range. The few confirmed Hungarian nesting records are from the very east of the country, suggesting an expansion of birds from Romania (though it is also very rare there). In 1962 three pairs were found breeding in the oakwoods of Nagyerdő near Debrecen, and though birds were seen in the same area, and elsewhere, in subsequent years breeding was not proven. Nesting was only confirmed again 32 years later, in 1994, when at least three pairs were found in plantations and parkland in Békés County in the very southeast of the country. A further three pairs, and several single birds, were found in the same area in 1995. Local ornithologists are now focusing on the species and the discovery of more nesting pairs is expected.

STATUS IN HUNGARY: Very rare breeder. From 2-6 pairs. Possibly overlooked in some areas. Migrant. Exact Hungarian status unclear. Strictly protected.

STATUS INTERNATIONALLY: Breeding range almost completely within Western Palearctic. Winters in Africa. Rare in Europe and probably declining, but exact status unknown.

DISTRIBUTION: Except for occasional vagrant birds, has only been found in woodland in Bihar and Békés Counties in the very east of country.

TIMING: Summer.

Common Buzzard *Buteo buteo*
Egerészölyv

This is Hungary's most common bird of prey, occurring in a wide range of landscapes and habitats. Birds breed above all in forested hill ranges but also in lowland plantations, floodplains, wooded *puszta* and farmland. In common with most other birds of prey, the species went through a post-war period of decline, though numbers began to increase again in the 1980s. In winter, birds from upland areas and influxes from further afield move to Hungary's lowlands. In areas rich in prey up to 50 birds can be seen in close proximity. There is also some movement, though not a visible migration, of birds through the country, including some of the *vulpinus* race.

STATUS IN HUNGARY: Common and widespread resident. The estimated 5,000-6,000 pairs represents a recent population increase. Protected.

STATUS INTERNATIONALLY: Palearctic breeding species. European population increasing.

DISTRIBUTION: Nationwide.

TIMING: All year round. Displaying birds can be seen as early as February. Classic months for *vulpinus* are March, and September-November.

Long-legged Buzzard *Buteo rufinus*
Pusztai ölyv

Long-legged Buzzards are regular visitors to Hungary in late summer and autumn. Usually single birds hunt in one area but there can be up to six on any large *puszta* with abundant prey. In recent years records have steadily increased with several adult birds oversummering and some seen in winter, particularly in the east of the country. It was not a total surprise therefore when a pair was confirmed as having bred on the Hortobágy in 1992 and then again in 1994. The birds occupied an artificial nest intended for Saker and, in common with other birds of prey in this area, hunted mainly Susliks.

STATUS IN HUNGARY: Very rare breeder. One pair. Regular late summer visitor. Protected.
STATUS INTERNATIONALLY: Palearctic breeding species. Endangered in Europe. Fairly common but rather local in parts of Asia and North Africa.
DISTRIBUTION: Rather nomadic. Visits lowland areas throughout Hungary but most linger on the Great Plain, particularly east of the River Tisza. Areas of *puszta* and farmland in Hortobágy and Kiskunság National Parks, Szolnok, Bihar and Békés Counties and the Szeged area are regular haunts. Now regularly seen on the Hortobágy throughout year which, with recent breeding, may indicate north and westward expansion of range from the Balkans.
TIMING: The classic time for the species is August when there is an influx of nomadic birds.

Rough-legged Buzzard *Buteo lagopus*
Gatyás ölyv

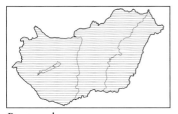

A Rough-legged Buzzard roosting atop a sweep-well or a telegraph pole is one of the most familiar sights of the Hungarian winter. Always fairly common from October on, some years see large influxes. It is not unusual to see several birds sitting in the company of Common Buzzards, all regularly spaced out, in a recently ploughed or mown field, preying on mammals disturbed by farm machinery.
STATUS IN HUNGARY: Fairly common winter visitor. Protected.
STATUS INTERNATIONALLY: Holarctic species. Stable breeding population in northern Europe.
DISTRIBUTION: Occurs in lowland farmland and *puszta* nationwide, with concentrations on the Great Plain.
TIMING: September to April, with peak numbers from November to January.

Lesser Spotted Eagle *Aquila pomarina*
Békászó sas

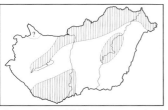

The most widespread *Aquila* species in Hungary, breeding mainly in hill forest and hunting in adjacent open areas of farmland, floodplains and stream valleys. Once again a translation of the Hungarian name is revealing as the 'Frog-hunting Eagle' does indeed feed to a large extent on amphibians, but reptiles, mammals and insects are also predated. Some birds from further north in Europe pass through Hungary in autumn but not in large concentrations. In the 1980s conservationists experimented in removing and later replacing the younger of the usually two eaglets in a nest in attempts to reduced sibling predation. There has since been some debate on the results and ethics of such methods.
STATUS IN HUNGARY: Uncommon, but with stable breeding population of 120-150 pairs.

Migrant. Strictly protected.

STATUS INTERNATIONALLY: Nominate race breeds almost exclusively in Western Palearctic. Rare in most of Europe.

DISTRIBUTION: Concentrated in central and northern hill ranges such the Bakony, Gerecse, Börzsöny, Mátra, Bükk and Zemplén. Some pairs in floodplain forest and a few scattered in lowlands. At the end of summer birds linger on the *puszta* before finally migrating.

TIMING: Possible from late March to early November. Most arrive in April and leave in September.

Spotted Eagle *Aquila clanga* (Greater Spotted Eagle)
Fekete sas

Although a rare and unpredictable visitor, a few Spotted Eagles are reported in Hungary each year. There is one unconfirmed record of a pair breeding in the Hanság in the 1950s and birds have occasionally overwintered. Single birds are the norm though there are some records of two together. More may well pass through Hungary on passage, but a lack of observers and difficulties in identification may in part account for the low numbers recorded.

STATUS IN HUNGARY: Rare but annual visitor. Protected.

STATUS INTERNATIONALLY: Palearctic breeding species. Globally threatened and considered endangered in Europe.

DISTRIBUTION: Possible nationwide, but two most regular sites are the Hortobágy and Kis-Balaton.

TIMING: Has occurred in almost every month of the year, although spring (March and April) and autumn (September and October) are most regular periods of occurrence.

Imperial Eagle *Aquila heliaca*
Parlagi sas

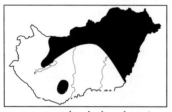

Hungary is an important country for this majestic and endangered species. Over the last 20 years there has been a gradual increase in the Hungarian population and today the species breeds in hill ranges, *puszta* and even lowland farmland. Some pairs have even taken to nesting in isolated trees in agricultural land when woodland proper is lacking. In some lowland areas, Imperial Eagles have benefited from the erection of artificial nests in trees adjacent to grassland abundant in prey. Other conservations measures have included insulating electric pylons and the introduction of Susliks, an important prey species, onto grassland near nests. Hungarian Imperial Eagles are traditionally considered to feed on Susliks, but hamsters, rabbits, hares and occasionally carrion are also eaten. Birds are nomadic rather than migratory, with most adults staying in their territories all year round whilst juvenile birds from the hills move to the *puszta* in winter. A few move further afield. A recent tendency to treat the eastern *heliaca* race as a distinct species from the Spanish *adalberti* probably has more to do with conservation politics and local pride than sound taxonomy.

STATUS IN HUNGARY: Rare breeder. 35-40 pairs. Increasing. Mainly resident but partially nomadic. Strictly protected.

STATUS INTERNATIONALLY: Palearctic species. Globally threatened. Endangered in Europe.

DISTRIBUTION: Most breeding pairs scattered in forested hills across the country, some in lowland *puszta* and agricultural areas.

TIMING: With exception of very harsh winters, all year round.

Imperial Eagle

Golden Eagle *Aquila chrysaetos*
Szirti sas

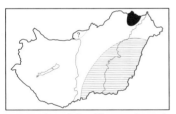

Historically there has been a steady decline in Hungary's breeding population of Golden Eagle. Recently a slight increase has occurred but the species is still a very rare and not all together successful breeder. Hungarian pairs might be regarded as the most southerly extension of the substantial Slovakian population and indeed inhabit inner parts of hill ranges near the Slovak border where felling has produced open areas. Here Golden Eagles hunt for hares, young deer, Moufflon and carrion.

STATUS IN HUNGARY: Very rare breeder. 2-4 pairs annually. Resident. Otherwise an uncommon but regular visitor, mainly in winter. Strictly protected.

STATUS INTERNATIONALLY: Holarctic species. Widespread but generally rare in Europe.

DISTRIBUTION: Breeding birds are mostly sedentary. Visitors, mostly nomadic young birds, wander over the Great Plain.

TIMING: All year round. Most visitors occur in November and December.

Booted Eagle *Hieraaetus pennatus*
Törpesas

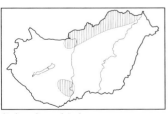

Booted Eagle is one of the most elusive of Hungary's birds of prey. In addition to being rare it is also secretive, inhabiting broadleaved woodland. Always a rare species in Hungary it has received less attention from local ornithologists than most other birds of prey. The limited available data suggests that little has changed in its status. Both light and dark phases probably occur in equal numbers though more often than not reports relate to the easier to identify light-phase birds.

STATUS IN HUNGARY: Very rare breeder. Small population of fewer than 20 pairs. Exact population trend unknown. Probably stable. Migrant. Strictly protected.

STATUS INTERNATIONALLY: Breeding range mainly within Palearctic. Rare in Europe and

generally declining.
DISTRIBUTION: Pairs scattered in the wooded hill ranges of central and northern Hungary. Otherwise lowland areas on passage.
TIMING: Arrives in April and leaves in August-September.

PANDIONIDAE (Osprey)

Osprey *Pandion haliaetus*
Halászsas

Hungary's innumerable and well-stocked fishponds are very attractive to migrating Ospreys. Single birds are very much the norm, though eight were seen together at Sumony fishponds in Transdanubia in April 1972, and there is a report from April 1969 of 14 birds at Szeged Fehér-tó. Artificial nests have attracted the interest of some spring birds but none has ever stayed to breed.
STATUS IN HUNGARY: Fairly common on passage. Strictly protected.
STATUS INTERNATIONALLY: Cosmopolitan species. Rare in Europe but population now stable after decades of decline.
DISTRIBUTION: Occurs at wetlands nationwide. Mainly fish-pond systems but also Kis-Balaton, Balaton, Lake Velence and Lake Tisza.
TIMING: Has occurred in every month of the year. Regular periods are April-May and from August to October. Majority observed in April.

FALCONIDAE (Falcons)

Lesser Kestrel *Falco naumanni*
Fehérkarmú vércse, Kis vércse

The current status of Lesser Kestrel in Hungary is shrouded in mystery. There have been unconfirmed breeding reports and misidentification blunders, but if the species does breed at all today then it is almost certainly in very low numbers. The last confirmed breeding was at Makó, Csongrád County, in the very southeast of the country in 1952. There were also reports from the Hortobágy in the 1980s. At the turn of the century small numbers bred in Vas County and interestingly there have been several recent reports of Lesser Kestrels from that region. Indeed, lying as it does in the southwest of the country, Vas County is close to southern Austria (where colonies have only recently become extinct) and to breeding populations in Slovenia and Croatia, which though small, are the nearest pairs to Hungary.
STATUS IN HUNGARY: Exact status unknown. Very rare and irregular breeder with 0-6 pairs. Migrant. Also accidental and nomadic birds occasionally occur. Strictly protected.
STATUS INTERNATIONALLY: Breeding range within Palearctic. Globally threatened. Vulnerable in Europe and declining.
DISTRIBUTION: Records scattered nationwide.
TIMING: If breeding, May to August. Otherwise accidentals mainly in April-May and August-September.

Kestrel *Falco tinnunculus* (Common Kestrel)
Vörös vércse

For many years numbers of this widespread bird of prey fell in Hungary, as indeed they did in most of Europe. Pesticides in the food-chain are thought to have been the main cause. The decline has now probably halted and the species is a familiar sight in both urban and rural Hungary. In some areas birds breed in loose colonies (for example on the Parliament building in Budapest) rows of *acacias* and particularly on lines of electricity pylons in farmland. Hungarian ornithologists are firm believers in artificial nests and nestboxes and Kestrels have been willing takers in many areas.

STATUS IN HUNGARY: Fairly common resident. Some migratory. Birds from further north and east in Europe winter. Between 3,500 and 4,000 pairs estimated. Population may now be stable after a long period of decline. Protected.
STATUS INTERNATIONALLY: Old World species. Has declined in much of Europe.
DISTRIBUTION: Urban and lowland rural areas nationwide.
TIMING: Usually all year round. Migratory birds return in February-March and leave in September.

Red-footed Falcons

Red-footed Falcon *Falco vespertinus*
Kék vércse

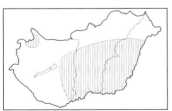

With only small populations remaining in neighbouring countries, the Hungarian breeding population of this endearing falcon is internationally important. Red-footed Falcons are essentially birds of Hungary's open lowland grassland, the *puszta*, though some occur on low-intensity farmland. They are the only true colonially breeding bird of prey in Hungary and mainly depend on rookeries for nesting sites, though some nest in loose colonies in colonnades and wind-breaks. Some pairs nest solitarily in isolated trees in Magpie and Hooded Crow nests. The availability of nests often dictates their local distribution, and the decline of Rooks, and hence rookeries, in Hungary has had its consequences for Red-footed Falcons. The days of large colonies of up to 200 pairs are gone. Besides a lack of nesting sites, numbers have been affected by a reduction in prey owing to intensive agricultural methods, by electrocution on pylons and the continued tradition of shooting-through corvid nests. Nevertheless, Red-footed Falcons swirling above an *acacia*-copse colony in eastern Hungary are still a familiar site and in many ways epitomise the *puszta* in summer.

STATUS IN HUNGARY: Uncommon nationally, common locally. Has steadily declined. With between 2,000 and 2,200 pairs, the bulk (Russian population possibly excepting) of Europe's breeding population is in Hungary. Migrant. Protected.

STATUS INTERNATIONALLY: Palearctic breeding species. Vulnerable and declining across most of European range.

DISTRIBUTION: Common locally east of the Danube where colonies of various sizes are scattered. The Kiskunság, Hortobágy and Csongrád, Bihar and Békés Counties are strongholds. Rare in Transdanubia, with only small isolated populations in Győr-Sopron, Tolna and Fejér Counties.

TIMING: Summer. First birds appear in early May. Large groups assemble in mid September before migrating to wintering areas in Africa.

Merlin *Falco columbarius*
Kis sólyom, Törpesólyom

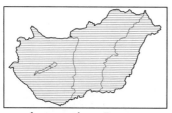

A Merlin over the *puszta* in pursuit of a lark or bunting is another of the regular sights of the Hungarian winter. With the exception of the forest of the Northern Hills and closed woodland in Transdanubia, birds can be seen almost anywhere nationwide. There have even been reports of three birds roosting together on Budapest's Basilica, from where they hunted urban House Sparrows. Usually solitary, but occasionally a pair seen together. The *aesalon* race from northern Europe occurs.

STATUS IN HUNGARY: Fairly common winter visitor. Protected.

STATUS INTERNATIONALLY: Holarctic breeding species. European population stable.

DISTRIBUTION: Lowlands nationwide. Mostly over farmland and *puszta,* occasionally around fish-pond reedbeds where songbirds roost.

TIMING: First birds usually occur at the end of September. Mainly from October through winter to March. Some reports from April.

Hobby *Falco subbuteo*
Kabasólyom

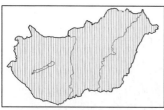

As is the case with Red-footed Falcon, Hobbies rely heavily on Magpies and Hooded Crows for nest sites, though in floodplains the nests of heron species and in farmland Raven nests on pylons are also occupied. The decline of the Hobby across much of Europe is owing to a combination of factors such as a general lack of habitat and declines in main prey species, but in some areas of Hungary a lack of nesting sites is often a problem when conditions otherwise seem ideal.

STATUS IN HUNGARY: Uncommon breeder. 1,000-1,200 pairs. Declined. Migrant. Protected.

STATUS INTERNATIONALLY: Palearctic species. European population probably now stable after decades of decline.

DISTRIBUTION: Scattered nationwide. Mostly in lowland areas with copses, wind-breaks and broadleaved woodland, but also in some upland areas, though rarely in forest proper.

TIMING: Mid May to September.

Saker *Falco cherrug* (Saker Falcon)
Kerecsensólyom, Kerecsen

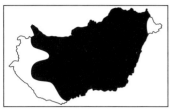

An increase in the Hungarian population of this enigmatic bird is owing to better protection of known nests (with nest robbing now virtually eliminated), the erection of artificial nests which the birds readily use, and a general improvement in monitoring. Hungarian ornithologists are fiercely proud and protective of their Sakers as this small country holds the largest population in Europe. In summer, many birds feed on Susliks, though upland birds mainly take pigeons, and, in winter, when Susliks hibernate, other prey, particularly birds, are taken. In general, Sakers which breed in uplands and floodplain forest hunt a wider selection of prey than lowland breeders. The species uses the nests of other large birds such as Raven, Hooded Crow, Common Buzzard and even Cormorant. Sites on cliffs, trees and electricity pylons are all used and Saker is yet another species which has been helped by the erection of artificial nests. If there is sufficient prey, adult birds stay in breeding territories all year. Upland breeders in particular move to the *puszta* in winter and there is a general post-breeding dispersal of juveniles. The official Hungarian nomenclature regards breeding birds as a Balkan subspecies '*danubialis*', though most authorities do not recognise this race.

STATUS IN HUNGARY: Rare breeder. 120-140 pairs. Increasing. Mainly resident. Some birds nomadic. Strictly protected.

STATUS INTERNATIONALLY: Palearctic species. Rare and considered endangered in Europe though numbers of breeding pairs actually increasing.

DISTRIBUTION: Scattered nationwide in both upland and lowland areas. Breeds in a wider range of habitats than most literature suggests. Forested hill ranges with open areas, riverine forest, *puszta* and even in farmland.

TIMING: All year round. Although numerically rare, Sakers are not too difficult to observe in Hungary, being large, mobile and loyal to *puszta* areas rich in prey.

Saker

Peregrine *Falco peregrinus* (Peregrine Falcon)
Vándorsólyom

Up to the 1960s, a few Peregrines still bred in hill ranges in the centre and north of Hungary. The exact reason for the disappearance of the species is unknown, but probably lies in a combination of pesticide use, nest robbing and lack of secure nesting sites. There have been occasional renewed breeding attempts, probably birds prospecting southwards from Slovakia or perhaps from the healthy populations in Austria and Croatia, but the species is now essentially a visitor to Hungary in autumn and winter. These birds are often juveniles, though

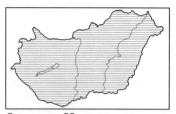

adults do occur, and are no doubt mostly birds from northern Europe which are migratory. As the species' name suggests these visitors are rather nomadic rarely staying in one area for long. Former breeding birds and most visitors are of the nominate race. The *calidus* (previously named *leucogenys*) race from the Eurasian tundra also occurs in winter. Perhaps strangely, the Mediterranean *brookei* race is not mentioned in the Hungarian literature.

STATUS IN HUNGARY: Uncommon autumn and winter visitor. Has bred. Strictly protected.
STATUS INTERNATIONALLY: Cosmopolitan. Rare in Europe but most populations have now recovered after years of decline.
DISTRIBUTION: Nationwide, particularly Great Plain but also lowlands in Transdanubia. Frequently seen over drained fishponds hunting waders and Teal.
TIMING: Possible all year round, but winter, October to March, is main period of occurrence.

TETRAONIDAE (Grouse)

Hazel Grouse *Bonasa bonasia* (Hazelhen)
Császármadár

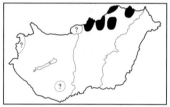

Hazel Grouse is Hungary's only breeding grouse species and one of the country's most elusive birds. Over the last 25 years there has been a drastic decline and the species is now almost certainly extinct in the hill ranges of Transdanubia and very rare in the Northern Hills where it was once widespread. The Aggtelek hills are the last stronghold with 50-100 pairs. One theory for the decline is that high numbers of Wild Boar, maintained artificially to ensure good hunting, have resulted in the clutches of this ground nesting bird being heavily predated. Although Wild Boar and other predators may be a problem in some areas, especially those with small localised Hazel Grouse populations, a more plausible reason for the national decline is that since the Second World War a more efficient forestry industry has produced unsuitable habitat. It may be useful to note that in parts of Poland the species is common in areas where Wild Boar are abundant. The Hungarian nomenclature regards birds as of an Alpine-Carpathian race 'styriacus'; other authorities regard these as the Central European race *rupestris*.

STATUS IN HUNGARY: Rare resident. Now very local with probably fewer than 200 pairs nationwide. Strictly protected.
STATUS INTERNATIONALLY: Palearctic species. Has decreased in both number and range across much of Europe.
DISTRIBUTION: Last real foothold is Aggtelek National Park, where fewer than 100 pairs are thought to remain. Smaller numbers hang on in the Börzsöny, Cserhát, Mátra, Bükk and Zemplén hills, though sightings in some of these areas are now few and far between.
TIMING: Present all year round.

PHASIANIDAE (Partridges, Quails and Pheasants)

Grey Partridge *Perdix perdix* (Common Partridge)
Fogoly

In line with the European trend, this species has declined drastically in Hungary in recent

decades. Pre-war numbers are considered to have been between one and two million birds, though such statistics were often produced by rather optimistic hunting bodies to justify shooting. By 1943, excessive hunting and a series of hard winters had reduced numbers to an estimated 285,000 birds scattered in fragmented populations around the country. Since the 1950s an intensification in farming, which included the use of herbicides, fertilisers and the creation of vast monocultures, caused a further crash in the population. In 1981 the population was estimated at 120,000 birds, and today numbers could be as low as a one tenth of that. Although Grey Partridge is still technically a gamebird in Hungary, permits are rarely issued because of the alarming decline in numbers.

STATUS IN HUNGARY: Uncommon to fairly common resident. Between 10,000 and 20,000 birds. Declining. Unprotected. Game species but shooting suspended.

STATUS INTERNATIONALLY: Palearctic species. Introduced populations in the New World. Vulnerable in Europe where it has declined drastically in almost every country.

DISTRIBUTION: Scattered nationwide. Mainly lowlands. Core populations in the Kiskunság and Békés County.

TIMING: All year round.

Quail *Coturnix coturnix* (Common Quail)
Fürj

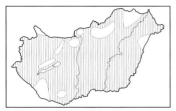

Although the familiar call of Quail is still rather common in much of Hungary's open country, the population has actually declined rather sharply since the war. Agricultural intensification has certainly reduced the population, with the use of chemicals and heavy machinery taking their toll, but Quail have proved more resilient and adaptable than Grey Partridge. In Hungary they have often transferred from grassland to crops, and in many regions are more common in the latter than the former. Quail occur mostly in open country across Hungary's lowlands but also in rolling hill country. Regularly inundated floodplains are avoided.

STATUS IN HUNGARY: Fairly common breeder. Population size unknown but probably between 15,000 and 25,000 birds. Has declined. Migrant. Protected.

STATUS INTERNATIONALLY: Old World species. Vulnerable in Europe and declining.

DISTRIBUTION: Dry open areas nationwide including meadows, fields of cereals and lucerne, and grassy *puszta*. More numerous on Great Plain, but also in some upland areas.

TIMING: Birds arrive from Africa in late April and early May. Return migration begins in August and peaks in September.

Pheasant *Phasianus colchicus* (Common Pheasant)
Fácán

Pheasant shooting is widespread in Hungary and the rearing and regular releasing of birds for both domestic and foreign guns is big business. At the turn of the century the nominate race *colchicus* is said to have bred wild in non-hybrid populations. Nowadays, the *torquatus* race is said to dominate in the colourful mix of hybrids that occurs in the Hungarian countryside. Although they may be 'impure', there are certainly wild breeding birds across Hungary, but it is impossible to decide exactly where and how these can be safely separated from captive-bred birds.

STATUS IN HUNGARY: Common resident. Around one million birds estimated. Wild birds supplemented by those bred for shooting. Unprotected. Game species. Season from 15

February to 1 September.
STATUS INTERNATIONALLY: Originally an Asian species, but widely bred and introduced into most areas of the world. Stable population in Europe.
DISTRIBUTION: Nationwide.
TIMING: All year round.

RALLIDAE (Rails and Crakes)

Water Rail *Rallus aquaticus*
Guvat

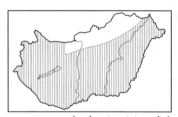

It is almost impossible to walk around a Hungarian reedbed in spring and not hear the characteristic squealing calls of Water Rail. No nationwide census has been conducted, but the species is undoubtedly widespread, occurring by lakes, fishponds, rivers, gravel pits, canals, marshes, ditches and backwaters with adequate vegetation. Although Water Rails are at present common, there is little room for complacency. There are fears that the current trend of privatizing fishpond systems, which are a key Hungarian habitat for the species, will lead to a 'tidying up' of bank vegetation and the regular harvesting of the reedbeds which surround many ponds. Clearly such a change in management would threaten Water Rails and other reed-dwelling birds.
STATUS IN HUNGARY: Fairly common breeder. Between 10,000 and 20,000 pairs estimated. Population probably stable. Partial migrant, some moving only short distances. Some overwinter. Protected.
STATUS INTERNATIONALLY: Palearctic species. Widespread in Europe where population considered stable.
DISTRIBUTION: Nationwide. Essentially lowland wetlands with suitable aquatic vegetation. Particularly common at Lakes Fertő, Velence and Balaton, Kis-Balaton, and fishponds and marshes at Hortobágy, Biharugra and Pusztaszer.
TIMING: Usually all year round. Migratory birds return in March and April. Most leave in October. Wintering birds congregate by flowing water and fishponds kept free of ice.

Spotted Crake *Porzana porzana*
Pettyes vízicsibe

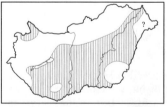

There is no classic Hungarian habitat for Spotted Crake and probably no stable breeding population. Numbers and distribution vary from year to year, with birds often inhabiting temporary or semi-permanent marshes and bogs. Also found in wet thickets, flooded pastures and even ditches and canals overgrown with rushes, reedmace *Typha* and sedge *Carex*. Much seems to depend on water levels, with pairs nesting in close proximity to each other in prime areas in one breeding season, and then being rather sporadic and scattered the next. Overall, Spotted Crakes have declined in Hungary, as the large scale drainage of wetlands earlier this century and later the conversion of others to fish-farms significantly reduced natural wetland habitats.
STATUS IN HUNGARY: Uncommon to rare. Fluctuating breeding population. Migrant. Protected.
STATUS INTERNATIONALLY: Palearctic breeding species. European population thought to be in decline.
DISTRIBUTION: Suitable lowland wetlands nationwide, but rather scattered. Regular breeding

sites include Dinnyés, Sárrét, Kis-Balaton, Tápió marshes, wetlands in the Kiskunság, Tisza floodplain and the Hortobágy.

TIMING: First birds arrive in March. Most leave in August. Some stay longer but those seen as late as November may well be passage birds from further north.

Little Crake *Porzana parva*
Kis vízicsibe

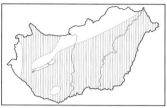

As a breeding bird, Little Crake is very much an Eastern European species and Hungary's wetlands host their share of the population. It is the most common *Porzana* species in Hungary, found in marshes, floodplains, lakes and around fishponds with vegetation cover. In contrast to Spotted Crake, Little Crake has probably benefited from the creation of Hungary's numerous fishpond systems, where tall *Phragmites* reeds are often left uncut and unburnt. Little Crakes are also less sensitive to the fluctuations in water levels which occur on fishponds. However, any move towards extensive reed harvesting or an intensification in fish-farming methods could reverse this apparent gain.

STATUS IN HUNGARY: Fairly common locally. National numbers unknown but probably 3,000-4,000 pairs. Population considered stable. Migrant. Protected.

STATUS INTERNATIONALLY: Palearctic breeding species. European population size and trends not accurately known but probably in decline.

DISTRIBUTION: Lowland wetlands nationwide. More common east of the Danube, notable sites being Tápió marshes, Péteri-tó, Csaj-tó, Szeged fishponds, the Hortobágy, Biharugra and Bodrogzug. In Transdanubia, Lake Velence, Kis-Balaton, Nagyberek, Pacsmag fishponds and Rétszilas.

TIMING: Birds return from unknown wintering areas in April. Most leave in September, though some remain into October.

Little Crake

Baillon's Crake *Porzana pusilla*
Törpe vízicsibe

This is probably the most difficult breeding bird to observe in Hungary, and anyone visiting, and indeed local ornithologists and birdwatchers, have little chance of encountering. In addition to the fact that it is small, often nocturnal and very rare, Baillon's Crake also breeds in some of Hungary's most impenetrable marshes, which are also invariably out-of-bounds. In Hungary as elsewhere in Europe the status of Baillon's Crake is somewhat unclear. The literature suggests it was widespread and even locally common in the last century. In common with Spotted Crake the species certainly suffered from a loss of suitable wetland habitats owing to drainage, and unlike Little Crake was unable to adapt to the fishpond habitats of open water and stands of tall *Phragmites* reed. In Hungary, Baillon's Crake is a bird of flooded meadows, marshes and fen-like wetlands with reedmace *Typha* and sedge *Carex*. The *intermedia* race occurs.

STATUS IN HUNGARY: Very rare breeder. Exact population size and recent trends unknown. Probably fewer than 50 pairs. Migrant. Strictly protected.

STATUS INTERNATIONALLY: Breeding range covers the Palearctic, southern Africa and Australasia. Rare in Europe where under threat.

DISTRIBUTION: Very local. Areas where breeding has been confirmed include Csákvár and Sárrét in Transdanubia, the Hortobágy (currently 15-20 pairs) and Szabadszállás in the Kiskunság. Problems in locating and identifying the species have no doubt hindered research, but birds may breed at such places as Pacsmag, Sumony, Tápió and Dabas among others.

TIMING: Present from the end of April to September.

Corncrake *Crex crex*
Haris

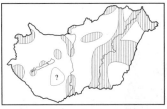

Corncrakes were apparently quite common in Hungary until the 1960s, but have since disappeared from many former haunts. Occurring mainly in wet meadows, marshy grasslands, peat bogs and floodplains, they have suffered from the drainage of habitat, the planting of poplars in floodplains and changes in farming methods. There is, however, some hope for the species in Hungary as many suitable habitats are under protection and the need for traditional farming practices to be maintained is high on the lobbying agenda of conservationists.

STATUS IN HUNGARY: Rare to uncommon breeder. Population fluctuates between 200 and 1,000 pairs. 420-450 calling males in 1994, which represents an overall decline. Migrant. Strictly protected.

STATUS INTERNATIONALLY: Palearctic breeding species. Globally threatened. Vulnerable in Europe and declining.

DISTRIBUTION: Rather scattered. Now rare in Transdanubia, the once important Hanság population is under threat and may now be as low as 10-15 pairs. Current stronghold is the Bodrogköz floodplain area between the Tisza and Bodrog rivers with 100-300 pairs. The Cserehát-Bódva valley hosts 20-25 pairs, and a few males call each year at Kis-Balaton, the Kali Basin, Őrség, Pacsmag, the Ipoly valley, Ócsa, Aggtelek, the Körös valley and on the Hortobágy (but very local here). The Tisza floodplain is important, with birds at Tiszadob, Tiszaalpár, Ároktő, Mártély and other suitable sites. Not all of the potential sites have been surveyed and areas such as Szatmár-Bereg may hold more birds than thought.

TIMING: First birds return at the end of April. Males call mainly from mid May to July. Leaves for African wintering areas in late August and September.

Moorhen *Gallinula chloropus* (Common Gallinule)
Vízityúk

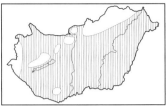

Visitors to Hungary are often surprised by the apparent lack of Moorhens on the country's wetlands. But the visual evidence is misleading. Moorhens are actually quite common in Hungary, occurring in all suitable wetlands. They are, however, much more secretive than, for example, British birds and are not as easily seen in urban areas such as parks. It is also unusual to see more than two or three adults together. Most Hungarian Moorhens are migratory, but some also regularly overwinter, moving locally to unfrozen waters. Birds from elsewhere pass through the country in both spring and autumn. The Hungarian nomenclature recognises occurring birds as of the '*lucida*' race; others regard this as one of the many clines of the nominate Eurasian race.

STATUS IN HUNGARY: Fairly common. Population size and trends unknown. Partial migrant. Protected.

STATUS INTERNATIONALLY: Cosmopolitan species. European population stable.

DISTRIBUTION: Nationwide, wetlands with suitable cover for nesting. Mostly lowland lakes, marshes with open water, fishponds, canals and ox-bows, but also in some hilly areas with ponds or reservoirs.

TIMING: Migrant birds arrive in April and leave in October. In mild winters many remain.

Coot *Fulica atra* (Eurasian Coot, Common Coot)
Szárcsa

After Mallard, the most widespread and common waterfowl species in Hungary. Some are resident, others move locally in winter and some are migratory. In addition, birds from further north pass through and winter in Hungary. The situation each winter depends on just how long wetlands remain frozen. In winter, many thousands gather on Lake Balaton even when most of the lake is completely iced-over. Coot are considered to take many small fish from fish-farms and are thus an unprotected species.

STATUS IN HUNGARY: Very common resident. Some migratory. Population size and trends unknown. Unprotected.

STATUS INTERNATIONALLY: Palearctic, Oriental and Australasian species. Stable population in Europe.

DISTRIBUTION: Nationwide. Found on almost all wetlands including freshwater lakes, salt lakes, fishponds, reservoirs, canals, rivers, ox-bows, gravel pits and angling ponds.

TIMING: All year round. Autumn sees numerous groups of several hundred each on larger waters. Migratory birds leave in October-November and return in March. In harsh winters, flocks congregate on open and flowing waters.

GRUIDAE (Cranes)

Common Crane *Grus grus*
Daru

The number of Common Cranes passing through Hungary on autumn passage has steadily increased in the last decade. Over 50,000 now stop on the Hortobágy, which makes this area probably the single most important stop-over site in Europe. The dusk fly-in of birds to their roosts here is without doubt one of Europe's ornithological spectacles. From a few hundred

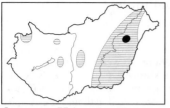

to some thousands also stop at other places on the Great Plain. Spring passage is less concentrated. The last confirmed breeding of the species was at Fonyód, Lake Balaton, in 1910, but, owing to a recent increase in over-summering birds on the Hortobágy, a return to breeding is expected and eagerly awaited. From some hundreds to a few thousand also winter depending on weather and feeding conditions.

STATUS IN HUNGARY: Numerous on autumn passage. Over 50,000 annually. Highest number *c.* 75,000 in eastern Hungary in October 1992. A few hundred present all year round. Protected.

STATUS INTERNATIONALLY: Palearctic breeding species. Vulnerable in Europe where has steadily declined throughout the century.

DISTRIBUTION: Main migration route is through a narrow 50-70 km corridor east of the Tisza. Regular stop-over areas are Hortobágy, Kardoskút, Pitvaros and Pusztaszer. Uncommon in Transdanubia, though some hundreds use the Lake Fertő area and small parties stop at Rétszilas and other wetlands. Surprisingly few pass through the Kiskunság though the area would seem to be suitable.

TIMING: Some birds present on the Hortobágy and elsewhere east of the Tisza all year round. Spring passage mainly in March. Highest numbers in October and November.

Common Cranes

OTIDIDAE (Bustards)

Great Bustard *Otis tarda*
Túzok

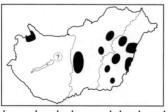

When one thinks of the birds of Hungary it is often Great Bustard that first comes to mind. The species is part of Hungarian folklore, has had more conservation attention (both domestic and international) than probably any other species, is the emblem of the ornithological society and is indeed regarded by many as the 'national bird'. In Hungary, Great Bustards inhabit agricultural land, especially when it is adjacent to *puszta*. As *puszta* areas have been ploughed up and developed throughout the century the birds have shown a tendency to nest and feed in crops, especially lucerne, barley and rape. In some ways this ability to adapt

Great Bustard

is positive, however, agricultural areas are fraught with dangers such as nest destruction by machinery and the numerous problems associated with an intensification in farming. At present, Hungary's Great Bustards do best in mosaic areas comprising open *puszta* for lekking and crops for nesting and feeding, though even here they are under great pressure. In hard winters, birds sometimes move southwards. This is dreaded by local ornithologists as power-lines and guns in the Balkans and Mediterranean invariably take their toll.

STATUS IN HUNGARY: Uncommon resident. Population currently stable at about 1,000 birds, though this represents a sharp decrease from the 3,000 estimated in the early 1980s. Hungary has an important European population, with only Iberia, Russia and perhaps the Ukraine having more birds. Strictly protected.

STATUS INTERNATIONALLY: Palearctic species. Globally threatened. Has declined drastically in Europe.

DISTRIBUTION: Except for two small, isolated and threatened populations in Transdanubia, Great Bustards are today very much birds of the Great Plain. The Kiskunság, Hortobágy and Heves, Bihar and Békés Counties are strongholds.

TIMING: All year round. After the breeding season, in the hot months of July and August, birds can be difficult to locate after early morning as they often sit in high vegetation. In winter groups of up to 100 occur.

HAEMATOPODIDAE (Oystercatchers)

Oystercatcher *Haematopus ostralegus* (Eurasian Oystercatcher)
Csigaforgató

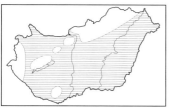

Although Hungary is completely land-locked, numerous maritime species occur on passage, mainly via the Danube and Tisza rivers. Although never numerous, Oystercatcher is one species that is conspicuous and annual. Usually single birds or up to three are seen, but groups of up to nine have been observed. Most birds are of the eastern *longipes* race. The nominate *ostralegus* has also been recorded.

STATUS IN HUNGARY: Uncommon on passage. Protected.

STATUS INTERNATIONALLY: European population increasing.

DISTRIBUTION: Wetlands nationwide including rivers, but particularly fishponds at Hortobágy, Pusztaszer, Szeged Fehér-tó and lakes in the Kiskunság. In Transdanubia, Lake Fertő, Kis-Balaton and the Danube are regular locations.

TIMING: Usual months are April and May, and September.

RECURVIROSTRIDAE (Stilts and Avocets)

Black-winged Stilt *Himantopus himantopus*
Gólyatöcs

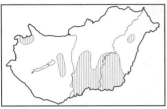

The number of pairs of Black-winged Stilt breeding in Hungary fluctuates greatly from year to year. Water levels at traditional salt-lake nesting sites and prevailing weather seem to determine whether birds attempt to nest or not. The species has never been common in Hungary, rather, a few pairs are found breeding alongside Avocets, in loose autonomous colonies or in isolation on small ephemeral waters. When the species does breed it is almost exclusively on salt lakes, though occasionally on partially drained fishponds, mainly east of the Danube. On passage, birds occur in a wider range of habitats such as rice fields, marshes and fishpond systems.

STATUS IN HUNGARY: Rare and irregular breeder. From 0-50 pairs. Migrant. Strictly protected.

STATUS INTERNATIONALLY: Almost cosmopolitan range. European population stable.

DISTRIBUTION: Very local. Rare in Transdanubia, though has bred at Dinnyés (three pairs, 1994) and elsewhere. East of the Danube, has bred at Szappanos-tó, Kelemen-szék and Zab-szék in the Kiskunság, Nagyszik, Akadémia-tó and Nagyiván-tó on the Hortobágy, Müller-szék and other sites in the Pusztaszer region.

TIMING: Groups of birds occur in April, some staying through the summer, others moving on. Breeding birds leave in September.

Avocet *Recurvirostra avosetta* (Pied Avocet)
Gulipán

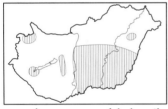

This is another species, which though mainly a bird of Europe's coastline, breeds inland on Hungary's salt lakes, drained fishponds and shallow marshes. Some of the latter habitats have been reconstructed by conservationists, the designs including islands for nesting colonies and the waters managed to encourage and safeguard not only Avocets but also terns. The number of pairs of Avocet in Hungary varies each year and the scattered loose colonies are often unsuccessful, heavily predated by mammals and corvids or destroyed by the untimely flooding of fishponds.

STATUS IN HUNGARY: Uncommon breeder. From 100-300 pairs. Migrant. Strictly protected.

STATUS INTERNATIONALLY: Old World species. Overall increase in European population.

DISTRIBUTION: On passage, lowland wetlands nationwide. Core breeding area is traditionally the Kiskunság, but recently conditions and numbers have declined. Other breeding birds are scattered east of the Tisza, particularly Hortobágy, Kardoskút, Biharugra and Pusztaszer region. In Transdanubia has bred at Lake Fertő, Sárrét and Sárszentágota.

TIMING: From March to September. In autumn, groups often gather on shallow fishponds.

BURHINIDAE (Stone Curlews)

Stone Curlew *Burhinus oedicnemus* (Eurasian Thick-knee)
Ugartyúk

Although Stone Curlews are in decline across most of Europe, Hungary's small and localised populations are stable if not increasing. Much suitable Stone Curlew habitat exists in

Hungary, but the species is extremely local, breeding on one area of arid *puszta* but missing from adjacent areas with similar habitat. Besides *puszta*, birds also breed on fallow land, ploughed fields and occasionally in gravel pits and vineyards. Given its potential for breeding in such man-made and managed habitats, which are numerous and widespread in Hungary, it is not unlikely that small undiscovered breeding populations exist outside the known and usually well-watched areas. On passage, groups of up to 40 occur.

STATUS IN HUNGARY: Uncommon breeder. Small but stable population of 200-250 pairs. Migrant. Strictly protected.

STATUS INTERNATIONALLY: Old World species. Vulnerable in Europe where has declined throughout this century.

DISTRIBUTION: Dry lowlands mainly east of the Danube. Breeds in the Tápió area, Mezőség, Pusztaszer and Dévaványa, but mainly in Kiskunság and Hortobágy National Parks. In Transdanubia, on the Moson Plain. Very local everywhere.

TIMING: Mainly from April to October. In mild weather delays migration until November.

Stone Curlew

GLAREOLIDAE (Pratincoles)

Collared Pratincole *Glareola pratincola*
Székicsér

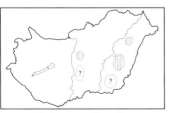

Although Collared Pratincoles were certainly more widespread in Hungary in the past than they are today, the population has always been fragmented and one typical of a species on the very edge of its range. In the 1970s, numbers in the core population of 150-200 pairs on the Hortobágy began to decline sharply. By the 1980s, numbers had fallen to around 50 scattered pairs. Although an overall nationwide decline this century is undeniable, some birds seemed to have moved from the Hortobágy *puszta* and Kiskunság salt lakes to breed on dried out rice fields, drained or disused fishponds, sunflower fields and even fallow land. Thus recent local declines may be owing to previously well monitored colonies relocating to unwatched areas rather than a true decline in numbers; Collared Pratincole numbers in Hungary have always fluctuated.

STATUS IN HUNGARY: Rare breeder. Most years see fewer than 100 pairs in four to six colonies. Migrant. Strictly protected.
STATUS INTERNATIONALLY: Old World species. Endangered in Europe and declining.
DISTRIBUTION: Very local. Seldom seen in Transdanubia though bred at various sites there earlier this century. East of the Danube in the Kiskunság, Hortobágy and scattered areas in Szolnok, Békés and Bihar Counties.
TIMING: First birds arrive in early May. Return migration in August and early September.

CHARADRIIDAE (Plovers)

Little Ringed Plover *Charadrius dubius*
Kis lile

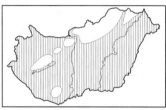

In keeping with its world distribution, Little Ringed Plover has a rather scattered range in Hungary, strongly linked to the availability of nesting sites. There is, however, a discernible pattern to its breeding distribution in the country as, apart from isolated fishponds and gravel pits, pairs are predominantly found along rivers and in suitable adjacent habitats. On passage, the species regularly occurs on drained fishponds and salt lakes, though breeding attempts at the former are often doomed owing to sudden increases in water levels. Not surprisingly, occurring birds are the Eurasian *curonicus* race.
STATUS IN HUNGARY: Fairly common breeder. Population size and trends unknown. Migrant. Many more on passage. Protected.
STATUS INTERNATIONALLY: Mainly Old World species. European population probably increasing.
DISTRIBUTION: Scattered in lowlands nationwide. In Transdanubia, at Lake Fertő, along the River Rába and its tributaries, Sárrét, and along the Danube. East of the Danube along the Tisza, Körös, Hernád, Sajó and other rivers, and in the Kiskunság and Hortobágy on salt lakes and drained fishponds.
TIMING: Most birds arrive and/or pass through in late March into April. Return passage lasts from August to October.

Ringed Plover *Charadrius hiaticula*
Parti lile

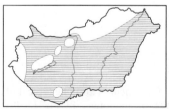

This is another bird from northern Europe's shores which occurs during migration in the heart of the continent on Hungary's wetlands. Single birds or small parties are usual, though in autumn flocks of 40-50 can occur in the Hortobágy and occasionally elsewhere. The majority of Ringed Plovers are seen on wet *puszta* and drained fishponds (in Hungary ponds are traditionally drained in autumn) and often in the company of Dunlins. Salt lakes across the Great Plain are also frequented. The majority of birds are of the smaller northern race *tundrae*, though the nominate *hiaticula* has occurred.
STATUS IN HUNGARY: Fairly common on passage. Protected.
STATUS INTERNATIONALLY: Mainly Palearctic breeding species, though also Greenland and Canada. Stable population in Europe.
DISTRIBUTION: Wetlands nationwide, but especially drained fishponds on the Great Plain.
TIMING: Has been recorded in every month except January and February. Regular in May and June, but majority from August to October.

Kentish Plover *Charadrius alexandrinus* (Snowy Plover)
Széki lile

Hungary is almost unique in Europe in being a land-locked country with a breeding population of this typically coastal species (a few pairs nest in neighbouring Austria). In recent decades, Kentish Plovers have declined in Hungary as elsewhere in Europe. Reasons include the heavy loss of clutches to a variety of predators (gulls, corvids, harriers, foxes, hedgehogs and even stray dogs) and the trampling of nests by cattle. The species tradition-ally breeds on areas of alkaline *puszta* and salt lakes across the Great Plain, though some pairs have occasionally nested on drained and dried out fishponds, though here the sudden refilling of ponds is a major hazard. Although very local, is relatively confiding and easy to observe at traditional sites.

STATUS IN HUNGARY: Rare breeder. Fewer than 150 pairs. Migrant. Population has declined. Strictly protected.

STATUS INTERNATIONALLY: Cosmopolitan. Although still fairly widespread, has declined across most of European range.

DISTRIBUTION: The Hungarian stronghold, with between 60 and 80 pairs, is Harta-Akasztó in the south of the Kiskunság. Other sites include Kelemen Szék, Fülöpszék, Miklapuszta, Balmazújváros Nagyszék, Kardoskút, Pusztaszer region, Kistelek and Szeged Fertő, though each site supports only a handful of pairs. Very rare in Transdanubia, though has bred at Lake Sárkány in Fehér County.

TIMING: First birds arrive from wintering areas in March. Most leave in September.

Dotterel

Dotterel *Charadrius morinellus*
Havasi lile

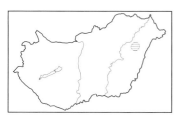

Although few would consider them typical Hungarian birds, the fact is some of Europe's Dotterels spend up to a quarter of their year in Hungary. On autumn passage, the first birds arrive on the Hortobágy in August and stay till November. Sometimes a flock of between 100-200 forms, though the birds often break up into smaller groups for some days before reforming. Maximum recorded was 224 at Szelencés Puszta, Hortobágy, in October 1993.

Dotterels are observed almost exclusively on the saline *pusztas* of the Hortobágy, where the vegetation is short and sparse. They moult here and often feed and roost in areas of spread and dried manure, especially around cattle pens. Birds are very loyal to these places, returning every year. In spring there are fewer birds and these invariably stay for only a few days.
STATUS IN HUNGARY: Uncommon on autumn passage. Usually around 200 birds. Protected.
STATUS INTERNATIONALLY: Palearctic species. European breeding population probably stable.
DISTRIBUTION: Regular but very local on Hortobágy during passage. Uncommon west of the Tisza and very rare in Transdanubia.
TIMING: Some from March to May but overall September-October is most reliable period in the south Hortobágy.

Golden Plover *Pluvialis apricaria* (European Golden Plover)
Aranylile

For many years, small groups of between two and 20 Golden Plover were the norm as the species moved through Hungary on a broad front in both spring and autumn. Flocks of over 100 were once rare; however, in recent years, such numbers have become more regular. Flocks of over 400 have been seen on the Hortobágy in recent years and 200 were at Apaj, Kiskunság, in November 1994. Birds are most often found on *puszta* and farmland, though dried-out fishponds are also frequented. The Hungarian nomenclature regards recorded birds as of a northern '*altifrons*' subspecies, though most authorities do not now recognise this race.
STATUS IN HUNGARY: Uncommon to fairly common on passage. Protected.
STATUS INTERNATIONALLY: Mainly Palearctic species. European population stable.
DISTRIBUTION: Lowlands nationwide but most regular across Great Plain, especially the Kiskunság, Hortobágy and southern *puszta* areas. In Transdanubia, Lake Fertő, Hanság, Kis-Balaton, Rétszilas and Sárvíz valley.
TIMING: Has been recorded in every month, but main passage is in autumn from September to November. In spring, March and April.

Grey Plover *Pluvialis squatarola* (Black-bellied Plover)
Ezüstlile, Ujjaslile

Although the most common passage plover to occur in Hungary, Grey Plovers are much more likely to occur in singles or pairs than their near relatives. Concentrations of birds at one site are unusual and large flocks rare.
STATUS IN HUNGARY: Common on passage. Usually singles and small groups. Protected.
STATUS INTERNATIONALLY: Cosmopolitan. European population probably stable.
DISTRIBUTION: Pastures, wet *puszta*, salt lakes, rice fields and drained fishponds nationwide. Most frequent on Great Plain, especially the Kiskunság and Hortobágy. Also found on sand and shingle banks along the Danube.
TIMING: With the exception of winter proper, almost all year round. Most in autumn, August to November. Main spring passage period is April-May.

Lapwing *Vanellus vanellus* (Northern Lapwing)
Bíbic

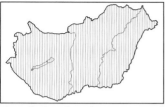

Hungary's most common and widespread breeding wader, Lapwings are found in open country across the country. Although agricultural work no doubt accounts for local losses of clutches, Lapwing numbers in Hungary are probably stable. The species breeds in a wide range of habitats from dry grassy *puszta*, saline *puszta,* the edges of salt lakes, pastures, meadows, ploughed fields and crops such as maize, lucerne and cereals. Less common in uplands though does breed in stream valleys and high meadows.

STATUS IN HUNGARY: Common and widespread breeder. Population size and trends unknown. Migrant. Protected.
STATUS INTERNATIONALLY: Palearctic species. European population probably stable.
DISTRIBUTION: Suitable habitats nationwide, particularly lowlands east of the Danube. On passage, flocks occur in farmland and on fishponds and rice fields.
TIMING: First birds return from Mediterranean wintering areas in February. Return passage mostly in September.

SCOLOPACIDAE (Sandpipers and Allies)

Knot *Calidris canutus* (Red Knot)
Sarki partfutó, Nagy partfutó

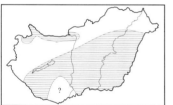

This is one of the rarer waders migrating through Hungary, with just a few records each year. The sparsity of observations may in part be owing to the very broad front across which the species passes through the country. Most observations are from drained fishpond systems.
STATUS IN HUNGARY: Rare to uncommon on passage. Protected.
STATUS INTERNATIONALLY: Circumpolar arctic breeding species. Cosmopolitan winter range. Common in Europe in winter but rather localised.
DISTRIBUTION: Possible on wetlands nationwide, particularly salt lakes, drained fishponds and open shingle banks along the Danube. Usually singles and small parties. More than a dozen together very rare.
TIMING: From April to November. Most reports from September.

Sanderling *Calidris alba*
Fenyérfutó

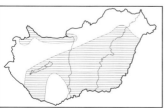

The recent increase in the number of birdwatchers in Hungary, particularly a new generation keen on waders, has been paralleled by an increase in Sanderling records. Most are seen in autumn, usually single birds or small parties, double figures being rare. Less frequent in spring.
STATUS IN HUNGARY: Uncommon on passage. Protected.
STATUS INTERNATIONALLY: Circumpolar arctic breeding range. European population considered stable.
DISTRIBUTION: No particular sites. Almost any salt lake or fishpond nationwide. Most records from Great Plain wetlands.
TIMING: Usual periods are in spring from March to May, and in autumn from August to November. The end of September is the classic period.

Little Stint *Calidris minuta*
Apró partfutó

One of the most common passage waders in Hungary, occurring on almost any suitable wetland in spring and autumn. Flocks can comprise anything from ten to over 100 birds. Although unusual, flocks of over a 1,000 have occurred.

STATUS IN HUNGARY: Common on passage. Protected.
STATUS INTERNATIONALLY: Palearctic breeding species. European population probably stable.

DISTRIBUTION: Wetlands nationwide. East of the Danube regular on Kiskunság salt lakes, drained fishponds on the Hortobágy, Szeged, Pusztaszer and Biharugra and Lake Tisza. In Transdanubia, drained fishponds everywhere, but also Lake Fertő, Kis-Balaton, Lake Tata, Dinnyés and the banks of the Danube.

TIMING: Occurs from April to November. Peak period in spring is May, in autumn, September and October.

Temminck's Stint *Calidris temminckii*
Temminck-partfutó

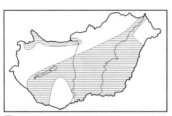

More often seen in singles and in smaller groups than Little Stint and never in such large flocks as the latter. Single figure flocks are the norm, double figures being very rare. Perhaps overlooked in some areas of the country.

STATUS IN HUNGARY: Uncommon to fairly common on passage. Protected.
STATUS INTERNATIONALLY: Palearctic breeding species. European population probably stable.

DISTRIBUTION: Salt lakes and drained fishponds nationwide, but mostly on Great Plain. Less common in Transdanubia.

TIMING: From April to November, with most in autumn. Peak period August-September. In spring, most records from May.

Curlew Sandpiper *Calidris ferruginea*
Sarlós partfutó

Records of Curlew Sandpiper in Hungary increase the further east one goes in the country. Wetlands in the flood-plain of the River Tisza dominate as stopover sites though birds are recorded further west, on well watched Transdanubian fishponds and even along the Danube. Single figure flocks were the norm in the 1980s, now up 20 birds are sometimes seen together.

STATUS IN HUNGARY: Fairly common on passage. Protected.

STATUS INTERNATIONALLY: Eastern Palearctic breeding species. Winters mainly in Africa, India and Australasia. Population size and trends unknown.

DISTRIBUTION: Nationwide, but mostly drained fishponds across the Great Plain. Unlike most other *Calidris* species is surprisingly uncommon on Hungary's salt lakes. Fewer records, but probably annual in Transdanubia.

TIMING: April to November. Spring passage records have increased, with most occurring in May. Autumn peak in September. Rare, but annually observed in summer.

Dunlin *Calidris alpina*
Havasi partfutó

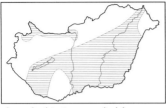

Dunlin are probably the most common of all the wader species which stop during migration on Hungary's wetlands. Numerous flocks of all sizes occur, from a few dozen to over 1,000 birds, mainly on large partially drained fishponds. The majority are of the nominate race *alpina,* though some of the western *schinzii* race also pass through. The Hungarian nomenclature also mentions a further race, *'centralis'*, as occurring in small numbers, though this is regarded by most authorities as an intermediate form.

STATUS IN HUNGARY: Very common on passage. Protected.
STATUS INTERNATIONALLY: Holarctic breeding species. Considered vulnerable on European wintering grounds.
DISTRIBUTION: Wetlands nationwide. Largest numbers on drained ponds east of the Danube.
TIMING: Main passage periods are March to May, and August to October. In most years, a few non-breeding birds oversummer.

Broad-billed Sandpiper *Limicola falcinellus*
Sárjáró

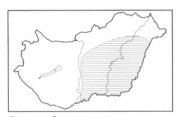

Although annual, Broad-billed Sandpiper is one of the rarer passage waders in Hungary, with solitary birds and groups in single figures the norm. Records have recently increased, with most observations from the Kiskunság and Hortobágy, but whether this is owing to the species preference for habitats in these regions or the higher number of observers is unclear.
STATUS IN HUNGARY: Rare, but annual on passage. Protected.
STATUS INTERNATIONALLY: Mainly Fenno-scandic breeding range. Considered vulnerable in Europe.
DISTRIBUTION: Occurs on salt lakes, marshes, goose and duck farm ponds, and partially drained fishponds, mainly east of the Danube.
TIMING: Most on autumn passage, August-September. May records have increased in recent years.

Ruff *Philomachus pugnax*
Pajzsoscankó

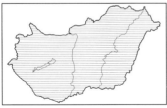

Tens of thousands of Ruff pass through Hungary on migration, stopping in wet meadows, flooded *puszta* and, particularly, partially drained fishponds. Recent estimates are 250,000-300,000 in spring and 50,000-60,000 in autumn. Some non-breeding flocks regularly oversummer and a few occasionally overwinter. A rare and irregular breeding bird in Hungary, it seems that whilst males continue passing north in spring, some mated Reeves remain to nest. A few may do so each year, though confirmed records are scarce. In April and May large flocks of birds stop over in lowland areas, where males in colourful breeding plumages display in flooded fields, pastures and marshes.
STATUS IN HUNGARY: Numerous on passage. Rare and irregular breeder. Protected.
STATUS INTERNATIONALLY: Palearctic breeding species. European breeding population considered stable.
DISTRIBUTION: On passage, at wet meadows, marshes and fishponds nationwide. Areas such

Ruff

as Dinnyés, the Kiskunság, Nagykunság, Biharugra and Pusztaszer regularly see 10,000 birds each in peak periods. Over 200,000 have been recorded in spring on the Hortobágy. Several breeding records from Csákvár in Transdanubia and the Hortobágy.

TIMING: First birds arrive in February. Largest numbers pass through in April and early May. Most return passage in September, continuing into November.

Jack Snipe *Lymnocryptes minimus*
Kis sárszalonka

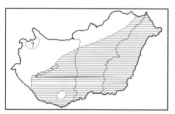

A rather inconspicuous bird on migration and one which moves through Hungary in scattered groups on a broad front. No doubt more Jack Snipe occur than reported observations indicate. Small groups or singles are usually seen at wetland edges or when accidentally flushed in marshes or flooded meadows. In recent years records have increased on the Hortobágy. A few stay through the winter by open waters such as channels and wetlands fed by warm springs.

STATUS IN HUNGARY: Uncommon on passage. Occasionally overwinters. Protected.

STATUS INTERNATIONALLY: Palearctic breeding range. Vulnerable in Europe where has declined throughout the century.

DISTRIBUTION: Possible on wet meadows, marshes and fishponds nationwide, but mainly Great Plain. Regular passage areas include the Sárvíz valley in Transdanubia, flooded meadows at Apaj and elsewhere in the Kiskunság, the Hortobágy and Csaj-tó fishponds.

TIMING: Birds move through in March-April and October-November. Overall, probably more in spring.

Common Snipe *Gallinago gallinago*
Sárszalonka

Although fairly widespread, Common Snipe is nowhere common in Hungary as a breeding species. More pass through in spring and autumn, often in large numbers. Breeding as it does

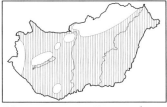

in sedge marshes, peat bogs, wet meadows and boggy *puszta,* all habitats which have been subject to drainage and exploitation in Hungary, the species has probably declined somewhat this century, though is not endangered. In peak autumn passage periods flocks of up to 100 birds, presumably from northern Europe, occur together.
STATUS IN HUNGARY: Uncommon to fairly common breeder. Population size and trends unknown. Migrant. More on passage. Protected.
STATUS INTERNATIONALLY: Almost cosmopolitan range. European population considered stable.
DISTRIBUTION: Scattered breeder in Transdanubia. More widespread on Great Plain. Some pairs in upland valleys. On passage, occurs on wetlands nationwide, especially drained fishponds.
TIMING: From March through to November. Spring peak in April, autumn peak September.

Great Snipe *Gallinago media*
Nagy sárszalonka

This is one visiting species which may well be slipping through Hungary largely unnoticed on a broad front in both spring and autumn. Only small numbers are recorded passing through each year, and observations are almost always of single birds flushed by chance. There are seemingly no favoured locations, though most are seen on fishpond systems and wet *puszta* east of the Danube.
STATUS IN HUNGARY: Uncommon on passage. Strictly protected.
STATUS INTERNATIONALLY: Palearctic breeding species. Vulnerable and declining in Europe.
DISTRIBUTION: Records are scattered around the country, but mainly from the east. Typical sites include fishponds, hatcheries, sewage farms, marshes, damp meadows, wet *puszta* and lakes.
TIMING: In spring, occurs from the end of March through to May, with April best overall. In autumn, from August to October, with main passage in late September.

Woodcock *Scolopax rusticola* (Eurasian Woodcock)
Erdei szalonka

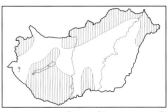

Some years see influxes of Woodcock into Hungary, whilst in others roding birds are scarce. Although the species can be legally hunted, this is probably not the main cause of any decline. Rather, woodland management has resulted in a lack of suitable breeding habitat, and no doubt problems exist on migration and in Mediterranean wintering areas. Most birds pass through the country, and indeed this may be the basis for its irregular breeding status as pairs breed or move on depending on weather and local conditions each year.
STATUS IN HUNGARY: Fairly common on passage. Rare breeder. Population size unknown but probably between 100-500 pairs. Migrant. Game species. Season from 1 March to 10 April.
STATUS INTERNATIONALLY: Palearctic breeding species. Vulnerable and declining in Europe.
DISTRIBUTION: Rather scattered in suitable lowland and upland woodland. Regular areas include the Hanság and the Kőszeg, Gerecse, Pilis, Börzsöny, Cserhát, Mátra, Vértes and Mecsek hill ranges. Nowhere common.
TIMING: Most birds move through in March and April. Return migration usually in September and can last into November. Some occasionally overwinter.

Black-tailed Godwit *Limosa limosa*
Nagy goda

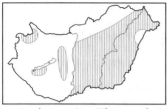

As a breeding species, Black-tailed Godwits are scattered around the country in floodplains, marshes, wet *puszta*, meadows, pastures and occasionally in grassland adjacent to fishpond systems or in suitable farmland. Several pairs often form loose colonies in favoured areas. Overall numbers in Hungary have fallen this century owing to a loss of wetlands for breeding and, locally, such problems as sudden flooding, trampling of nests by livestock and untimely mowing. The population has, however, now stabilised. On passage, most numerous on shallow or drained fishponds and rice fields, where flocks of between 100 and 1,000 birds are regular.

STATUS IN HUNGARY: Uncommon breeder. Between 1,000 and 2,000 pairs. Has declined. Migrant. More on passage. Protected.

STATUS INTERNATIONALLY: Palearctic breeding species. Vulnerable and declining in Europe.

DISTRIBUTION: Lowland wetlands nationwide. Breeding birds scattered in Transdanubia at Lake Fertő, Hanság, Kis-Balaton, Nagyberek, Dinnyés and Sárrét. Locally common across the Great Plain.

TIMING: From March to October. Spring passage peak in March. Main post-breeding passage in August-September.

Bar-tailed Godwit *Limosa lapponica*
Kis goda

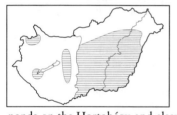

Once regarded as a rarity, this is another wader from Europe's coastline which is now recorded annually. This is no doubt partly owing to the increase in local wader enthusiasts. Hungary is not on the main migration route of this species and only small numbers occur. For many years the largest flock on record was ten birds at Zabszék in the Kiskunság in September, 1972. Nowadays, flocks of a dozen, usually juvenile birds, are annual on drained fishponds on the Hortobágy and elsewhere east of the Danube.

STATUS IN HUNGARY: Rare but annual on passage. Protected.

STATUS INTERNATIONALLY: Breeds across arctic Eurasia and Alaska. Considered vulnerable on its European wintering grounds.

DISTRIBUTION: Possible at wader sites nationwide, but mainly on drained fishponds and salt lakes on the Hortobágy, Kiskunság and other wetlands across the Great Plain.

TIMING: Most regular period the end of summer into autumn, from July to October, with September best overall. In spring, March to May.

Whimbrel *Numenius phaeopus*
Kis póling

Pre-war data states that up to 20,000 Whimbrel passed through Kardoskút, Szeged Fehértó and other salt lakes and *puszta* in southeast Hungary. Whether such figures are accurate or not, it is certain that no such numbers pass through Hungary today. Rather, flocks of fewer than 100 birds occur on wet *puszta*, rice fields and fishpond systems. Unlike most of the other waders which pass through Hungary, Whimbrel are more numerous in spring than autumn. A few non-breeding birds often oversummer.

STATUS IN HUNGARY: Fairly common on passage. Protected.

STATUS INTERNATIONALLY: Holarctic breeding species. Population stable in Europe.
DISTRIBUTION: Mainly Great Plain, with largest flocks east of the River Tisza in spring. Uncommon in Transdanubia.
TIMING: Best period March to May, with peak in mid April. Although fewer birds in autumn, some passage in August and September.

Curlew *Numenius arquata* (Eurasian Curlew)
Nagy póling

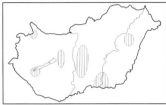

Curlews are essentially passage visitors to Hungary, though small and irregular numbers do nest most years. These breeding birds constitute one of the most southerly breeding populations of the species in Europe and nest in habitats such as floodplain meadows, wet pastures, marshes and peat bogs. Although Curlews have never been widespread as breeding birds, numbers have certainly fallen since the Second World War owing to the loss of suitable habitat. In late summer, flocks from northern Europe often linger on drained fishponds, rice fields, salt lakes and wet *puszta*. On passage, flocks of several hundred occur in these same habitats and remain to moult before moving further south. Breeding birds and the majority of visitors are of the nominate race, though *orientalis* from further east also occurrs.
STATUS IN HUNGARY: Common on passage. Rare breeder, with fewer than 50 pairs annually. Migrant. Strictly protected.
STATUS INTERNATIONALLY: Palearctic breeding species. Declining in much of Europe.
DISTRIBUTION: A few breeding pairs thinly scattered. Sites include the Hanság, Kis-Balaton, Sárrét, Dabas and parts of the Kiskunság. On passage, large flocks occur on lowland wetlands nationwide, particularly in the Hortobágy and Pusztaszer regions.
TIMING: Mainly from February to November. A few hundred sometimes overwinter.

Spotted Redshank *Tringa erythropus*
Kormos cankó, Füstös cankó

One of the most familiar passage waders in Hungary, with flocks of several hundred and even up to a thousand birds regular. Small groups of non-breeding birds often over-summer, and some have occasionally stayed on through milder winters. Most birds occur in winter plumage, but in late spring birds in breeding plumage are regular.
STATUS IN HUNGARY: Common on passage. Protected.
STATUS INTERNATIONALLY: Breeding range confined to arctic Eurasia. European population considered stable.
DISTRIBUTION: Wetlands nationwide, but majority through large fishpond systems in the east of country. Smaller numbers can occur on just about any marsh, salt lake or drained fishpond.
TIMING: In spring, large numbers from the end of February to May. Peak in early May. In autumn, from August to November, with most in September. In most years a few birds can be seen almost all year round.

Redshank *Tringa totanus* (Common Redshank)
Piroslábú cankó

Although nowhere common, Redshanks breed in various lowland wetland habitats, typically in wet meadows, pastures, marshes and disused rice fields, but above all on salt lakes and damp saline *puszta*. On passage, autonomous flocks, and sometimes just a few individuals, gather on fishponds in the company of Ruff, Spotted Redshanks and Dunlins. This is another

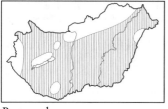

wader species which has been affected by changes in land use in Hungary. Firstly, by the drainage of breeding habitats and, secondly, by a general intensification in farming methods since the Second World War. After decades of decline the current breeding population is relatively small but stable.

STATUS IN HUNGARY: Uncommon breeder, with 500-750 pairs estimated. Migrant. Very common on passage. Protected.

STATUS INTERNATIONALLY: Palearctic breeding species. Has declined in much of Europe.

DISTRIBUTION: Breeds locally in lowland wetlands. Strongholds east of the Danube, especially in the Kiskunság and Hortobágy. On passage, wetlands nationwide. In autumn, numerous on drained fishponds.

TIMING: From March to October. Absent only in winter.

Marsh Sandpiper *Tringa stagnatilis*
Tavi cankó

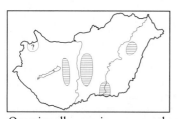

In the first half of this century Marsh Sandpiper was a scattered breeding bird on wetlands nationwide. The last confirmed breeding was in 1958 and the reasons for the subsequent disappearance are largely unknown. For many years only singles or small numbers were seen on passage on wet saline *puszta,* drained fishponds and salt lakes. Nowadays, small flocks of up to a dozen occur on the Kiskunság, Hortobágy and Pusztaszer fishponds. Occasionally seen in summer, though there has been no recent sign of a return to breeding.

STATUS IN HUNGARY: Uncommon to rare, but annual on passage. Strictly protected.

STATUS INTERNATIONALLY: Palearctic breeding species. Small European population increasing.

DISTRIBUTION: Nationwide, but most records from Great Plain. Former breeding areas included predominantly saline habitats at Lake Fertő, Hanság, Sárszentágota, Apaj, Kiskunság, Hortobágy and the Szeged area.

TIMING: Most regular periods April and early May, and from July to September.

Greenshank *Tringa nebularia* (Common Greenshank)
Szürke cankó

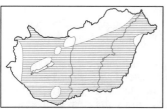

This is another wader species which today passes through Hungary in much smaller numbers than occurred only a few decades ago. Small groups of Greenshank are now the norm, with flocks of more than 40 birds rare. Quite often only single birds are seen, in the company of other *Tringa* species.

STATUS IN HUNGARY: Fairly common to uncommon on passage. Numbers have declined. Protected.

STATUS INTERNATIONALLY: Palearctic breeding species. European population stable.

DISTRIBUTION: Wetlands nationwide, particularly drained fishponds, salt lakes, the shores of reservoirs and lakes but also along the Danube and Tisza rivers.

TIMING: April and May are best spring months, though does occur as early as February. In autumn, numbers peak in August and September, though regular through to early November.

Green Sandpiper *Tringa ochropus*
Erdei cankó

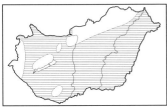

Although a widespread passage species, Green Sandpipers never occur in flocks proper, rather in twos or threes, and more often than not as single birds. Birds seem to move through Hungary over a quite long period in both spring and autumn and on a broad front. A few non-breeding birds oversummer, and some have been recorded in winter by free-flowing canals and streams and in floodplain woodland.

STATUS IN HUNGARY: Common on passage. Protected.
STATUS INTERNATIONALLY: Palearctic breeding species. European population considered stable.
DISTRIBUTION: Wetlands nationwide, in particular riverine forest, canals, river banks, lakesides, smaller fishponds and the feeder channels of fish-farms.
TIMING: Possible all year round, but essentially on passage, with main periods March to May and August to October.

Wood Sandpiper *Tringa glareola*
Réti cankó

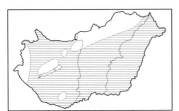

One of the most common passage waders in Hungary. Flocks of over 100 birds are regular, though often small parties are scattered across recently drained fishponds, flooded meadows or other shallow wetlands. Unlike Green Sandpiper, the species moves through in concentrations. A few non-breeding birds, sometimes in small groups, regularly oversummer.

STATUS IN HUNGARY: Very common on passage. Protected.
STATUS INTERNATIONALLY: Palearctic breeding species. In decline in Europe.
DISTRIBUTION: Wetlands nationwide. In particular wet *puszta*, marshes, salt lakes and drained fishponds.
TIMING: From March to mid October. Largest numbers on spring passage at the end of April into May. In autumn, mainly August and September.

Terek Sandpiper *Xenus cinereus*
Terekcankó

With only a few recorded annually, Terek Sandpiper is one of the rarest of the regular passage waders in Hungary. Typically, single adult birds are seen in the company of other waders on drained fishponds. Although a very particular and easily identified species, it is likely that the relative scarcity of birdwatchers and the innumerable possible sites of occurrence in Hungary have limited the number of records.

STATUS IN HUNGARY: Rare but annual passage visitor. Protected.
STATUS INTERNATIONALLY: Palearctic breeding species. Small European population considered stable.
DISTRIBUTION: One or two records every year, mainly from larger fishponds on the Great Plain such as Hortobágy-halastó, Csécsi, Csaj-tó and Szeged Fehértó. Fewer records from Transdanubia where birds probably move through unnoticed.
TIMING: Occurs in both spring and autumn, with most regular months being May and September. Some records from summer.

Common Sandpiper *Actitis hypoleucos*
Billegetőcankó

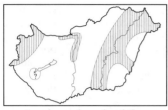

The scarcity of breeding Common Sandpipers in Hungary is probably owing to the lack of suitable nesting habitats. Very few of Hungary's rivers have adequate stretches of the pebble- and gravel-covered banks or islands that the species requires. A few pairs nest away from rivers in gravel pits and by ponds, but such sites are often temporary or subject to constant disturbance. Indeed, most Common Sandpipers which occur in Hungary are birds passing through and, whilst on migration, a much wider range of wetlands are frequented.

STATUS IN HUNGARY: Uncommon breeder. Population size and trends unknown. Migrant. Common on passage. Protected.

STATUS INTERNATIONALLY: Palearctic breeding species. European population considered stable.

DISTRIBUTION: Breeding population scattered along the Danube, Rába, Tisza, Hernád and other rivers, by canals and in gravel pits. On passage occurs on drained fishponds and lake shores, sometimes in small groups.

TIMING: First birds arrive in late March, with numbers peaking in April. Most continue on north. Return passage mostly in August, though birds can be seen as late as November.

Turnstone *Arenaria interpres*   (Ruddy Turnstone)
Kőforgató

Once again, another species where more local wader watchers has meant a rapid increase in records in recent years. Although a bird very much associated with Europe's coastline, most of land-locked Hungary's birdwatchers no longer get too excited about this species. Singles were the norm for many years, recently flocks of up to a dozen birds have become regular on salt lakes, drained fishponds, flooded *puszta* and the goose and duck farm ponds of the Great Plain.

STATUS IN HUNGARY: Uncommon but annual on passage. Protected.

STATUS INTERNATIONALLY: Circumpolar arctic breeding species. European populations considered stable.

DISTRIBUTION: Wetlands nationwide, but mostly the Kiskunság and larger fishponds east of the Tisza. In Transdanubia, regular along the shoreline of Lake Balaton, at Dinnyés, and no doubt on the innumerable fishponds of the region.

TIMING: Regular periods are May, and particularly mid August to mid September.

Red-necked Phalarope *Phalaropus lobatus*
Vékonycsőrű víztaposó

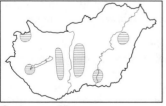

Records of this species have increased in the last ten years. Before 1988 there was only one spring record from the Hortobágy, whereas pairs are now regular here in May. At the end of summer, groups of between one and three birds are usually reported from several sites around the country. The largest single flock on record is 17 birds at Sárszentágota salt lake in Transdanubia before the Second World War.

STATUS IN HUNGARY: Uncommon but annual on passage. Protected.

STATUS INTERNATIONALLY: Circumpolar arctic breeding species. European populations probably stable.

DISTRIBUTION: Wetlands nationwide, but most observations from the Kiskunság and Hortobágy. Also marshes, salt lakes and shallow or partially drained fishponds at Pusztaszer and Szeged Fehértó. In Transdanubia, probably annual at Lake Fertő, Kis-Balaton, Sárszentágota, Rétszilas and Dinnyés.

TIMING: Occurs from April to October. Overall, best months August and September.

STERCORARIIDAE (Skuas)

Arctic Skua *Stercorarius parasiticus* (Arctic Jaeger, Parasitic Jaeger)
Ékfarkú halfarkas

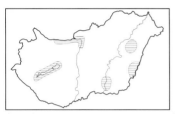

Arctic Skua is the most frequently occurring skua species in Hungary and, though far from numerous, the only one which does occur annually. From June to August it is not unusual for up to four birds to be seen together, whereas from September mostly singles are seen. Two-thirds of all records relate to adult birds.

STATUS IN HUNGARY: Rare but annual visitor. Protected.
STATUS INTERNATIONALLY: Mainly circumpolar arctic breeding species. European population stable.

DISTRIBUTION: Most sightings at Lake Balaton, the Danube, and fishponds in the Szeged and Hortobágy areas.

TIMING: Occurs mainly between June and November, with most observed in September.

LARIDAE (Gulls)

Mediterranean Gull *Larus melanocephalus*
Szerecsensirály

This relatively new Hungarian breeding species first nested in 1940 on the fishponds of Szeged-Fehértó. A few pairs have bred annually since 1953 and the population has increased steadily since the early 1980s. New colonies have since been established in Transdanubia. Pairs are often grouped together at the edges of Black-headed Gull colonies on fish-pond systems and salt lakes.

STATUS IN HUNGARY: Rare to uncommon breeder. Rather local. Increasing. Currently between 120 and 150 pairs. Migrant. Protected.

STATUS INTERNATIONALLY: Breeding range confined to Europe where population is increasing.

DISTRIBUTION: Pairs scattered around the country. In 1994 breeding pairs distributed as follows: in Transdanubia, 23 pairs at Rétszilas-Soponya fishponds and eight pairs Lake Fertő on the Austrian border; on the Great Plain, 55-60 pairs in the Pusztaszer area and 28 at Kelemen Szék, Kiskunság National Park.

TIMING: First birds return from wintering areas in the Mediterranean and Black Sea basins in March and occupy nesting colonies in April. With the exception of winter proper, wandering birds possible almost all year round.

Mediterranean Gull

Little Gull *Larus minutus*
Törpesirály, Kis sirály

A few Little Gull are present over Hungary's larger wetlands almost all year round. Some regularly winter and summer over Lake Balaton, larger fishponds and no doubt elsewhere. Single-figure parties are the norm, though up to 50 together do occur. Flocks of more than 100 birds are unusual. Birds in breeding plumage are rather uncommon. STATUS IN HUNGARY: Common on passage. Some in summer and winter. Protected.

STATUS INTERNATIONALLY: Palearctic breeding species. European breeding population stable, perhaps increasing.

DISTRIBUTION: Occurs over wetlands nationwide but main areas are the Danube, Kiskunság salt lakes, Lakes Fertő, Balaton, Velence and Tisza, all reservoirs and larger fishpond systems such as Biharugra, Pusztaszer, Szeged and those on the Hortobágy.

TIMING: Main spring passage from March to May. In autumn, September and October.

Black-headed Gull *Larus ridibundus*
Dankasirály

By far the most common gull in Hungary, though overall breeding numbers have actually fallen in recent decades. Flocks can be seen all year round but most breeding birds leave for the Mediterranean in autumn, whilst birds from northern Europe move in to winter. Others disperse in all directions or move locally. Colonies are dotted on wetlands around the country, especially larger fishpond systems with suitable islands for nesting.

STATUS IN HUNGARY: Very common resident. Some partially migratory. Between 15,000 and 30,000 pairs estimated. Has declined. Protected, though can be killed on unprotected fish-farms between 1 August and 31 March.

STATUS INTERNATIONALLY: Mainly Palearctic breeding species. European breeding population increasing.

DISTRIBUTION: Nationwide. Colonies of up to 1,000 pairs usually at Szeged Fehértó, Kelemen-szék in the Kiskunság, Kis-Balaton, Balaton-Boglárlelle, and on fishponds in the Mezőföld region. 720 pairs counted at Lake Velence-Dinnyés, Transdanubia, in 1994.
TIMING: All year round. Migratory birds arrive mainly in March and leave in September.

Common Gull   *Larus canus*   (Mew Gull)
Viharsirály

Common Gulls (mainly immatures) occur in Hungary in numbers ranging from single birds to flocks of over 100. A Hungarian breeding record was expected for several years before the first at Kiskunláchaza, Kiskunság, in 1988. Non-breeding birds occur every summer, particularly at Hortobágy-halastó. The majority of autumn and winter visitors are of the nominate *canus* race, though *heinei* from further east has also been recorded.

STATUS IN HUNGARY: Common autumn and winter visitor. Very rare breeder. From 0-3 pairs annually. 1,014 counted wintering nationwide in January 1994. Protected.
STATUS INTERNATIONALLY: Holarctic breeding species. European breeding population stable but declining in Scandinavia.
DISTRIBUTION: Any large wetlands but especially the Danube Bend, Danube in Budapest, the River Tisza, Lakes Balaton, Velence, Tata, Tisza, reservoirs and larger fishponds nationwide. Also over farmland. A few pairs breed each year at Kiskunlacháza.
TIMING: Possible all year round but mainly from September to April when scattered nationwide.

Lesser Black-backed Gull   *Larus fuscus*
Heringsirály

Something of a nomad in Hungary, rather than a true migrant, this species usually occurs in ones and twos. The local literature refers only to the nominate *fuscus* race, however, the *intermedius* race also occurs in small numbers. Mostly single adult birds occur, at almost anytime on just about any wetland nationwide.
STATUS IN HUNGARY: Uncommon but annual visitor. Protected.

STATUS INTERNATIONALLY: Palearctic breeding species. European population increasing.
DISTRIBUTION: Wetlands nationwide. In winter, particularly on Lake Balaton and the Danube. Nomadic birds always possible on fishpond systems.
TIMING: A few birds occur all year round but main periods are April-May and August-October when there is often a small influx of birds.

Herring Gull   *Larus argentatus*
Ezüstsirály

The status of Herring Gull needs clarifying in Hungary, as elsewhere in the region, as previously races of the far more common *cachinnans* group were lumped with the *argentatus* group. Certainly small numbers of Herring Gulls do occur with other large gulls at roosts and on larger wetlands and the Danube.
STATUS IN HUNGARY: Uncommon but annual visitor. Unprotected.
STATUS INTERNATIONALLY: Holarctic breeding species. European population increasing.

DISTRIBUTION: Mainly Transdanubia and the Danube but can occur anywhere nationwide with other gulls.

TIMING: Mainly autumn though possible all year round.

Yellow-legged Gull *Larus cachinnans*
Sárgalábú sirály

Although a rare breeder, this species is a regular though somewhat nomadic resident in Hungary. Numbers fluctuate from season to season and most birds are immatures. Birds of the nominate Black Sea *cachinnans*, Mediterranean *michahellis* and Baltic *omissus* races probably all occur, but for the moment the ratio for each is unknown. In autumn and early winter several thousand roost at favoured sites. Breeding was first confirmed at Sárszentmihály, Fejér County, in 1988 and a few pairs are now regular here each year. In 1994 breeding was also confirmed at Mexikópuszta, Lake Fertő National Park and, most recently, in 1995 at Kis-Balaton.

STATUS IN HUNGARY: Fairly common visitor. Very rare breeder. From 1-3 pairs annually. Unprotected.

STATUS INTERNATIONALLY: Palearctic breeding species. European status unclear but population probably stable.

DISTRIBUTION: Wetlands nationwide, particularly the Danube, reservoirs and larger fishpond systems. Also found at rubbish dumps and occasionally farmland. A few pairs regularly breed at Sárszentmihaly, Fejér County, Transdanubia.

TIMING: All year round.

Yellow-legged Gull

Kittiwake *Rissa tridactyla* (Black-legged Kittiwake)
Csüllő

It may come as a surprise to find that Kittiwakes are regular, though rare, visitors to land-locked Hungary. With most Hungarian records in the west of the country, it seems that, as for many maritime species, the Danube is the route into the Carpathian basin. Single immature birds are the norm, though small parties have been recorded. Most observations from early winter.

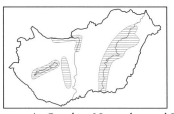

STATUS IN HUNGARY: Rare but annual visitor. Protected.
STATUS INTERNATIONALLY: Holarctic breeding species. European populations stable.
DISTRIBUTION: Occurs nationwide but mainly the Danube, Lake Balaton and fishponds in the rest of Transdanubia. Although less frequent, also occurs on the River Tisza and Great Plain wetlands.
TIMING: Records from August through winter to April but most in October, November and December.

STERNIDAE (Terns)

Caspian Tern *Sterna caspia*
Lócsér

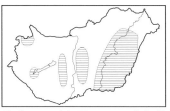

The Caspian Terns which occur each spring on Hungary's wetlands are thought to originate from the Baltic population, though birds from the Black Sea may also occur. Usually single birds or up to four individuals in loose association are recorded. Double figures at one site are very rare.
STATUS IN HUNGARY: Uncommon on passage. Protected.
STATUS INTERNATIONALLY: Almost cosmopolitan species. Endangered in Europe and declining.
DISTRIBUTION: Occurs nationwide, but more frequent on salt lakes and fishponds across the Great Plain, particularly in the Kiskunság.
TIMING: From March to November, though classic months are April and September.

Common Tern *Sterna hirundo*
Küszvágó csér

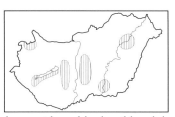

The most widespread and common *Sterna* species in Hungary, Common Terns nest in scattered colonies across the country's lowlands. Large autonomous colonies of several hundred birds no longer exist, and over a 100 pairs together is now rare. Rather, colonies of dozens of pairs breed on lakes, salt lakes, fishponds and reservoirs, often in the company of Black-headed Gulls. Nests are often destroyed by flooding, drainage of ponds, and predation by corvids and both wild and domestic mammals. There has been some success with nesting rafts and artificial islands, particularly in Lake Fertő National Park.
STATUS IN HUNGARY: Uncommon to fairly common breeder. Fewer than 1,000 pairs. Has declined. Migrant. Protected.
STATUS INTERNATIONALLY: Mainly Holarctic breeding range. European population stable.
DISTRIBUTION: Small scattered colonies nationwide. Regularly at Lake Fertő, Kis-Balaton, ponds on the south shore of Lake Balaton, Sárszentmihály and Lake Tisza. Rather rare breeder in the Hortobágy and Kiskunság.
TIMING: Summer. Birds arrive in April and leave in September.

Whiskered Tern *Chlidonias hybridus*
Fattyúszerkő

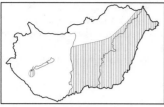

The most communal of the three *Chlidonias* 'marsh' terns, nesting in colonies on reservoirs, lakes, marshes and fish-ponds which have floating vegetation such as water-lilies. Often breeds in the company of Black Terns, Black-headed Gulls and Black-necked Grebes. In such mixed colonies, Whiskered Terns can number anything from ten to 100 pairs. Colonies of over 200 pairs are sometimes established on the Hortobágy. Breeding sites are at a premium and colonies shift from year to year depending on local conditions. Although many natural wetlands have been lost, Whiskered Terns have adapted well to man-made fishponds, with probably half the population now nesting at such places.

STATUS IN HUNGARY: Uncommon to fairly common breeder. From 800-1,000 pairs. Population probably stable. Migrant. Strictly protected.

STATUS INTERNATIONALLY: Old World species. Declining in most of Europe.

DISTRIBUTION: Uncommon in Transdanubia where largest colony, of around 100 pairs, is at Kis-Balaton. Locally common on Great Plain wetlands such as Bodrogzug, Lake Tisza, Hortobágy-halastó, Hajdúság area, Pusztaszer and numerous smaller salt lakes and ponds.

TIMING: Summer. First birds arrive in late April. Most leave in September.

Whiskered Terns

Black Tern *Chlidonias niger*
Kormos szerkő

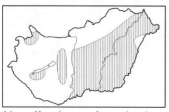

Black Terns are more widespread in Hungary than Whiskered Terns and probably slightly more numerous, but they never nest in such large colonies as their congener. Rather, the species breeds in small numbers on numerous ox-bows, fishponds with emergent vegetation, salt lakes, flooded pastures and sedge marshes. When breeding in mixed colonies with Whiskered Terns, Black Terns are invariably in the minority. Overall, the species has proba-bly suffered more from the drainage of natural wetlands than Whiskered Tern.

STATUS IN HUNGARY: Fairly common to uncommon breeder. Estimated population of 800-1,000 pairs probably stable. Migrant. More on passage. Protected.
STATUS INTERNATIONALLY: Mainly Holarctic species. Declining in most of Europe.
DISTRIBUTION: Scattered nationwide. Transdanubian sites include Hanság, Sárrét, Dinnyés, Kis-Balaton, Nagyberek and several fishpond systems. More common but localised east of the Danube at Lake Tisza, Ároktő, Tiszadob, Bodrogzug, Pusztaszer and in the Kiskunság and Hortobágy regions.
TIMING: Summer. From mid April to September. Late records in October probably passage birds.

White-winged Black Tern *Chlidonias leucopterus*
Fehérszárnyú szerkő

The rarest of the three 'marsh' terns, White-winged Black Tern is on the very western edge of its breeding range in Hungary. Traditionally, pairs nest on the Hortobágy in alkaline marshes typified by tussocks of sedge, but numbers here now fluctuate greatly each year. A few pairs occasionally nest in temporary flooded pastures and others are sometimes found in colonies of Black or Whiskered Terns, though the species rarely breeds on fishponds. On the other hand, White-winged Black Terns frequent a much wider range of wetlands when feeding, hawking for insects over fishponds, reedbeds, rice fields, wet meadows, pastures and flooded *puszta*. Numbers have always fluctuated, but overall there has been a sharp decline in recent decades. In the 1970s, 250-300 pairs were estimated in the core Hortobágy population, with numbers dropping to 150-200 in the 1980s and to a low of 80-90 pairs in the early 1990s.
STATUS IN HUNGARY: Rare and irregular breeder. From 50 to 150 pairs. Migrant. More on passage. Strictly protected.
STATUS INTERNATIONALLY: Mainly Palearctic breeding species. European population probably stable.
DISTRIBUTION: Mostly restricted to the Great Plain. Only regular breeding pairs very local on the Hortobágy. Has bred on the Kiskunság salt lakes. Outside the nesting period, small numbers occur over wetlands around the country.
TIMING: Arrives in spring in mid April. In autumn, breeding birds leave in early September.

COLUMBIDAE (Pigeons and Doves)

Feral Pigeon *Columba livia domestica*
Parlagi galamb, Házi galamb

Widespread in Hungary as elsewhere in Europe. Placed in Category C owing to being 'of captive origin but having established wild populations'.
STATUS IN HUNGARY: Very common and widespread resident. Unprotected.
STATUS INTERNATIONALLY: Cosmopolitan. Large stable populations in Europe.
DISTRIBUTION: Nationwide, especially urban areas and settlements.
TIMING: All year round.

Stock Dove *Columba oenas*
Kékgalamb

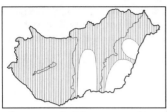

Stock Doves have one of the clearest demarcations between summer and winter ranges of any Hungarian bird species, being restricted to woodland in the north and west in summer and dispersing to lowlands in the southeast in autumn and winter. In many areas the breeding range of the species closely follows that of Black Woodpecker, on which it often relies for nest holes. Broken or hollow trees and even buildings are also utilised. The felling of stands of mature deciduous trees has affected Stock Doves locally. The overall population size has probably not been affected unduly, though no nationwide survey has been done to clarify the situation.

STATUS IN HUNGARY: Fairly common breeder. Population size and trends unknown. Partial migrant though some do winter. Protected.

STATUS INTERNATIONALLY: Palearctic species. European population increasing.

DISTRIBUTION: Breeds mostly in forested uplands in Transdanubia and the Northern Hills, to a lesser degree in parkland and floodplain woodland. On passage and in winter on farmland.

TIMING: Migrants return in February and leave in October-November. In most winters, some flocks gather on lowland farmland.

Woodpigeon *Columba palumbus*
Örvös galamb

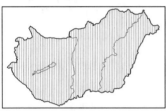

Visiting birdwatchers are often surprised by the status of this species. Although far from rare, Woodpigeons in Hungary are seldom seen in the large flocks which are commonplace in, for example, the British Isles. This is because most Hungarian birds disperse and leave the country in winter rather than gathering in roaming flocks. Being a very resilient species, they have remained common though they are regularly shot.

STATUS IN HUNGARY: Common breeder. Population size unknown but certainly large and probably increasing. Mainly migratory. Unprotected. Game species.

STATUS INTERNATIONALLY: Palearctic species. European population stable.

DISTRIBUTION: Nationwide. Breeds in both upland and lowland woods, parkland, windbreaks and copses. Some on farmland in winter.

TIMING: Some usually present all year round. Most leave for the Mediterranean in November, returning in February.

Collared Dove *Streptopelia decaocto* (Eurasian Collared Dove)
Balkáni gerle

After first being recorded breeding in 1932, in Berettyóújfalu in Bihar County on the Romanian border, Collared Doves quickly began to populate Hungary's lowlands. In the 1950s they had colonised villages in hilly regions and today have become one of the most common and widespread birds in Hungary. In August, flocks of several thousand each invade sunflower fields, and though regularly shot, the species remains abundant. The Hungarian name 'Balkan Dove' was once perhaps appropriate, reflecting the direction from which the species invaded the country, but as is well known the species has now reached northern Scotland.

STATUS IN HUNGARY: Very common and widespread resident. Population size unknown, but

certainly large and stable if not increasing. Unprotected.
STATUS INTERNATIONALLY: Palearctic and Indian subcontinent. Introduced populations elsewhere. Numbers increasing.
DISTRIBUTION: Nationwide. Breeds in settlements, farms, gardens, cemeteries, parks and also in open country in copses and wind-breaks. Never found in forest proper. Large feeding flocks in agricultural areas nationwide.
TIMING: All year round. From July to September for post-breeding flocks in rural areas.

Turtle Dove *Streptopelia turtur* (European Turtle Dove)
Vadgerle

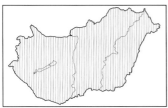

Although still widespread in rural areas, Turtle Doves have been forced out of many parks, cemeteries and other habitats in settlements by their dominant relative the Collared Dove. After the breeding season, Turtle Doves join their congener in flocks of many thousands on Hungary's vast sunflower fields. A contentious problem lies in the fact that Turtle Dove is a protected species whereas Collared Dove is not. It is doubtful whether the mainly foreign guns that shoot these flocks at the end of summer are able, or willing, to discriminate between the two species.
STATUS IN HUNGARY: Common and widespread breeder. Population size and trends unknown but probably over 100,000 pairs. Migrant. Protected.
STATUS INTERNATIONALLY: Palearctic breeding species. Declining in Europe.
DISTRIBUTION: Nationwide. Breeds in open woodland, *acacia* copses, parkland, orchards, poplar plantations, wind-breaks and floodplain woodland. Never found in forest proper. Largest post-breeding flocks mainly on Great Plain.
TIMING: In spring, arrives mostly in April. In autumn, leaves in September after feeding in large flocks on crops.

CUCULIDAE (Cuckoos)

Cuckoo *Cuculus canorus* (Common Cuckoo, European Cuckoo)
Kakukk

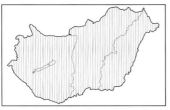

Cuckoos generally arrive in Hungary in mid April. In the Northern Hills they are usually first heard around the 16th of the month, with the exact date seemingly linked to the arrival of Robins, their main host here. The most frequent host in lowland areas is Great Reed Warbler. In total, 30 different species have been found hosting Cuckoo eggs in Hungary. Other regulars include White Wagtail, Redstart, Wood Warbler, Red-backed Shrike and Wren. In hill ranges male Cuckoos have been observed to arrive a fortnight earlier than females. This is thought to be owing to the male's role of seeking out in advance potential host nests for the female.
STATUS IN HUNGARY: Common and widespread. Numbers have fallen locally owing to declines in available host species. National population size and trends unknown. Migrant. Protected.
STATUS INTERNATIONALLY: Old World species. Stable population in Europe.
DISTRIBUTION: Nationwide. Inhabits a wide range of habitats linked to the abundance of host birds.
TIMING: From April to September. Males arrive before females. Adults leave in early September whilst young birds leave later in the month.

TYTONIDAE (Barn Owls)

Barn Owl *Tyto alba*
Gyöngybagoly

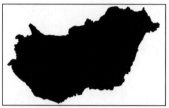

Throughout Hungary the renovation of buildings where Barn Owls nest and roost has become a serious problem. In some counties, nestbox schemes have proved successful in countering this. In addition, intensification in farming has reduced hunting habitat and prey though not on the scale of parts of western Europe. The number of breeding pairs each year fluctuates depending on weather and prey availability, but overall the population has declined in recent decades. Hungarian Barn Owls apparently prefer to nest in the buildings of the Reform Church rather than in Catholic ones. Simply, the Reform Church is less well funded than the Catholic and thus its churches are seldom renovated, have their attics and bell-towers cleaned or windows repaired. If one is in search of Barn Owls in Hungarian villages, then it may be wise to first learn how to separate Reform from Catholic churches! The *guttata* race occurs. There is one record of a pair of the nominate *alba* breeding in Tolna County in 1983.

STATUS IN HUNGARY: Fairly common to uncommon resident. Has declined. Mainly sedentary though some disperse before winter. Between 1,000 and 2,000 pairs estimated. Strictly protected.

STATUS INTERNATIONALLY: An almost cosmopolitan species but absent from much of Asia. Declining in Europe.

DISTRIBUTION: Nationwide, though not in forested hills. Locally common in parts of Transdanubia. Scattered on the Great Plain.

TIMING: All year round.

STRIGIDAE (Owls)

Scops Owl *Otus scops* (European Scops Owl)
Füleskuvik

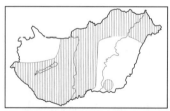

This species is probably more widespread in Hungary than is generally believed and the local literature suggests. Its distribution is, however, limited by a lack of natural nesting cavities. The number of breeding pairs fluctuates greatly as is typical of a migratory species on the edge of its range as Scops Owl is in Hungary. Good years see birds occurring in suitable habitat nationwide, whilst in others, traditional strongholds are almost deserted. Classic Hungarian habitats are vineyards, allotments, grassy areas with scattered old oaks or walnut trees and abandoned orchards. The species never occurs in the country's forests or higher hills. To counter the problem of insufficient natural nesting sites, nestboxes have been erected in several regions and have increased the density of some local populations.

STATUS IN HUNGARY: Uncommon to rare breeder. Fewer than 400 pairs. Fluctuating population. Migrant. Protected.

STATUS INTERNATIONALLY: Palearctic breeding species. Overall decline in Europe.

DISTRIBUTION: Rather scattered nationwide. Often breeds in cultivated areas and by settlements. Locally common in parts of Transdanubia such as the Tolna hills and Baranya County. Invariably on the south-facing slopes of low hills. Rare on Great Plain.

TIMING: Summer. (May to August).

Scops Owl

Eagle Owl *Bubo bubo* (Eurasian Eagle Owl)
Uhu

Once a widespread species, Eagle Owl is now the rarest breeding owl and indeed one of the rarest birds in Hungary. Earlier this century, pairs bred in all the country's forested hills. Today a small population hangs on in the Zemplén region, with occasional birds in the Bükk, Mátra, Cserhát and Börzsöny ranges. Before the Second World War, nest-robbing was common, with eggs taken by collectors or destroyed by 'hunters'. Adults and young were taken for taxidermy or for use as lures in corvid shoots. Later, Eagle Owls no doubt suffered from an increase in the use of chemicals, as main prey species such as rats and hedgehogs feed on village dumps, whilst hamsters and voles feed in agricultural areas where pesticides are used. Birds often nest in quarries where power-lines have proven deadly for both fledging young and roosting adult birds. In response to the decline, owlets from Germany were released into previously occupied areas in the 1980s, but though well-meant, the project failed to tackle the fundamental problems which had caused the decline of the species or indeed to artificially increase the population.

STATUS IN HUNGARY: Very rare resident. Small but stable population of 10-12 pairs. Strictly protected.

STATUS INTERNATIONALLY: Mainly Palearctic range, but extending deeper into Africa, the Middle East and the Indian subcontinent. Considered vulnerable in Europe, though overall numbers may have increased.

DISTRIBUTION: Confined to and very local in Northern Hills. Only regular breeding pairs in the Zemplén hills.

TIMING: Present all year round. Young birds disperse when forced from parental territory in autumn.

Little Owl *Athene noctua*
Kuvik

As is the case with the overall European population, numbers of this species have declined sharply in Hungary since the Second World War. Changes in agriculture are thought to be the main cause. Feeding predominantly on large insects, Little Owls have been particularly affected by the use of pesticides. Yet in many parts of the Great Plain, Little Owls are still a familiar sight by day, sitting on thatched barns, cattle-sheds, farmhouses, haystacks and sweep-wells. Birds usually nest in farmyard lofts, under tile roofs and sometimes in haystacks. On the Hortobágy and Kiskunság, run-down farms and military bases are favourite haunts. Little Owls also occur in the foothills of Hungary's hill ranges, often in orchards and vineyards where old trees and buildings provide nesting sites.

STATUS IN HUNGARY: Fairly common to uncommon resident. Around 2,000-2,500 pairs. Population probably now stable. Strictly protected.

STATUS INTERNATIONALLY: Mainly Palearctic range, extending further south into the Middle East and parts of Africa. European population declining.

DISTRIBUTION: Open country nationwide, but mainly in lowlands, especially east of the Danube where locally common. Never found in forest proper. Adult birds remain in breeding territories whilst young birds disperse short distances at the end of summer.

TIMING: All year round. Birds become particularly active in February and March as they confirm their territories.

Tawny Owl *Strix aluco*
Macskabagoly

The most common owl of Hungary's woodlands, breeding in forested hill ranges, remnant lowland woods, floodplain forest, parks, orchards and even gardens. A limiting factor in the distribution of the species is the availability of nesting sites. Holes and hollows in old trees are preferred but birds will also use buildings and nestboxes. Tawny Owls have probably not been affected too negatively by forestry practices in Hungary, indeed they may have benefited in upland areas, as clearings adjacent to stands of trees provide a combination of hunting and nesting habitat. In lowlands the replacement of old riverine forest with poplar plantations has probably been detrimental but the overall afforestation of lowlands may have countered this.

STATUS IN HUNGARY: Common resident. Population size and trends unknown, no nationwide survey having been done: probably 8,000-10,000 pairs. Numbers stable if not increasing. Protected.

STATUS INTERNATIONALLY: Mainly Palearctic species. European population stable.

DISTRIBUTION: Occurs in deciduous but also coniferous woodland nationwide, particularly in hill ranges. Adults stay in breeding territories whilst young disperse locally throughout the summer.

TIMING: All year round.

Ural Owl *Strix uralensis*
Uráli bagoly

Hungary's small population of this enigmatic species can be regarded as the southerly extension of the Slovakian population to the north and northeast. Indeed, several pairs nest within a few miles of the Slovak border in the Aggtelek and Zemplén hills. In some years, increased numbers in Hungary may have coincided with a fall in the number of breeding pairs in Slovakia. Movements of Ural Owls into the northeast of the country occur periodically, and occasionally there are classic influxes, the winter of 1905-1906 and recently 1993-1994 being

such years. As elsewhere, fewer birds, or none at all, breed in years with low numbers of voles and other small mammals. Overall, the gradual movement into Hungary mirrors the westward trend of the species in central Europe. Most pairs are resident, nesting above all in old beech forest, but also coniferous and mixed woodland with adjacent meadows or clear fellings where birds hunt. There has also been a movement towards woods at lower elevations. Nesting sites include the old nests of Common Buzzard, Goshawk and tree-nesting Ravens, and some pairs have readily taken to nestboxes. Hungarian birds are of the Carpathian *macroura* race.

STATUS IN HUNGARY: Rare resident. Breeding pairs fluctuate between ten and 60 annually. Periodical influxes. Strictly protected.

STATUS INTERNATIONALLY: Palearctic species. European population probably stable.

DISTRIBUTION: Restricted to Northern Hills. Only regular in the Zemplén and Aggtelek hills, perhaps the Cserehát and occasionally the Bükk.

TIMING: All year round.

Ural Owl

Long-eared Owl *Asio otus*
Erdei fülesbagoly

Although often inconspicuous, Long-eared Owls are quite common in lowland areas and, after Tawny Owl, are the second most common owl species in Hungary. This is also another species which often relies on the much maligned Magpie for nesting sites, though those of Hooded Crow, Rook and even Common Buzzard are also used. A quietly brooding Long-eared Owl among the clamour of Red-footed Falcons and Rooks in a Hungarian *acacia* copse is typical. Wind-breaks, clumps of conifers, thickets, floodplain willows, colonnades, plantations, even isolated bushes are occupied if they contain a suitable nest and adjacent grassland or farmland for hunting. Long-eared Owls never inhabit the heart of forest. The species is a highly specialised predator, with voles often comprising up to 90% of prey items. The number of breeding pairs and of offspring raised each year is closely linked to the abundance of voles. In years with very low vole numbers, many pairs do not breed at all. In good years the Hungarian breeding population is higher in density than in most of Europe. Birds from further north and east in Europe move into Hungary in winter. Although protected, Long-eared Owls not uncommomly fall victim to the 'tradition' of spring shooting-through of corvid nests.

STATUS IN HUNGARY: Fairly common resident. Between 5,000 and 10,000 pairs. Population fluctuates greatly annually. Overall trend a slight decline. Protected.

STATUS INTERNATIONALLY: Holarctic species. European population probably stable.

DISTRIBUTION: Lowlands, foothills and floodplains nationwide. In winter, roosts of from ten to 20 and sometimes up to 50 birds occur, especially on the Great Plain in conifer plantations and copses. Also found in semi-urban parks and cemeteries.

TIMING: All year round.

Short-eared Owl *Asio flammeus*
Réti fülesbagoly

Short-eared Owl is something of a maverick in Hungarian ornithology. It is a rare and irregular breeder and at best a rare to common winter visitor depending on the year. In short, its occurrence in Hungary is erratic. The reasons for this no doubt lie elsewhere in the species' regular northern European range where the abundance of prey dictates movements. Some years see invasions and breeding pairs reported from Hungary's lowlands, particularly post-glacial habitats, whilst in other years the species is absent. Noted invasion years were in 1930, 1973, 1976 and most recently 1992 when around 40 pairs bred in the Fertő-Hanság area. Groups of around ten and sometimes up to 30 may be seen on areas of *puszta* in autumn and winter.

STATUS IN HUNGARY: Rare and irregular breeder. From 0-100 pairs each year. Breeding birds nomadic. Mainly winter visitor. Occasional large influxes. Strictly protected.

STATUS INTERNATIONALLY: Holarctic and South American species. European population vulnerable and in decline overall.

DISTRIBUTION: Occurs on lowland grassland and marshes nationwide. Usual breeding areas are Lake Fertő, Hanság, Sárrét, Kis-Balaton, Ócsa, Heves grasslands, Hortobágy and *puszta* in Békés and Bihár Counties.

TIMING: Possible all year round. Autumn and winter visitors generally arrive in August-September and leave in March. Breeding birds generally display in April and May.

CAPRIMULGIDAE (Nightjars)

Nightjar *Caprimulgus europaeus* (Eurasian Nightjar)
Lappantyú

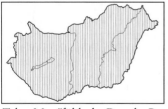

Being crepuscular hunters and largely inactive by day, Nightjars are probably overlooked in many areas of Hungary. This is not to suggest that this is a common species, it is fairly widespread, however, occurring around the country in forest clearings, woodland edges, wooded dry grassland, vineyards, orchards, parkland, scrub-dotted karst and plantations. Nightjar is locally common in areas with sandy and well drained soils such as the Kiskunság, Tolna Mezőföld, the Danube Bend and the Hajdúság, and on the warmer slopes of hill ranges such as the Börzsöny, Pilis, Mátra and Zemplén. Nightjars rarely occur in Hungary's closed forests or treeless open *puszta*. The *meridionalis* race breeds, and birds from northern Europe of the nominate *europaeus* occur on migration.

STATUS IN HUNGARY: Fairly common breeder. Population size and trends unknown. Probably between 5,000 and 10,000 pairs. Migrant. Protected.

STATUS INTERNATIONALLY: Palearctic breeding species. Overall European population in decline.

DISTRIBUTION: Widespread, though nowhere abundant. Occurs in suitable habitats in both lowlands and uplands nationwide.

TIMING: Summer. First birds arrive at the end of May. Most leave in September. Birds seen in October may well be through-migrants.

APODIDAE (Swifts)

Swift *Apus apus* (Common Swift)
Sarlósfecske

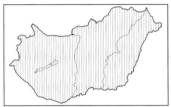

The vast majority of Swifts in Hungary nest in colonies on urban buildings. Yet this is a relatively recent trend, resulting from the post-war construction of tower-blocks and the like. In rural areas the species nests in castle ruins, sandy banks and holes in high beech trees. Records of the latter are few, but given the number of potential sites there may well be more woodland nesting pairs.

STATUS IN HUNGARY: Fairly common and widespread breeder. Population size unknown but has apparently increased in the last 40 years. Migrant. Protected.

STATUS INTERNATIONALLY: Palearctic breeding species. European population stable.

DISTRIBUTION: Nationwide. Mainly urban areas, especially cities such as Budapest, Sopron, Debrecen, Szeged, Szekszárd and Pécs. Some breeding records from woodland in the Zemplén and Bükk hill ranges.

TIMING: Birds arrive in late April and early May; most leave at the end of August. In summer, mainly in the vicinity of breeding sites. Birds range over wider areas before migrating south.

ALCEDINIDAE (Kingfishers)

Kingfisher *Alcedo atthis* (Common Kingfisher, River Kingfisher)
Jégmadár

Outside the breeding season, Kingfishers are widespread in Hungary, occurring along rivers, streams, canals, and on fishponds, reservoirs and lakes, in areas where they do not necessarily nest. The breeding range of the species is limited by the availability of nesting sites. As elsewhere in Europe, loamy or sandy banks near water are sought. In winter, much depends on the weather, some birds migrate whilst others move locally to open waters such as thermal springs, flowing feeder channels, fishponds and the Danube. In spring and autumn, and to a lesser extent winter, Kingfishers are common on fishponds such as those at Hortobágy and Pusztaszer, though very few breed at such places. Hungarian breeding birds are of the *ispida* race.

STATUS IN HUNGARY: Uncommon breeder. Exact population size unknown. Around 1,000 pairs estimated, though numbers fluctuate. Overall, has probably declined. Partial migrant.

Influxes in winter. Protected.

STATUS INTERNATIONALLY: Range covers Palearctic, India and South-East Asia. European population in decline.

DISTRIBUTION: Breeding range mainly follows Hungary's lowland rivers. Outside nesting period occurs on a wider variety of wetlands nationwide.

TIMING: All year round. Birds disperse in harsh winters.

MEROPIDAE (Bee-eaters)

Bee-eater *Merops apiaster* (European Bee-eater)
Gyurgyalag

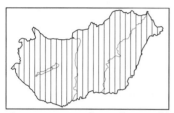

As with other hole nesting species, the distribution of Bee-eaters in Hungary is mainly determined by the availability of breeding sites. Colonies are scattered around the country wherever there are sand pits, quarries of soft sandstone or loamy clay and high river banks. In the absence of such nesting sites, loose colonies are formed in the ground in sandy soils. Occasionally widely scattered single pairs are found. The species does best if suitable nesting sites are on the warmer southern slopes of hill ranges, where birds hawk for insects over adjacent vineyards, orchards, allotments, pastures and areas of scrub. In the past, colonies of 100 burrows existed, nowadays the largest usually comprise around 50. A nationwide survey in 1949 found 1,271 nests, in 1977 1,390, and today between 1,000 and 2,000 pairs are estimated. Historically, birds were killed by bee-keepers, but being a strictly protected species this is now illegal and in any case no longer a serious problem. Rather, the species is often threatened at its colonies, from the illegal excavation of sand, rubbish dumping and by general disturbance as they are often located by roads and villages.

STATUS IN HUNGARY: Fairly common to uncommon breeder. Localised colonies, with between 1,000 and 2,000 nests nationwide. Numbers fluctuate locally, but overall population probably stable. Migrant. Strictly protected.

STATUS INTERNATIONALLY: Mainly Palearctic breeder. European breeding population in decline.

DISTRIBUTION: Suitable habitats nationwide. Very local breeder.

TIMING: Summer. Most birds arrive in the second week of May. In July and August, flocks of several hundred birds can be seen away from colonies before they leave in late August and early September.

CORACIIDAE (Rollers)

Roller *Coracias garrulus* (European Roller)
Szalakóta

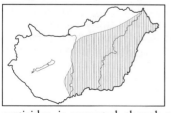

Travelling on certain roads across the Great Plain in summer one might be forgiven for thinking that Rollers are common birds in Hungary. Being brilliantly coloured and often sitting exposed on wires or dry branches from where they hunt for mostly insect prey, they are conspicuous birds. In fact, the species has steadily declined in Hungary over the last 25 years and the precise reasons remain unclear. Agricultural intensification, particularly the use of pesticides, is suspected, though problems no doubt also exist on migration and in African

Roller

wintering areas. Rollers are essentially birds of dry wooded *puszta* but also occur in open floodplain woodland, nesting in hollows in oaks, poplars, willows and in the old holes of Black or Green Woodpeckers. There are cases of nesting in soft sandstone walls and some pairs have also taken to specifically erected nestboxes.

STATUS IN HUNGARY: Uncommon breeder. Fewer than 500 pairs. Has declined. Migrant. Strictly protected.

STATUS INTERNATIONALLY: Palearctic breeding species. Drastic decline across most of Europe.

DISTRIBUTION: Lowlands nationwide. Now very rare in Transdanubia. Predominantly *puszta* and pastures on the Great Plain, especially the Kiskunság and Jászság regions. Also, open woodland along the Tisza and southern stretches of the Danube.

TIMING: Summer. Birds arrive at the end of April and early May. Small groups assemble in August before migrating in early September.

UPUPIDAE (Hoopoes)

Hoopoe *Upupa epops* (Eurasian Hoopoe)
Búbosbanka

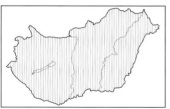

Typical Hoopoe habitat in Hungary is sparsely wooded *puszta*, open scrub areas and pasture, though the species is also found by settlements in allotments, vineyards, orchards and even village gardens. An adaptable species it nests in ruins, farm-buildings, tree hollows and holes, posts in vineyards, rabbit burrows, and will readily take to nestboxes. Unlike other lowland birds such as Roller, Hoopoes have adapted quite well to man-made habitats and have thus to a certain extent avoided the worst effects of the post-war intensification in agriculture. Overall numbers have probably declined but no nationwide surveys have been carried out to clarify the situation.

STATUS IN HUNGARY: Fairly common breeder. Population size unknown, probably between 5,000 and 10,000 pairs. Has declined. Migrant. Protected.

STATUS INTERNATIONALLY: Old World species. European population fluctuates, but overall considered stable.

DISTRIBUTION: Nationwide. Common and widespread in lowlands. Fairly common in hilly regions, with the exception of conifer plantations and dense woodland. Particularly common

in the Kiskunság, Hortobágy, Hajduság, Nyírség, Tolna Mezőföld and locally around Balaton.
TIMING: First birds arrive in late March and early April. Most leave in August.

PICIDAE (Woodpeckers)

Wryneck *Jynx torquilla* (Northern Wryneck, Eurasian Wryneck)
Nyaktekercs

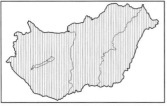

Wrynecks are widespread in Hungary, occurring in gardens, parks, orchards, woodland edges and clearings, copses, floodplain woodland and wooded *puszta*. Oakwoods bordered by grassland are prime Wryneck habitat as the two most important requirements of the species are met, namely tree holes for nesting and ants on which to feed. Around settlements, Wrynecks often nest in old woodpecker or natural holes in walnut trees. This is yet another species which has benefited from Hungarian ornithology's passion for nestbox schemes.

STATUS IN HUNGARY: Common and widespread breeder. Population size and trends unknown. Probably between 10,000 and 20,000 pairs. Migrant. Protected.
STATUS INTERNATIONALLY: Palearctic breeding species. European population in decline.
DISTRIBUTION: Woodland nationwide, though not in dense forest or conifer plantations.
TIMING: First birds heard at the end of March, though most arrive in mid April. Return migration mainly in September.

Grey-headed Woodpecker *Picus canus* (Grey-faced Woodpecker)
Hamvas küllő, Szürke küllő.

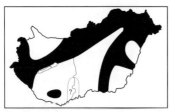

The Hungarian range of this species is mainly tied to old broadleaved woodland in floodplains and hilly regions. Some birds also breed in parkland and lowland woods. Although essentially ground feeders with a preference for anthills and rotten tree stumps, Grey-headed Woodpeckers nest high on the trunk of mature trees, mainly beech, oak, and hornbeam, but also in willows, conifers and occasionally even in telegraph poles. The felling of suitable woodland, the forestry trend towards managed poplars and conifers and the degradation of adjacent grassland where this woodpecker feeds have all certainly affected the species. In winter, some birds disperse, occurring in gardens, orchards and woods along lowland rivers where they do not breed. Outside the incubation period, invariably responds to imitations of its calls.

STATUS IN HUNGARY: Uncommon to fairly common resident. Probably between 1,000 and 2,000 pairs. Rather local. Some nomadic in winter. Population has declined. Protected.
STATUS INTERNATIONALLY: Palearctic and Oriental species. European population in decline.
DISTRIBUTION: Scattered nationwide. Mainly Northern Hills and the Őrszég, Bakony, Vértes and Pilis hill ranges in Transdanubia.
TIMING: All year round. Some influx of native birds from hills, and probably others from further afield, into lower hills and lowland woodland in winter.

Grey-headed Woodpecker

Green Woodpecker *Picus viridis* (European Green Woodpecker)
Zöld küllő

By far the most common and widespread of the two *Picus* species in Hungary, occurring in both upland and lowland woodland. Green Woodpeckers are, however, absent from closed forest, breeding rather in parks, gardens, orchards, floodplains, colonnades, copses, poplar plantations and open deciduous woodland. Green Woodpeckers excavate their nest holes on the main trunk of large trees but only in soft or rotten wood and will also enlarge the entrance holes of nestboxes intended for other smaller species. Although little concrete data are available on trends, Green Woodpeckers are seemingly more adaptable in terms of habitat requirements than Grey-headed Woodpeckers, and have thus probably been less affected by post-war Hungarian forestry practices. Locally there have been declines, but overall the population remains healthy. Outside the breeding season some birds disperse and occur in areas where they do not breed.

STATUS IN HUNGARY: Common and widespread resident. Between 8,000 and 10,000 pairs estimated. Population has probably declined slightly. Protected.

STATUS INTERNATIONALLY: Global range almost completely within Western Palearctic. European population in decline.

DISTRIBUTION: Nationwide. Rarely in dense woodland. Rather plantations, floodplain woodland, glades, copses, parkland, orchards, gardens and wood edges. Some dispersal from breeding areas in autumn.

TIMING: All year round.

Black Woodpecker *Dryocopus martius*
Fekete harkály

The classic habitat of Black Woodpeckers in Hungary is old stands of beech in hill areas, though birds inhabit a wide range of woodland with mixed deciduous and conifer species. In recent decades, Black Woodpeckers have expanded their range in Hungary and are now found in upland conifer plantations and in lowland areas in parkland, riverine forest, open wooded

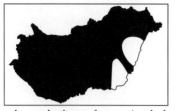

floodplains, poplar plantations and remnant lowland oakwoods. Pairs typically excavate holes high up in the sound hard wood of wide trunks. In closed conifer forest any sign of prolonged work on the ground or a stump betrays the presence of Black Woodpecker, as Green Woodpecker, the only other species capable of this, does not occur in such habitat. Stock Doves in a woodland also usually indicate the presence of the species as the former rely on the latter for nesting holes.

STATUS IN HUNGARY: Fairly common and widespread resident. Population size unknown but probably somewhere between 2,000-5,000 pairs. Seems to be increasing in range and number. Protected.

STATUS INTERNATIONALLY: Mainly Palearctic species. European population considered stable.

DISTRIBUTION: Woodland nationwide. All upland forest. In lowlands, especially woodland along the Danube and Tisza, the Hajdúság and the southern Kiskunság. Sedentary, though young birds disperse at the end of the breeding season and are sometimes seen moving across open country.

TIMING: All year round.

Great Spotted Woodpecker *Dendrocopos major*
Nagy fakopáncs, Nagy tarkaharkály

By far the most common and widespread woodpecker species in Hungary, Great Spotteds are found in almost every type of wooded habitat. They are the least specific of the family in terms of habitat choice, breeding in urban gardens and parks *alongside* Syrian Woodpecker, and in extensive tracks of hill forest with Black and Grey-headed Woodpeckers. Nest holes are usually excavated in the trunk, main boughs and sometimes in telegraph poles. Nestboxes intended for passerines are also adapted and utilised. Breeding birds are of the *pinetorum* race, and there are some winter records of the northern European nominate *major*. There have been several documented occurrences in Hungary of hybridisation between Great Spotted and Syrian Woodpeckers.

STATUS IN HUNGARY: Very common and widespread resident. Population size and trends unknown. Protected.

STATUS INTERNATIONALLY: Mainly Palearctic species. European population stable.

DISTRIBUTION: Nationwide. Found in all types of lowland and upland woodland. Some birds move short distances from nesting sites in winter.

TIMING: All year round.

Syrian Woodpecker *Dendrocopos syriacus*
Balkáni fakopáncs, Balkáni tarkaharkály

First recorded breeding at Kiskunfélegyházá in the Kiskunság in 1937, Syrian Woodpecker swept through Hungary in less than 20 years. The Budapest area was colonised in the early 1940s, and in 1948 the first birds were seen across the Danube in Transdanubia. By 1950 the species was reported beyond Hungary's borders in southern Slovakia and eastern Austria. Syrian Woodpecker is very much a bird of settlements, occurring in urban gardens, parks, cemeteries, allotments, orchards and colonnades. Some also inhabit open floodplain woodland along the Danube and other rivers, copses in farmland and the edges of woodland. Favoured trees for nesting include *acacia,* willow, poplar, cherry and other fruit trees. Nestboxes are also occupied. Unlike Great Spotted Woodpecker, the species never breeds in the heart of woodland, and contrary to many accounts, Syrians do not replace their congener in lowland areas. Rather both occur in lowlands whilst only the former species occurs in hill forest. The Hungarian nomenclature regards occurring birds as a European race '*balcanicus*', though this is not recognised by most authorities.

STATUS IN HUNGARY: Common and widespread resident. Population size and current trends unknown. Probably between 5,000 and 10,000 pairs. Population probably now stable after decades of increase and expansion. Protected.

STATUS INTERNATIONALLY: Palearctic species. Gradually increasing and expanding range in Europe.

DISTRIBUTION: Nationwide, especially in and around settlements. Very rarely in woodland proper. Locally common in Budapest and other urban areas. In winter some dispersal locally.

TIMING: All year round.

Syrian Woodpecker

Middle Spotted Woodpecker *Dendrocopos medius*
Közép fakopáncs, Közép tarkaharkály

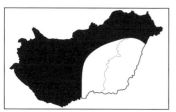

This species is found mainly in Hungary's oakwoods, though some also occur in parks with oaks and hornbeam, old orchards, wooded pastures and in floodplains with old willows. Middle Spotted Woodpeckers are rarely seen in conifers. Birds are highly sedentary, seldom moving far from their breeding territories though in winter there is some dispersal locally. In spring the species is very vocal, though birds rarely drum, and their very characteristic calls often betray their presence at the top of exposed branches. On the other hand, when nesting and feeding young, birds can be rather silent and elusive as they feed mainly in the canopy of broadleaved trees, gleaning insects from foliage and probing into bark rather than boring into wood.

STATUS IN HUNGARY: Fairly common resident. Population size and trends unknown. Probably between 5,000 and 10,000 pairs. Protected.

STATUS INTERNATIONALLY: Range mostly within Western Palearctic. European population probably stable.

DISTRIBUTION: Deciduous woodland in Transdanubia and the Northern Hills. Some in floodplain forest. Locally common in the Sopron, Mecsek, Vértes, Buda, Pilis, Börzöny, Mátra and Zemplén hill ranges.

TIMING: All year round.

White-backed Woodpecker *Dendrocopos leucotos*
Fehérhátú fakopáncs, Fehérhátú harkály

The rarest of Hungary's woodpeckers, this species is very local in the Northern Hills, with some pairs also in forested regions in Transdanubia. White-backed Woodpeckers have never been common in Hungary but today are scarcer than ever. A very specialised feeder, their preferred Hungarian habitat is old, unmanaged beech with abundant standing and fallen dead wood and rotten stumps. In the last 40 years, much of such woodland has been cleared. Several scattered populations hang on in steep and rocky terrain where forestry machinery cannot be used or in protected areas. Some breed in mixed forest and very occasionally in quite open areas with scattered fruit trees. The already small population is rather fragmented, with most areas holding fewer than 20 pairs each. Largest numbers are in Bükk National Park, where around 50 pairs are estimated to breed.

STATUS IN HUNGARY: Rare resident. 100-150 pairs. Has declined. Strictly protected.
STATUS INTERNATIONALLY: Mainly Palearctic species. European population in decline.
DISTRIBUTION: Localised. Found only in suitable forest in the Börzsöny, Mátra, Bükk, Aggtelek and Zemplén hills and in Transdanubia in the Kőszeg and possibly Bakony hills.
TIMING: All year round. Sedentary, but some movement locally in winter.

Lesser Spotted Woodpecker *Dendrocopos minor*
Kis fakopáncs, Kis tarkaharkály

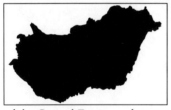

Although fairly common and widespread, Lesser Spotted Woodpeckers can be rather elusive. The classic habitat for the species in Hungary is oakwoods, but they also occur in mixed deciduous woods, orchards, parks, gardens and in floodplains with willow, alder and poplar. Very rarely seen in closed forest or conifer plantations. Has readily taken to nestboxes of which plenty have been erected for songbird studies in such areas as the Pilis hills. Hungarian birds are of the Central European *hortorum* race.

STATUS IN HUNGARY: Fairly common resident. Population size and trends unknown. Protected.
STATUS INTERNATIONALLY: Palearctic species. European population probably stable.
DISTRIBUTION: Woodland nationwide. Mainly rolling hills in Transdanubia, suitable woodland in the Northern Hills and floodplain forest along the Danube, especially Gemenc. Also Debrecen forest and the Hajdúság. Rare in lowlands but does breed in some scattered Great Plain woodland.
TIMING: All year round. Some local dispersal in autumn and winter.

ALAUDIDAE (Larks)

Short-toed Lark *Calandrella brachydactyla*
Szikipacsirta

In 1956 an endemic Hungarian race '*hungarica*' of Short-toed Lark was described. Some ornithologists have disputed this, among other things querying how a migratory bird with a fluctuating population can be endemic, but at present this race remains in the official Hungarian nomenclature. The nominate *brachydactyla* is also mentioned as having occurred. If Hungarian birds are of a clearly defined subspecies, then the race is in danger of extinction as numbers have crashed. Before the 1980s, over 200 singing males were regularly counted in

the core Hortobágy population, and a small population bred at Kardoskút in the very south of the Great Plain. The Kardoskút birds have since disappeared and the Hortobágy population has steadily declined, with now only 5-20 pairs found each year, though the previously favoured habitat remains intact. In the late 1980s, some birds were found breeding in farmland in Heves County, and though there has been no confirmation since, it is possible that isolated populations are scattered in other areas in eastern Hungary. Interestingly, the species has been replaced as the symbol of Hortobágy National Park and has recently started to breed just to the north in Slovakia from where it was previously absent.

STATUS IN HUNGARY: Very rare breeder. 10-30 pairs. Strong decline. Migrant. Strictly protected.

STATUS INTERNATIONALLY: Palearctic breeding species. European population vulnerable and in decline.

DISTRIBUTION: Breeds exclusively on Great Plain and then very local. Alkaline grazing *puszta* at Kunmadaras-Nagyiván and Szelencés-Angyalháza in Hortobágy National Park were long regarded as the core breeding areas. Has also bred in farmland. Rare elsewhere, possibly overlooked.

TIMING: First birds arrive in early April. Return migration mainly in August.

Crested Lark *Galerida cristata*
Búbospacsirta

Originally a bird of the *puszta* and edges of open farmland, Crested Larks now also frequent railway sidings, motorway hard-shoulders, wasteland, dumps, cart-tracks, vineyards and stock-yards across lowland Hungary. Recently, birds have spread into the urban desert habitats of car parks and forecourts around high-rise blocks. Two races are said to occur, the nominate *cristata* in northwest and western Transdanubia and *tenuirostris* mainly east of the Danube. Some overlap no doubt occurs.

STATUS IN HUNGARY: Very common and widespread resident. Stable if not increasing population. 50,000-80,000 pairs estimated. Protected.

STATUS INTERNATIONALLY: Old World species. Although still common and widespread, European population in decline.

DISTRIBUTION: Unforested areas nationwide, but mainly lowlands. Highly sedentary.

TIMING: All year round. In winter small flocks congregate but do not move far from breeding areas.

Woodlark *Lullula arborea*
Erdei pacsirta

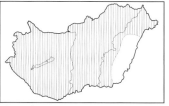

Woodlarks occur across Hungary in lightly wooded hills, wooded pasture and karst, forest edges, plantations, clearings, vineyards with scattered trees and old orchards. Although no doubt affected in some areas by urbanisation and intensive farming and forestry methods, the small population in Hungary is not considered to be threatened. In some areas the species is still locally quite common. Woodlarks were once common around Budapest, and though some pairs can still be found, the expansion of the city into the Buda hills has eliminated many suitable habitats.

STATUS IN HUNGARY: Fairly common breeder. Population probably stable. 3,000-5,000 pairs. Migrant. Protected.

STATUS INTERNATIONALLY: Mainly Western Palearctic species. European population considered vulnerable and mostly in decline.

DISTRIBUTION: Suitable woodland nationwide. Mainly foothills and rolling country but also lowland plantations. Locally common on the southern slopes of the Pilis, Börzsöny, Mátra, Bükk and Aggtelek hills, Balaton uplands and the Hajdúság region.

TIMING: First birds return from the Mediterranean in February. Most leave late September into October. Some may overwinter in mild years.

Crested Lark

Skylark *Alauda arvensis* (Eurasian Skylark, Common Skylark)
Mezei pacsirta

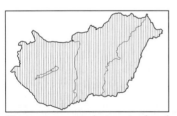

One of the most common and widespread birds of Hungary's lowlands, Skylarks are often abundant on expanses of *puszta*, arable land, pasture, and indeed occur everywhere except forest and wetlands. Although much suitable habitat exists in Hungary, Skylark numbers have declined, once again agricultural intensification, changes in land use and loss of habitat to development are considered the causes. There is, however, no need for alarm as the Hungarian population is far from threatened and large core populations breed in the Hortobágy, Kiskunság and other protected areas on the Great Plain. Birds breeding in the northwest of the country and the majority passing through and wintering are of the nominate *arvensis* race; elsewhere, the *cantarella* race breeds, though some consider these birds to be '*lunata*', an additional race from the Balkans.

STATUS IN HUNGARY: Very common and widespread breeder. Population size and trends unknown. Probably over 200,000 pairs. Breeding birds mainly migratory. Influxes in autumn and winter. Protected.

STATUS INTERNATIONALLY: Palearctic species. European population considered vulnerable and mostly in decline.

DISTRIBUTION: Nationwide, particularly the Great Plain.

TIMING: First birds arrive from the Mediterranean in early February. Autumn passage depends on weather but usually in September-October. In mild winters, some stay on and are joined by birds from further north and northeast.

Shore Lark *Eremophila alpestris* (Horned Lark)
Fülespacsirta

The number of Shore Larks visiting Hungary each winter fluctuates greatly. Some years see small parties of single figures and others influxes of flocks of more than 100 birds each. The norm is rather flocks of between ten and 20 birds at known and regularly watched sites on the Hortobágy, with unknown numbers at the numerous underwatched but similar areas across the Great Plain. Occurring birds are of the *flava* race.

STATUS IN HUNGARY: Rare but annual winter visitor. Protected.
STATUS INTERNATIONALLY: Mainly Holarctic species. European population probably stable.
DISTRIBUTION: Mainly *puszta* and salt lakes east of the Tisza, particularly the Hortobágy and Bihar, Békés and Csongrád Counties. Less frequent, perhaps overlooked, in the Kiskunság. Very rarely observed in Transdanubia.
TIMING: Winter. From beginning of November to February.

HIRUNDINIDAE (Swallows and Martins)

Sand Martin *Riparia riparia* (Bank Swallow)
Partifecske

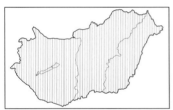

There are numerous Sand Martin colonies along the River Tisza, with the largest at Tiszatelek being also one of the largest in the world. In 1989, 2,537 pairs, and in 1990, 2,118 bred here. In 1990, 33,000 pairs in 211 colonies were counted along the whole length of the Tisza. This figure constituted around half the total Hungarian Sand Martin population. The average size of colonies varies between 120-157 pairs, with 45% of colonies holding over 500 pairs. The Tisza colonies are on average larger than usual and high vertical banks have been found to be the most important factor in choice of nesting sites. Numbers at these colonies fluctuate from year to year depending on water levels. Recent studies have shown that the annual sizes of the River Tisza populations are strongly linked to conditions on migration and in African wintering areas. Besides large colonies, many of fewer than 20 pairs can be found dotted around the country, often far from rivers in sand pits and both working and abandoned soft-sandstone quarries. Sand Martins are often in the company of Bee-eaters, Tree Sparrows and other species at such sites.

STATUS IN HUNGARY: Common breeder. Fluctuating population of between 60,000 and 80,000 pairs. Migrant. Protected.
STATUS INTERNATIONALLY: Holarctic breeding species. Declining in Europe.
DISTRIBUTION: Nationwide. As a breeding species somewhat local owing to need for suitable nesting sites. Essentially lowlands. Large colonies on the upper reaches of the River Tisza. Between 1,500 and 2,600 pairs (2,500-4,200 holes) at Tiszatelek annually.
TIMING: Spring and summer. April to early September.

Swallow *Hirundo rustica* (Barn Swallow)
Füstifecske

Swallows are common and widespread throughout Hungary, though numbers in hilly areas are restricted by a lack of suitable buildings for nesting. In lowland areas they nest in loose colonies on houses and farm buildings, particularly inside stables and cattle sheds on the Great Plain. On the Hortobágy, Swallows nest on wooden beams in the porches of inns and

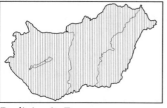

even inside buildings which have permanently open windows. Loose colonies of up to 25 pairs are formed when nesting possibilities permit.
STATUS IN HUNGARY: Very common and widespread breeder. Locally very common. Overall population probably stable. 150,00-200,000 pairs estimated. Migrant. Protected.
STATUS INTERNATIONALLY: Holarctic breeding species. Declining in Europe.
DISTRIBUTION: Nationwide, but mainly lowlands.
TIMING: Spring and summer. End of March to early October. Flocks gather in August and leave in September. Some reports from winter.

House Martin *Delichon urbica*
Molnárfecske

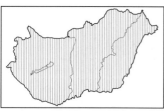

Not as numerous as Swallow, but just as widespread, House Martins are more of an urban species than their congener. Most pairs nest in small colonies of 5-20 nests under the eaves of houses and other buildings in villages, towns and even large cities. Some are found on isolated rural buildings and occasionally in quarries. In rural areas the two species often nest in loose association on farm buildings owing to the limited availability of nesting sites. In such cases, House Martins are invariably in the minority. Although not generally persecuted, it is not unusual to see improvised anti-nesting devices on dwellings, often plastic bunting or strips of coloured paper suspended from gutters.
STATUS IN HUNGARY: Common and widespread breeder. Population size and trends unknown. Locally common. Migrant. Protected.
STATUS INTERNATIONALLY: Mainly Palearctic breeding species. European population has declined.
DISTRIBUTION: Nationwide. Predominantly urban and lowland areas.
TIMING: Spring and summer. Birds arrive back from winter quarters in April. Flocks congregate in August before leaving late in the month and early September.

MOTACILLIDAE (Pipits and Wagtails)

Tawny Pipit *Anthus campestris*
Parlagi pityer

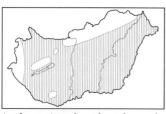

A bird of dry open country, Tawny Pipit is locally common east of the Danube on expanses of *puszta*, fallow, grazing land, arable land and particularly sandy soil regions such as the Kiskunság. In the west and north of the country the species is somewhat scattered and localised. Birds also occur in linear habitats such as farm tracks and the dry grassy tops of dykes around fishponds and along canals. Hungary has one of the largest populations of Tawny Pipit in the region, but though much suitable habitat currently exists, changes and intensification in land use may threaten those birds outside protected areas such as the Hortobágy and Kiskunság.
STATUS IN HUNGARY: Fairly common breeder. Locally common. Population size and trends unknown. Probably around 10,000 pairs. Migrant. Protected.
STATUS INTERNATIONALLY: Palearctic breeding range. Considered vulnerable in Europe and

declining.
DISTRIBUTION: Nationwide, but essentially lowlands. Uncommon in most of Transdanubia. More widespread across Great Plain. Core populations in the Kiskunság, Hortobágy, and in Heves, Csongrád, Bihar and Békés Counties.
TIMING: Spring and summer. Birds arrive throughout April. Most leave in late September into early October.

Tawny Pipit

Tree Pipit *Anthus trivialis*
Erdei pityer

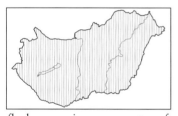

Tree Pipits are widespread across Hungary, nesting wherever there is suitable habitat. The majority of the population breeds at the edges of upland forest, by clearings, tracks and fire-breaks. The species is also fairly common around lowland conifer and poplar plantations which are bordered by farmland or grassy scrub. Some also breed in isolated woodland, copses and wind-breaks on the Great Plain. At the end of summer, prior to migration, small flocks occur in open country, often in the company of other pipit and lark species.
STATUS IN HUNGARY: Common and widespread breeder. Population size and trends unknown. Migrant. Protected.
STATUS INTERNATIONALLY: Palearctic breeding range. European population stable.
DISTRIBUTION: Woodland nationwide. Mainly Northern Hills and Transdanubia. Rather local on Great Plain.
TIMING: Spring and summer. Most arrive in April. Return migration in August-September.

Meadow Pipit *Anthus pratensis*
Réti pityer

Although it does not breed, Meadow Pipit is one of the most common *Anthus* species in Hungary, occurring in a variety of wet and semi-wetland habitats on passage and through most winters. In autumn, flocks of over 100 birds can occur, though smaller groups of around a dozen are more typical. In winter, often associates with larks, buntings and finches in open farmland and *puszta*.

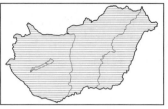

STATUS IN HUNGARY: Very common and widespread on passage. Some winter. Protected.
STATUS INTERNATIONALLY: Breeding range mainly within Western Palearctic. European population probably stable.
DISTRIBUTION: Nationwide, but predominantly lowlands.
TIMING: Almost all year round. Easily encountered on autumn passage in September and October. In spring, from March to early May.

Red-throated Pipit *Anthus cervinus*
Rozsdástorkú pityer

Once considered uncommon in Hungary, Red-throated Pipits are regular migrants through Hungary's lowlands as they move southwards from northern Europe to winter in Africa. The species is still probably overlooked somewhat, as birds are often mingled in flocks of other pipits and larks. Rarely more than ten birds seen together in spring, whereas small flocks are regular in autumn across the Great Plain. Most birds move through Hungary in mid May after the last Meadow Pipits have already passed through.
STATUS IN HUNGARY: Fairly common on passage. Protected.
STATUS INTERNATIONALLY: Breeding range covers the Arctic and sub-Arctic Palearctic extending to Alaska. European population probably stable.
DISTRIBUTION: Moves through on a broad front nationwide. In Transdanubia, is regular at sites along the Sárviz valley such as Sárrét, Sárszentágota and Rétszilas. East of the Danube, small flocks pass through the Kiskunság, Hortobágy, Pusztaszer region and probably many other areas.
TIMING: Mainly lowlands, from September to November. In spring, April to May.

Water Pipit *Anthus spinoletta*
Havasi pityer

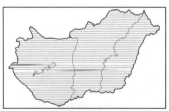

Although never numerous on passage, being for example less common than Red-throated Pipit, small flocks and single birds occur by flowing canals, feeder channels, marshes, wet *puszta* and lakesides. Most winters see a few birds remaining. Flocks of around 100 birds have been recorded, but rather small groups scattered across the country are the norm.
STATUS IN HUNGARY: Uncommon on passage. Some winter. Protected.
STATUS INTERNATIONALLY: Holarctic breeding range. European population stable.
DISTRIBUTION: Occurs nationwide, with exception of wooded areas.
TIMING: From September to April. Main wintering period from November to February.

Blue-headed Wagtail *Motacilla flava*
Sárga billegető

Three of the various races of *flava* Wagtail regularly occur in Hungary. The nominate Blue-headed predominates and breeds in wet meadows, pastures, boggy *puszta* and sedge marshes across the country's lowlands and in river valleys in hilly regions. A few of the Balkan Black-headed *feldegg* race are annual, mainly east of the Tisza. On several occasions pairs of this race have bred on the Hortobágy and at Kardoskút. The Fenno-Scandic Grey-headed race *thunbergi* is regular on migration. There are also four collected records of '*dombrowskii*'

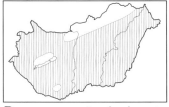

birds, which are regarded by some as yet another race from the Balkans. Whilst on passage, feeding mixed-race flocks of several hundred birds can be seen following cattle and sheep across the *puszta*.

STATUS IN HUNGARY: Common and widespread breeder. Population size and trends unknown. Migrant. Protected.

STATUS INTERNATIONALLY: Breeding range mainly within Palearctic. European population probably declining.

DISTRIBUTION: Lowlands nationwide. Some suitable habitats in uplands.

TIMING: First passage flocks appear at the end of March into April. Autumn migration mainly in September, though some pass through in early October.

Blue-headed Wagtail

Grey Wagtail *Motacilla cinerea*
Hegyi billegető

Grey Wagtails have never been common in Hungary as the country has little mountainous terrain with the fast-flowing streams that the species requires. Yet up to the 1980s, pairs were found in small numbers in all of Hungary's hill ranges. Today, Grey Wagtails are a scattered and uncommon breeding bird. Although the decline has not been as drastic as that of the other hill stream species the Dipper, the disappearance of many streams in successive dry years has been a factor which has forced many pairs elsewhere. Water management methods and poor water quality have also played their part in the decline.

STATUS IN HUNGARY: Rare breeder. Between 150 and 200 pairs. Has declined. Some resident, others partial migrants. Influxes in winter. Protected.

STATUS INTERNATIONALLY: Palearctic breeding range. European population considered stable.

DISTRIBUTION: Localised. Breeding pairs scattered in hills on the Austrian border and the Mecsek, Bakony, Pilis, Börzsöny, Bükk, Zemplén and Aggtelek areas.

TIMING: Most remain in breeding areas for much of year. Some occur in winter by unfrozen lowland wetlands. Parties nationwide during spring migration in March and April.

White Wagtail *Motacilla alba*
Barázdabillegető

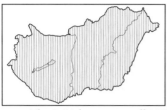

I will always have a soft spot for White Wagtail as it took me so long to learn how to pronounce its Hungarian name correctly. Most birds breed by lakes, gravel pits, reservoirs, ponds, canals, streams and the like, though some also nest in villages, stock-yards and farmland some way from water. In late summer, birds congregate around stables, cattlesheds and other places with farm animals and manure heaps. Hungarian birds are of the nominate *alba* race. The British race *yarrellii* (Pied Wagtail) has been recorded as a vagrant.

STATUS IN HUNGARY: Very common and widespread breeder. Population size and trends unknown. Mainly migratory, though some birds occasionally winter in the south of the country. Protected.

STATUS INTERNATIONALLY: Mainly Palearctic breeding range. European population probably stable.

DISTRIBUTION: Nationwide. Very common in lowlands, especially around farms and rural settlements.

TIMING: All year round. Small numbers sometimes overwinter.

First migratory birds arrive back in February. More pass through the country during spring and autumn migration.

BOMBYCILLIDAE (Waxwings)

Waxwing *Bombycilla garrulus* (Bohemian Waxwing)
Csonttollú

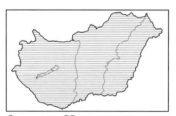

A typical invasion species, with flocks all around the country in some winters and few if any birds the next. Much depends on weather and food supplies and it seems that the first birds to arrive in Hungary often move on to the Balkans before midwinter, with new flocks replacing them. In recent years scattered flocks of some hundreds have been recorded rather than truly large invasions. The last significant invasion was in 1958 with *c.* 5,000 birds estimated.

STATUS IN HUNGARY: Common to rare winter visitor. Numbers fluctuate greatly from year to year. Protected.

STATUS INTERNATIONALLY: Holarctic species. European population considered stable.

DISTRIBUTION: Occurs nationwide, usually in urban gardens, orchards and parks.

TIMING: Has occurred from October to June, main period, however, is November to March.

CINCLIDAE (Dippers)

Dipper *Cinclus cinclus* (White-throated Dipper)
Vízirigó

In the last 20 years Dippers have all but vanished from Hungary. The cause of the drastic decline of the species is not entirely clear, but, as with Grey Wagtail, birds have lost much stream habitat owing to several years with hot, dry summers. Poor water quality, water management and forestry practices have also been factors. At the time of writing, only one known pair regularly breeds. In the early 1980s the total Hungarian population was estimated

to be 30 pairs with, for example, 15 in the Bükk hills, 1-3 Mátra, 1-5 Zemplén, 1-3 Börzsöny and a few near Sopron and other areas on the Austrian border. The *aquaticus* race occurs.

STATUS IN HUNGARY: Very rare resident. 1-2 pairs. Strictly protected.

STATUS INTERNATIONALLY: Palearctic species. European population has declined slightly.

DISTRIBUTION: Last known breeding pair confined to the Aggtelek hills, occasionally in the Pilis-Visegrád area. Some, presumably Austrian birds, winter in the Sopron hills.

TIMING: All year round. Some birds, perhaps from neighbouring countries, occasionally seen in winter along the Danube and other rivers.

TROGLODYTIDAE (Wrens)

Wren *Troglodytes troglodytes* (Northern Wren, Winter Wren)
Ökörszem

Wrens are common woodland birds in Hungary, occurring in almost any deciduous wooded area with an understory of brush, tangled vegetation or scrub. Highest numbers are in damp woods with earth walls, stream banks, root-plates, logs and piles of branches which provide nesting sites.

STATUS IN HUNGARY: Common and widespread resident. Population size and trends unknown. Protected.

STATUS INTERNATIONALLY: Holarctic species. European population considered stable.

DISTRIBUTION: Wooded habitats nationwide. Mainly hill and floodplain woodland. Also parks, gardens, vineyards and allotments. Common in Transdanubia and Northern Hills, scattered on Great Plain. Some dispersal to more open country in winter, especially reedbeds.

TIMING: All year round. Some birds disperse from breeding areas in winter.

PRUNELLIDAE (Accentors)

Dunnock *Prunella modularis* (Hedge Accentor)
Erdei szürkebegy

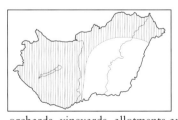

Dunnocks are much more of a woodland bird in Hungary than in, for example, the British Isles. A somewhat secretive species, inhabiting thickets, forest edges and stream valleys, it has taken time for its Hungarian breeding distribution to be clarified. Until very recently it was regarded as a rare breeding species, however, in the last 20 years nesting has been confirmed in most hill ranges and some floodplain woodland. On migration, birds occur in orchards, vineyards, allotments and lowland copses and reedbeds.

STATUS IN HUNGARY: Uncommon breeder. Fairly common locally. Migratory. Some may be resident. Population size and trends unknown. Protected.

STATUS INTERNATIONALLY: Range almost completely within Western Palearctic. European population probably stable.

DISTRIBUTION: Breeding first confirmed in the early 1960s at Szigetköz in the very northwest; later in several areas in the Northern Hills and along the Danube. Almost certainly breeds elsewhere.

TIMING: All year round. Small numbers of passage birds pass through lowlands in April. In autumn occurs nationwide. Some overwinter.

Alpine Accentor *Prunella collaris*
Havasi szürkebegy

Alpine Accentors usually arrive from the high mountains, which almost encircle Hungary, in November. Single birds or small parties, rarely double figures, often stay at one site all winter. Birds wintering on Gellert Hill in the centre of Budapest have been observed heading high across the Danube at dusk, presumably to roost on downtown buildings rather than on the rocky hill itself.

STATUS IN HUNGARY: Uncommon but regular winter visitor. Protected.

STATUS INTERNATIONALLY: Mainly Palearctic species. European population stable.

DISTRIBUTION: Regular at favoured quarries, rocky areas and castle ruins in the Buda, Pilis, Gerecse, Cserhát, Börzsöny, Medves, Zemplén and no doubt other hill ranges.

TIMING: Has occurred from November to May, though December and January are most regular months.

TURDIDAE (Chats, Thrushes and Allies)

Robin *Erithacus rubecula* (European Robin)
Vörösbegy

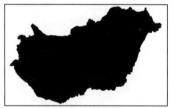

A truly woodland bird in Hungary, Robins are rarely confiding and seldom seen in urban gardens. Typical nesting habitats are damp woodland with tangled undergrowth and particularly stream valleys with root-plates and banks with overhanging vegetation. Some Robins do, however, inhabit suburban allotments, vineyards, gardens, parks and floodplain forest. Most Hungarian Robins are migratory, the birds seen in winter being from further north and east in Europe, though some breeding birds may be resident. The species is the most frequent host of Cuckoos in Hungary's wooded hills. Being mainly migratory, Robins are not associated with Christmas in Hungary.

STATUS IN HUNGARY: Common and widespread. Population size unknown. Has probably declined. Mainly migratory, though some regularly overwinter. Protected.

STATUS INTERNATIONALLY: Palearctic species. European population stable.

DISTRIBUTION: Woodland nationwide, but mainly Transdanubia and Northern Hills. On migration in lowland copses, reedbeds and other areas where they do not breed.

TIMING: All year round. Migratory birds return in March and April. Most leave in October.

Thrush Nightingale *Luscinia luscinia* (Sprosser)
Nagy fülemüle

The European breeding range of this species extends into Hungary in the very northeast of the country. An irregular number of pairs breed in the wet willow and poplar thickets of the upper River Tisza, particularly the Bodrogzug floodplain. Boggy terrain, often impenetrable shrubbery and innumerable mosquitoes go hand in hand with Thrush Nightingale habitat here. To complicate matters further, the range of the much more common Nightingale *L. megarhyn-*

chos overlaps with Thrush Nightingale, and there have been cases of hybridisation and convergence in the songs of the two species. Occasionally there are hints of an expansion of range further into Hungary via the Tisza, and with the species common in neighbouring Ukraine and Romania, this has long seemed probable. However, such an expansion, which would be in line with the general westward trend of the species in Europe, has not materialised. Local observers have in fact reported fewer birds in recent years.

STATUS IN HUNGARY: Rare and localised breeder. Status unclear. Probably fewer than 100 pairs. Migrant. Regular on passage. Strictly protected.

STATUS INTERNATIONALLY: Palearctic breeding range. European population stable.

DISTRIBUTION: Confined as a breeding bird to the very northeast of the country. The Tiszatelek-Tiszaberceli Nature Conservation Area was a regular area until the early 1980s but numbers here have since declined. Possible elsewhere in the upper Tisza floodplain and the Szatmár-Bereg region.

TIMING: First birds arrive in late April into May. Steady numbers occur in August and September at ringing camps.

Nightingale *Luscinia megarhynchos* (Common Nightingale)
Fülemüle

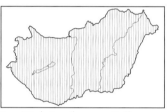

In summer it sometimes seems as if every patch of bushes in the country holds a singing Nightingale. Certainly, the species inhabits a wide range of habitats including thickets, copses and woods with rank vegetation, parkland, overgrown orchards, vineyards and gardens. Highest numbers breed in floodplains in wet willow and alder thickets and damp poplar plantations with lush undergrowth. The official Hungarian nomenclature regards the country's breeding Nightingales as a Balkan race '*baehrmanni*'. However, current opinion regards this 'race' as somewhat dubious, the features described being too slight to warrant separation from the nominate *megarhynchos*.

STATUS IN HUNGARY: Very common and widespread breeder. Population size and trends unknown. Migrant. Protected.

STATUS INTERNATIONALLY: Breeding range within Palearctic. European population stable.

DISTRIBUTION: Suitable habitats nationwide. Very common in Transdanubia, parts of the Northern Hills, along most rivers and in floodplains. More scattered, but still fairly common, on the Great Plain.

TIMING: First birds arrive in April. Most leave in late August and early September.

Bluethroat *Luscinia svecica*
Kékbegy

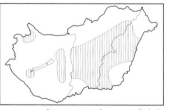

Bluethroats are rather localised breeders in Hungary and numbers fluctuate annually in any given area. Given the amount of apparently suitable wetland habitat in the country numbers might be considered low. Typical breeding sites are the edges of reedbeds or merely patches of reed, along canals, around fishponds, overgrown ditches and marshes as long as there are scattered willow bushes and trees, which males use as singing posts. Birds can often be seen on the exposed tops of dykes when feeding. Males often sing from the tops of stacks of cut reed and, as elsewhere, Hungarian birds are expert mimickers. The white-spotted *cyanecula* race breeds. There is one record of the red-spotted *svecica* race, from Fertőújlak in May, 1992.

STATUS IN HUNGARY: Uncommon to locally common breeder. Population between 900 and 1,000 pairs. Migrant. Protected.

STATUS INTERNATIONALLY: Mainly Palearctic breeding range. European population stable.

DISTRIBUTION: Scattered around lowland wetlands nationwide. In Transdanubia regular areas are Lake Fertő, the Hanság, Lake Velence and Dinnyés (40 pairs 1994), Rétszilas and Kis-Balaton. East of the Danube on the Hortobágy (100-120 pairs most years), Kiskunság, Szeged area, Biharugra and other fishpond systems.

TIMING: First birds arrive in March, most in April. Return migration in August and September.

Bluethroat (White-spotted)

Black Redstart *Phoenicurus ochruros*
Házi rozsdafarkú

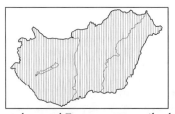

The shrill song of male Black Redstarts is one of the first to be heard in spring. Mainly migratory, males return from wintering areas in the Mediterranean before females, and in early March sing from rooftops, chimneys and rocky outcrops. Black Redstarts breed in both rural and urban settlements and also away from populated areas in vineyards, working and abandoned quarries, on cliffs and rocky karst terrain. Hungarian birds are of the western and central European race *gibraltariensis*.

STATUS IN HUNGARY: Common and widespread breeder. Population size and trends unknown. Migratory, though some regularly winter, especially in urban areas. Protected.

STATUS INTERNATIONALLY: Palearctic breeding range. European population stable.

DISTRIBUTION: Nationwide. Anywhere with buildings or quarries in both lowlands and uplands.

TIMING: Almost all year round. Migrants return in March and leave in October.

Redstart *Phoenicurus phoenicurus* (Common Redstart)
Kerti rozsdafarkú

This species has a rather patchy distribution in Hungary, frequenting orchards, vineyards with trees, parkland and even gardens around the country but being nowhere common. Highest numbers nest in oakwoods, old willow woods and poplar groves along rivers. The steady felling of such woodland and planting with introduced tree species along the Tisza and other

rivers has, however, meant the loss of much prime habitat. With the exception of floodplain woodland, Redstarts are generally scarce in many parts of Hungary's lowlands.

STATUS IN HUNGARY: Uncommon to fairly common breeder. Rather local. 5,000-10,000 pairs estimated. Has probably declined. Migrant. Protected.

STATUS INTERNATIONALLY: Palearctic breeding range. European population considered vulnerable having steadily declined in recent decades.

DISTRIBUTION: Scattered nationwide. Sopron and Kőszeg hills, Balaton uplands, woodland on the Danube, Pilis hills, Aggtelek, Debrecen forest and the Middle Tisza floodplain are core areas.

TIMING: First birds arrive in late March, with majority in April. Return passage in September.

Whinchat *Saxicola rubetra*
Rozsdáscsuk, Rozsdás csaláncsúcs

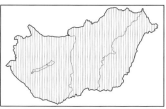

Whinchats are widespread birds in both upland and lowland areas. They inhabit wet meadows, pasture, bogs, sedge marshes and wetland edges with bushes or scattered trees which they need as songposts. Although some overlap exists, Whinchats frequent wetter habitats than their congener Stonechat and hence in the breeding season they are rarely seen on the large dry areas of *puszta* east of the Danube. Although no national population trend data exists, Whinchats have probably declined in Hungary as much suitable habitat has been drained, degraded or planted with trees throughout this century.

STATUS IN HUNGARY: Fairly common breeder. Population size and trends unknown. More on passage. Migrant. Protected.

STATUS INTERNATIONALLY: Breeding range within Palearctic. European population declining.

DISTRIBUTION: Breeds in suitable habitat nationwide. Widespread in Transdanubia. Rather local east of the Danube.

TIMING: Breeding birds arrive and others pass through from mid-April into May. Return passage in August and September.

Stonechat *Saxicola torquata* (Common Stonechat)
Cigánycsuk, Cigány csaláncsúcs

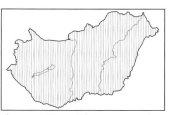

Perching on fence posts, telegraph wires and stalks of vegetation, Stonechats are one of the most conspicuous roadside birds in Hungary. They are far more common and widespread than their close relative Whinchat, being birds of the drier habitats of which Hungary has plenty. Lowland habitats include arid *puszta,* pasture, wasteland, allotments, canal banks, dykes, railway sidings and roadsides. Stonechats are also found in farmland but rarely in the vast Great Plain monocultures of sunflowers, maize and other crops. In upland regions, karst hillsides, forest fire-breaks and clearings, river valleys, vineyards and scrub are frequented. Breeding birds are of the *rubicola* race. In recent years there have been reports of 'Eastern' Stonechats.

STATUS IN HUNGARY: Very common and widespread breeder. From 70,000-100,000 pairs estimated. Probably increased in number in recent years. Mostly migratory. Protected.

STATUS INTERNATIONALLY: Breeding range in the Palearctic and parts of Africa. Western European population declining.

DISTRIBUTION: Suitable habitats nationwide.

TIMING: Most of year. Some may overwinter. Migrant birds return in early March. Autumn passage in September and October.

Northern Wheatear *Oenanthe oenanthe* (Wheatear)
Hantmadár

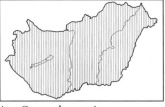

Essentially a bird of drier *puszta*, stony pastures and rocky hillsides, this species has proved to be very adaptable as regards breeding habitat. Pairs are also found in a range of secondary habitats in Hungary such as wasteland, stockyards, ruins, cart-tracks, dykes, gravel pits, vineyards and allotments. On migration, birds also occur in arable and other farmland where they do not necessarily nest. Northern Wheatears are Hungary's only regularly breeding *Oenanthe* species.

STATUS IN HUNGARY: Fairly common breeder. Population size and trends unknown. Migrant. Protected.

STATUS INTERNATIONALLY: Holarctic breeding range. European population probably declining.

DISTRIBUTION: Open rolling country and lowlands nationwide. Locally common in parts of the Great Plain.

TIMING: Males usually arrive back first in late March, with females soon after. Return migration rather staggered, lasting from August to October.

Rock Thrush *Monticola saxatilis* (Rufous-tailed Rock Thrush)
Kövirigó

The Hungarian population of Rock Thrush has declined drastically over the last 30 years and the species is now in danger of extinction in the country. The reasons for this, and indeed the overall decline throughout Europe, remain unclear. The number of pairs at regular sites in the Vértes and Pilis hills, Budaörs and Badacsony started to fall in the 1960s before finally disappearing in the late 1970s and early 1980s. Nowadays pairs breed only occasionally in these areas. A small but regular population hangs on in the Northern Hills. In Hungary, the species usually breeds on the warm south-facing slopes of limestone hills, tree- and bush-dotted karst and in both working and abandoned stone quarries. Such places are invariably surrounded by vineyards and orchards which provide feeding habitat. Although disturbance, changes in land use and degradation of feeding habitat have certainly contributed locally, the Rock Thrush's decline may well be owing to wider ranging factors such as climatic change and problems on migration and in wintering areas.

STATUS IN HUNGARY: Very rare breeder. 20-40 pairs. Migrant. Strong post-war decline. Strictly protected.

STATUS INTERNATIONALLY: Breeding range within Palearctic. European population has declined steadily throughout the century.

DISTRIBUTION: Very local. Only regular breeding sites are in the Bükk, Zemplén and Tokaj hills. Odd pairs occasionally in the Gerecse and Börzsöny hills. Now very rare in Transdanubia.

TIMING: Birds usually arrive in late April and leave in August and early September.

Rock Thrush

Ring Ouzel *Turdus torquatus*
Örvös rigó

As Hungary is almost encircled by the Alps and Carpathians, it is perhaps not surprising that Ring Ouzels of the *alpestris* race occur in Hungary. However, the species is only partially migratory and little regular through-passage occurs. Mostly from one to three birds are seen together. Flocks are very rare, and indeed it seems that Hungary does not lie on any main migration route of the species, if indeed one exists. Very occasionally a few winter, usually in the company of other thrush species. Birds of the nominate *torquatus* race from further north and west were recorded twice at ringing camps in the 1960s.

STATUS IN HUNGARY: Uncommon spring visitor. Occasional in autumn and winter. Protected.

STATUS INTERNATIONALLY: Breeding range mainly within Western Palearctic. Some breed further east in Transcaspia. European population stable.

DISTRIBUTION: Scattered nationwide, but most observations from Transdanubia, followed by the Northern Hills. One or two birds regular in early April on the Hortobágy and in the Kiskunság.

TIMING: From September to April. Most regular in spring; mid March to mid April.

Blackbird *Turdus merula*   (Eurasian Blackbird)
Fekete rigó

One of the most common birds in Hungary, Blackbirds inhabit woodland of all kinds, from deciduous forest to urban parks and gardens. Some even nest in conifer plantations. Many birds migrate to the Mediterranean for the winter, though good numbers also remain, especially in towns and cities.

STATUS IN HUNGARY: Very common and widespread. Population size unknown but large and probably increasing. Mainly resident and sedentary, some migratory. Protected.

STATUS INTERNATIONALLY: Range covers Palearctic, Indian subcontinent and parts of

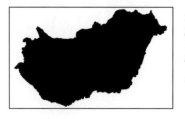

Australasia. European population increasing.

DISTRIBUTION: Nationwide. Very common in Transdanubia, Northern Hills and settlements everywhere. More scattered on Great Plain.

TIMING: All year round. Migrant birds leave in September and return in February.

Fieldfare *Turdus pilaris*
Fenyőrigó

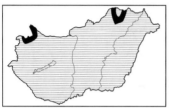

With Fieldfares being common breeding birds to the west, north and east in neighbouring Austria, Slovakia, Ukraine and Romania, it is perhaps surprising that relatively few pairs nest in Hungary, especially as the species is known to be spreading in a southwestern direction in Europe. A few pairs nest in the Hernád and Sajó valleys in the northeast and the Hanság-Fertő area in the northwest. Some years see pairs in the Budapest area and occasionally at scattered sites on the Great Plain. As is typical of a species on the edge of its range, breeding numbers fluctuate from year to year, though it is likely that some pairs have been overlooked in border regions. In winter, large flocks of from hundreds to several thousand each invade and feed in urban parks, orchards, farmland, pastures and often on wet *puszta*.

STATUS IN HUNGARY: Very common winter visitor. Very rare breeder. 5-20 pairs. Protected.

STATUS INTERNATIONALLY: Palearctic species. European population considered stable.

DISTRIBUTION: In winter nationwide. Most breeding birds very local in the north of the country.

TIMING: Some all year round. Large flocks invade in October and November. Some of these birds stay till March, others move further south before returning in late winter.

Song Thrush *Turdus philomelos*
Énekes rigó

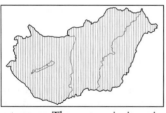

This is another species which in Hungary is still very much a woodland rather than a garden or park bird. Song Thrushes nest in deciduous and coniferous woodland of all sizes, provided there is plenty of damp undergrowth, adjacent moist vegetation and leaf-litter. Although some do nest in parks and allotments, they have not colonised urban habitats as readily as Blackbirds have done and are generally less numerous and widespread than their congener. The vast majority migrate to the Mediterranean, though a few sometimes overwinter.

STATUS IN HUNGARY: Common and widespread breeder. Migrant. Population size and trends unknown. Protected.

STATUS INTERNATIONALLY: Palearctic species. European population stable.

DISTRIBUTION: Wooded areas nationwide. Common in Transdanubia and Northern Hills. Rather local on Great Plain.

TIMING: Mainly March to October. Some may overwinter.

Redwing *Turdus iliacus*
Szőlórigő

Redwing numbers in Hungary build up in November and then fall off through the winter as birds migrate further south. Small groups are regular throughout the winter in gardens, parks, orchards and open woodland. On open farmland, wet pastures and *puszta,* Redwings often mingle with their almost always more numerous relative Fieldfare. Large autonomous flocks of Redwings are unusual. In March and April numbers rise again as returning migrants stop off *en route* to breeding areas in northern Europe.

STATUS IN HUNGARY: Fairly common passage and winter visitor. Protected.
STATUS INTERNATIONALLY: Palearctic species. European population stable.
DISTRIBUTION: Occurs nationwide.
TIMING: From September to May. Main passage periods are in March and October-November. Some birds remain throughout most winters.

Mistle Thrush *Turdus viscivorus*
Léprigó

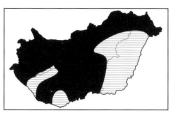

Although still a rather uncommon breeding bird, Mistle Thrushes seem to be on the increase in Hungary, particularly in wooded hills along the Austrian and Slovakian borders. Elsewhere, pairs are scattered in hilly regions with tall stands of oak, beech and to a lesser extent conifers. Some also breed in lowland plantations. In winter, small groups, but never large flocks, move into parks, plantations and colonnades with mistletoe. Some of these are no doubt migratory birds from further north and east in Europe. Unlike many parts of western Europe, there is as yet little sign of a movement of Mistle Thrushes to breed in urban habitats in Hungary.

STATUS IN HUNGARY: Uncommon resident. Common autumn and winter visitor. Breeding population size unknown but may be increasing in number and range. Protected.
STATUS INTERNATIONALLY: Palearctic species. European population stable if not increasing.
DISTRIBUTION: Scattered in Transdanubia and Northern Hills. Rather uncommon breeder in lowlands. In winter disperses as far as adequate food sources and occurs more in lowlands and urban parks.
TIMING: All year round. More easily encountered in winter when many birds, but not all, move from upland breeding areas to more open country.

SYLVIIDAE (Warblers)

Grasshopper Warbler *Locustella naevia*
Réti tücsökmadár

The rarest of Hungary's three breeding *Locustella* warblers and the species least likely to be heard east of the Danube. Along with such species as Curlew, Short-eared Owl and Montagu's Harrier the Hungarian breeding range of Grasshopper Warbler falls mainly in 'post-glacial relict' regions such as the Hanság and Ócsa. Typical habitats here include tussock sedge marshes and wet scrubby grassland, though the species also nests in bogs, wet meadows and floodplains. Numbers at regular sites vary annually, probably owing to changes in water levels.

STATUS IN HUNGARY: Uncommon breeder. Population size unknown but recent increase apparent. Migrant. More on through passage. Protected.

STATUS INTERNATIONALLY: Palearctic breeding range. European population considered stable.

DISTRIBUTION: Scattered nationwide, but mainly Transdanubia where regular areas include the Hanság, Őrség, Kis-Balaton, Tolna Mezőföld, Sárrét, Csákvár and Dinnyés. East of the Danube at Ócsa, Dabas, parts of the Kiskunság and Bodrogzug. Rare breeder on the Hortobágy.

TIMING: Summer. Breeding birds arrive in May and leave in September.

River Warbler *Locustella fluviatilis*
Berki tücsökmadár

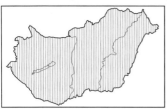

The westward expansion in range of River Warbler in Europe is mirrored within Hungary where the species has moved closer to settlements, into damp poplar plantations and even into isolated damp pockets in upland forest. Traditionally occupied habitats are located in floodplains, scrubby meadows and marshes, bush-dotted nettle beds, willow-lined ditches and backwaters, stream valleys and all types of damp woodland including alder carr and oak copses. River Warblers are locally common in such places throughout Hungary. The species never breeds in reedbeds. Although no national census has been carried out, probably the most common of the *Locustella* warblers.

STATUS IN HUNGARY: Very common and widespread breeder. Population size unknown but between 50,000-100,000 pairs has been estimated. Increasing in range. Migrant. Protected.

STATUS INTERNATIONALLY: Breeding range within Palearctic. European population increasing and expanding in range.

DISTRIBUTION: Suitable habitats nationwide. Predominantly lowlands but expanding into high meadows and damp clearings in hill ranges. Very common in the Tisza floodplain.

TIMING: Summer. Early May to September.

River Warbler

Savi's Warbler *Locustella luscinioides*
Nádi tücsökmadár

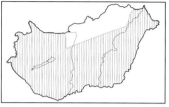

With one of largest populations in Europe, Hungary is an important country for this species. Of the three Hungarian breeding *Locustella* warblers it is the one most attached to reedbeds. In fact, it is almost exclusively a bird of extensive stands of *Phragmites,* though some do occur in reedmace and rushes. In summer, males produce their very characteristic reeling song from the tops of reeds around fishponds, reservoirs, lakes, marshes and along canals and rivers with such vegetation. The only reedbeds the species does not frequent are those which are regularly burnt or cut for thatch.

STATUS IN HUNGARY: Common and widespread breeder. No exact population data but around 50,000 pairs has been estimated. Migrant. Protected.

STATUS INTERNATIONALLY: Breeding range mostly within Palearctic. Increasing and expanding range in Europe.

DISTRIBUTION: Wetlands with reedbeds nationwide. Large numbers at Lake Fertő, Kis-Balaton, Lake Velence, Hortobágy, Biharugra and Pusztaszer. Pairs also on smaller wetlands.

TIMING: Summer. First males are heard at the end of April. Autumn migration in August and September. Some pass through in early October.

Moustached Warbler *Acrocephalus melanopogon*
Fülemülesitke

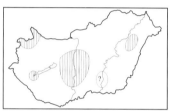

This species is perhaps more common in Hungary than the local literature suggests. First of all, being far less conspicuous and vocal than other *Acrocephalus* species, its congeners are more easily located and studied. Sedge and Great Reed Warblers are numerically and vocally dominant and Aquatic Warbler is local, easily observed and well watched. Although certainly not abundant, Moustached Warbler is perhaps an overlooked species in some areas. Traditional habitats are the reedmace *Typha* beds of large marshes and the margins of *Phragmites* reedbeds around fishponds. Being a relatively short-distance migrant, Moustached Warblers arrive back in Hungary before their congeners, and are best sought in late March and early April when they have wetlands almost to themselves. Once the other *Acrocephalus* species arrive, the less vocal Moustached is rather difficult to locate. When it can be heard its distinctive song easily indicates its presence. The Nightingale-like start of the song is acknowledged by its Hungarian name which translates as 'Nightingale warbler'.

STATUS IN HUNGARY: Uncommon to fairly common breeder. Population size and trends unknown. Estimates vary from a few hundred to several thousand pairs. Migrant. Protected.

STATUS INTERNATIONALLY: Palearctic breeding range. Rather scattered European populations probably stable.

DISTRIBUTION: Scattered and rather local. Regular areas are Lake Fertő, Kis-Balaton, Lake Velence, Ócsa and parts of the Kiskunság and Hortobágy.

TIMING: Present for a longer period than other *Acrocephalus* warblers, arriving back from wintering areas in the Mediterranean as early as March and staying until October and early November. In mild years some may even overwinter in the south of the country.

Aquatic Warbler *Acrocephalus paludicola*
Csíkosfejű nádiposzáta

Whilst this globally threatened species has declined and even become extinct in neighbouring countries, Hungary has seen an increase in the breeding population. First confirmed breeding in 1971, Aquatic Warblers are, however, still very rare breeding birds, only found very locally

129

on the Hortobágy. In 1977, 10-20 pairs were found and in subsequent years the population steadily increased. Although the name may suggest otherwise, Aquatic Warblers are, in fact, the *Acrocephalus* warbler least likely to occur by deep or open water, and never nest in reedbeds. In Hungary the species inhabits tracts of reedmace *Typha* and sedge *Carex* and quite dry *Festuca* meadows, but is essentially found in damp hay fields. Interestingly, this choice of habitat differs from that of the substantial Polish population where birds breed predominantly in peat bogs and marshes with tall sedge tussocks. Hungarian breeding sites lie in strictly protected areas within the Hortobágy National Park, so habitat loss to drainage schemes is slight; fires, and to some extent trampling by cattle, however, remain a threat.

STATUS IN HUNGARY: Rare breeder. From 400-420 pairs (1994). Rather local. Increasing. Migrant. Strictly protected.

STATUS INTERNATIONALLY: Breeding range almost totally confined to Western Palearctic. Globally threatened. Endangered in Europe and in decline.

DISTRIBUTION: Breeds only on the Hortobágy and here very local. Otherwise, scattered on passage across Great Plain. Very rare in Transdanubia, though some old breeding records from Lake Fertő and Csákvár.

TIMING: Arrives in late April. Breeding birds leave in late August and early September. Others may move through later.

Aquatic Warbler

Sedge Warbler *Acrocephalus schoenobaenus*
Foltos nádiposzáta

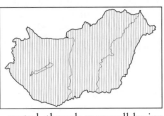

The most common and widespread of the *Acrocephalus* warblers in Hungary, found in all kinds of wetland margins, especially reedbeds, ditches, reed-fringed canals, streams, ponds and lakes, sedge and rush beds, rice fields and marshes. Birds can also be found in quite dry habitats such as nettlebeds, copses and damp patches in farmland.

STATUS IN HUNGARY: Very common and widespread breeder. Stable population of around 200,000 pairs estimated, though may well be increasing. Migrant. Protected.

Status Internationally: Palearctic breeding range. European population considered stable.

Distribution: Wetland habitats nationwide. Some in farmland.

Timing: Breeding birds occur from April to August, others pass through in September and October.

Marsh Warbler *Acrocephalus palustris*
Énekes nádiposzáta

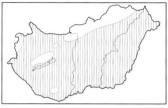

Seldom found near open water or reedbeds, Marsh Warblers are rather birds of damp scrub and copses, willow-lined ditches, canal banks with rank vegetation, nettlebeds and bush-dotted marshes and bogs. Occasionally, birds are found in weedy crops and at the edges of maize or cereal fields. Some habitat overlap occurs between Marsh and Sedge Warblers, with the latter often breeding in the above mentioned habitats. Marsh Warblers, however, are seldom found in the wetter areas where Sedges occur in highest numbers.

Status in Hungary: Fairly common breeder. Population size and trends unknown. Certainly not as common as Reed and Sedge Warblers. Migrant. Protected.

Status Internationally: Palearctic breeding range. European population stable, perhaps increasing.

Distribution: Suitable habitat nationwide, but essentially lowlands. In some areas, such as Hortobágy, surprisingly local.

Timing: Breeding birds arrive at the end of April into May and leave mainly in August. Birds from further north pass through in September.

Reed Warbler *Acrocephalus scirpaceus*   (European Reed Warbler)
Cserregő nádiposzáta

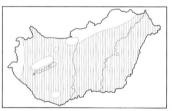

A very common bird of Hungary's numerous *Phragmites* reedbeds around both natural and man-made wetlands. Highest numbers occur in extensive stands of mature reed, but a few birds can also be found in quite small patches or belts of reed along canals, ditches and rivers. Less common in mixed reed, sedge *Carex* and rush *Typha* beds. There is considerable overlap in habitat with Great Reed and Sedge Warblers, less so with Marsh Warbler. Although not so conspicuous and vocal as Great Reed Warbler, the species is probably more common. Reed Warblers are also a favoured host of Cuckoos.

Status in Hungary: Very common and widespread breeder. Population size and trends unknown. Migrant. Protected.

Status Internationally: Palearctic breeding range. European population increasing.

Distribution: Breeds in all extensive and many smaller stands of reed nationwide. Large numbers at Lakes Fertő and Velence, Hortobágy fishponds and Biharugra fishponds.

Timing: First birds heard in early April, though majority arrive late in the month. Return passage in August and September.

Great Reed Warbler *Acrocephalus arundinaceus*
Nádirigó

Although widespread in reed-fringed canals, rivers, gravel pits and marshes across the country, Great Reed Warbler is essentially a bird of fishponds and lakes with stands of mature *Phragmites*. It is also the *Acrocephalus* warbler most likely in high vegetation over deeper

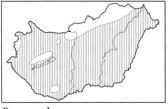

water. An extremely conspicuous and vocal bird, almost any patch of reed, even village ponds and damp depressions in farmland, seems to hold a singing male in spring. Great Reed Warbler is the most common host of Cuckoo in Hungary's lowlands.

STATUS IN HUNGARY: Very common and widespread breeder. Population size and trends unknown. Certainly numerous, and population probably stable. Migrant. Protected.

STATUS INTERNATIONALLY: Mainly Palearctic breeding range. European population stable.

DISTRIBUTION: Wetlands nationwide.

TIMING: First birds arrive mid April. Most leave in September, though some, possibly through-migrants, occur in October.

Olivaceous Warbler

Olivaceous Warbler *Hippolais pallida*
Halvány geze

By far the rarest of the two Hungarian *Hippolais,* Olivaceous Warbler is another species which is perhaps more widespread than the available literature suggests. Before the 1950s, Olivaceous Warbler was very rare in Hungary but has since expanded its European range northwards into the country from the Balkans via the Danube and Tisza rivers. This range expansion has been noticeably faster along the Tisza. If the trend continues, the first breeding record for Slovakia and regular breeding in eastern Austria can be expected, however, the expansive trend may well have ceased. In Hungary, Olivaceous Warbler is strongly riparian, occurring in riverside willows *Salix*, tamarisk, poplar *Populus* plantations and parkland with a good understory of lush vegetation, though some pairs have colonised town parks away from rivers. Nowhere abundant, it regularly nests at Gemenc and probably Szigetköz on the Danube and probably along the whole length of the Tisza. The *elaeica* race occurs.

STATUS IN HUNGARY: Rare to uncommon breeder. Between 200 and 400 pairs. Slowly increasing and expanding range. Migrant. Protected.

STATUS INTERNATIONALLY: Mainly Palearctic breeding range, extending into central Africa. Despite range expansion in Europe, declining in core areas and considered vulnerable.

DISTRIBUTION: Largely riparian. Rare away from the Tisza and Danube floodplains. Has expanded Hungarian range via these major rivers. In the 1940s recorded along the River Maros and lower stretches of the Tisza. In the 1960s recorded along the Middle Tisza, and in the 1970s began to move up the Danube. In the 1980s recorded at Szigetköz in the very northwest of Hungary.

TIMING: Summer. One of the latest warblers to arrive in Hungary, often only in late May. Leaves in August and September.

Icterine Warbler *Hippolais icterina*
Kerti geze

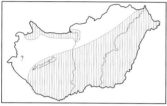

In Hungary, Icterine Warblers breed mainly in floodplain woodland, especially damp poplar plantations and willow, oak and ash woods, though some occur in other open broadleaved woodland such as scrubby glades and parkland. In some areas also gardens, cemeteries and orchards as long as there is a dense and moist understory of vegetation and sufficient mature trees. Nowhere common, this is, however, one species which may have been little affected if not assisted by post-war lowland forestry management. Although certainly not as confined to riparian habitats as its only Hungarian congener, Olivacious Warbler, the species is still essentially a bird of the country's floodplain woodland.

STATUS IN HUNGARY: Uncommon to fairly common breeder. Population size and trends unknown. Has probably increased in recent decades. Protected.

STATUS INTERNATIONALLY: Breeding range within Palearctic. European population considered stable.

DISTRIBUTION: Rather scattered in lowlands nationwide, particularly key areas include Gemenc and Szigetköz on the Danube and most of the Tisza floodplain. Also habitats adjacent to tributaries. Occasionally parks and other semi-urban habitats. Rare in uplands.

TIMING: Occurs from late April through to September.

Barred Warbler *Sylvia nisoria*
Karvalyposzáta

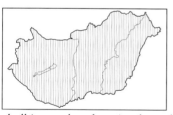

The least likely of the Hungarian *Sylvia* warblers to be found in gardens and other urban habitats, Barred Warblers are nevertheless common birds in both lowlands and uplands throughout the country. Typical habitats are tree- and bush-dotted karst areas, regenerating woodland, untidy clearings and margins in deciduous woods, drier parts of floodplains, overgrown quarries and old orchards, indeed almost anywhere with scrub. Although rather skulking, males often give themselves away by their harsh rattling call and looping song flight. Once incubation begins, usually in late May, birds can be decidedly difficult to observe. As has been noted elsewhere, Barred Warblers in Hungary often nest in close proximity to Redbacked Shrikes, sometimes even in the same bush.

STATUS IN HUNGARY: Common breeder. Population size and trends unknown. Between 20,000 and 40,000 pairs has been estimated. Migrant. Protected.

STATUS INTERNATIONALLY: Breeding range within Palearctic. European population stable.

DISTRIBUTION: Suitable habitats nationwide.

TIMING: First birds arrive in late April. Most leave in August, though some remain and others pass through in September.

Barred Warbler

Lesser Whitethroat *Sylvia curruca*
Kis poszáta

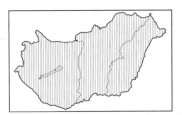

This very common breeding bird nests in a wide variety of habitats such as gardens, parks, cemeteries, thickets, untidy or overgrown orchards and vineyards, woodland edges, clearings, fire-breaks, scrubby hillsides and open floodplain woodland. It occurs on willow-lined dykes and *acacia* wind-breaks during passage and is only absent from closed forest and the most open treeless *puszta*.

STATUS IN HUNGARY: Very common and widespread breeder. Population size and trends unknown. Migrant. Protected.

STATUS INTERNATIONALLY: Palearctic breeding range. European population probably stable.

DISTRIBUTION: Suitable habitats nationwide.

TIMING: Males are first to arrive, in mid April. Most leave in September, though some, possibly through-passage birds, occur in October. Some overwintering records.

Common Whitethroat *Sylvia communis* (Whitethroat)
Mczci poszáta

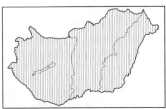

In Hungary, Whitethroats inhabit similar habitats to Barred Warbler, though unlike the latter they also frequently nest in gardens, urban parks, allotments, vineyards, villages and other sites close to or within human settlements; also along ditches and in smaller clumps of scrub and bushes where Barred Warblers seldom occur. During passage, birds occur and sing in areas where they do not necessarily breed such as around fishponds.

STATUS IN HUNGARY: Common and widespread breeder. Population size unknown. Has probably declined in recent decades, though still widespread. Migrant. Protected.

STATUS INTERNATIONALLY: Palearctic breeding range. European population probably stable.

DISTRIBUTION: Suitable habitats nationwide.

TIMING: Second half of April to September. As with other *Sylvia* warblers, males are the first to arrive in spring.

Garden Warbler *Sylvia borin*
Kerti poszáta

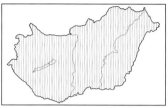

Garden Warbler has the most scattered distribution of the *Sylvia* warblers breeding in Hungary. At times it is rare in seemingly ideal habitat, or absent altogether. Birds mainly inhabit floodplain willow and poplar thickets, copses with adequate bush cover, regenerating woodland, especially oakwoods, and scrubby fire-breaks and clearings in deciduous woods. Despite being named 'Garden' in both English and Hungarian, the species is essentially a woodland bird in Hungary, rarely found nesting in settlements.
STATUS IN HUNGARY: Fairly common to common breeder. 10,000-20,000 pairs estimated. Has probably declined slightly in recent years. Migrant. Protected.
STATUS INTERNATIONALLY: Breeding range within Palearctic. European population probably stable.
DISTRIBUTION: Possible in suitable habitat nationwide.
TIMING: Often arrives slightly later than its congeners, at the end of April. Birds begin to migrate in August, with most leaving in September.

Blackcap *Sylvia atricapilla*
Barátposzáta

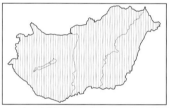

The most common and widespread *Sylvia* species, and indeed one of the most common of all Hungarian breeding birds, Blackcaps occur in wooded habitats in both lowlands and uplands. In urban areas the species breeds in gardens, parks and allotments with shrubs, brambles or other thick low vegetation. In rural areas, in floodplain thickets and copses, riverine forest, broadleaved woods, bush-dotted hillsides and overgrown orchards and vineyards. Although Hungarian birds are essentially migratory, a few occasionally overwinter, particularly in urban areas.
STATUS IN HUNGARY: Very common and widespread breeder. Population size and trends unknown but certainly numerous. Migrant. Protected.
STATUS INTERNATIONALLY: Mainly Western Palearctic breeding range. European population increasing.
DISTRIBUTION: Suitable habitats nationwide.
TIMING: First males arrive mid March. Most birds have returned from wintering areas by mid April. Autumn migration lasts from August to October.

Wood Warbler *Phylloscopus sibilatrix*
Sisegő füzike

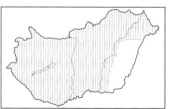

Typically occurring in mature broadleaved woodland, Wood Warblers are sometimes locally common but then absent from other seemingly suitable woodland. In several hill ranges the species is most numerous in shady beech forest but pairs also breed in mixed woods, particularly with hornbeam and oak. Also found occasionally in mixed deciduous and conifer woodland.
STATUS IN HUNGARY: Fairly common to locally very common breeder. Population size and trends unknown. Migrant. Protected.
STATUS INTERNATIONALLY: Breeding range within Palearctic. European population stable.
DISTRIBUTION: Predominantly woodland in Transdanubia and Northern Hills. Often rather scattered. Rare on Great Plain.

TIMING: Males are the first to arrive, in the second half of April. Return passage is in late August and early September.

Chiffchaff *Phylloscopus collybita*
Csilpcsalp-füzike

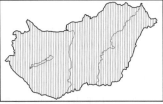

By far the most common of the three *Phylloscopus* warblers breeding in Hungary, and one of the most common of all Hungarian birds. Chiffchaff breed in a wide variety of woodland of all sizes in both uplands and lowlands and many more pass through the country in both spring and autumn. The nominate race breeds. The *abietinus* race from further north and east has also been recorded. The *tristis* race has been recorded three times, first in the field at Dinnyés in 1970, and then at ringing camps in 1993 and 1994.

STATUS IN HUNGARY: Very common and widespread breeder. Population size and trends unknown. Certainly abundant. Migrant. Protected.

STATUS INTERNATIONALLY: Palearctic breeding range. European population stable if not increasing.

DISTRIBUTION: Nationwide.

TIMING: Almost all year round. First birds often heard in early March. Breeding birds leave in September and October. Others move through in November. Some have occasionally over-wintered.

Willow Warbler *Phylloscopus trochilus*
Fitisz füzike

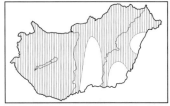

The rarest of the three breeding *Phylloscopus* warblers. Willow Warbler is a scattered breeding bird, mainly occurring in Hungary's upland woodland, though some do breed in lowland *acacia* copses and floodplain woods. Most nest in mixed broadleaved woods though some also occur in young conifer plantations. The official Hungarian nomenclature regards breeding birds as a central European race '*fitis*', though other observers do not recognise this, regarding such birds as the nominate race. The *acredula* race from further north and east has also been recorded.

STATUS IN HUNGARY: Uncommon breeder. Population size and trends unknown. Fairly common on passage. Migrant. Protected.

STATUS INTERNATIONALLY: Palearctic breeding range. European population stable.

DISTRIBUTION: Rather scattered. Mainly in wooded hills. Rare breeder in lowlands. Occurs nationwide on passage.

TIMING: Most birds arrive in mid April. Return passage is in September.

Goldcrest *Regulus regulus*
Sárgafejű királyka

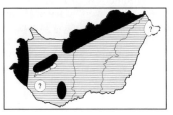

By far the most common of the two *Regulus* species in Hungary. Although the Hungarian breeding population is rather scattered, Goldcrests can be locally common in dense conifer plantations, arboretums, and parks with suitable stands of conifers. From September, birds begin to wander from breeding sites and occur more regularly in gardens, parks, lowland copses, and even patches of shrubs and reedbeds. Influxes from further north and east move through before the onset of winter and good numbers also overwinter. In March and April returning parties of migratory birds pass through.

STATUS IN HUNGARY: Uncommon to fairly common resident. Common winter visitor. Breeding population size and trends unknown but may well be increasing. Protected.

STATUS INTERNATIONALLY: Palearctic breeding range. European population stable.

DISTRIBUTION: Scattered in Northern Hills and forest in Transdanubia. Most common in coniferous forest bordering Austria such as those in the Őrség, Kőszeg and Sopron regions. Rare breeder in lowlands but regular here in winter and on passage.

TIMING: All year round.

Firecrest *Regulus ignicapillus*
Tüzesfejű királyka

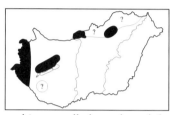

Firecrest is a relatively new Hungarian breeding bird, with nesting first confirmed only in 1978 in the Őrség hills, Transdanubia. This region and the adjacent Sopron and Kőszeg hills, which all lie in the Alp Foothills region on Hungary's border with Austria, remain the Hungarian breeding stronghold, though it is also far from common here. In the breeding season Firecrest is much more likely in mixed deciduous-coniferous woodland than Goldcrest, and is generally less arboreal than its congener.

STATUS IN HUNGARY: Rare resident. Breeding population probably fewer than 200 pairs. More on passage. Protected.

STATUS INTERNATIONALLY: Breeding range within Western Palearctic. European population stable.

DISTRIBUTION: Breeding birds scattered in conifer plantations and mixed woodland in the very west of Transdanubia and the Bakony range. East of the Danube found in the Börzsöny, Bükk and perhaps Aggtelek and Zemplén hills. Although still uncommon, occurs in lowland gardens, parks, thickets and copses in winter.

TIMING: Possible all year round. Birds from elsewhere move through in September-October and particularly March.

MUSCICAPIDAE (Flycatchers)

Spotted Flycatcher *Muscicapa striata*
Szürke légykapó

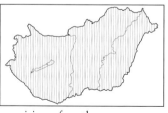

The most common and widespread flycatcher species in Hungary. Spotted Flycatchers typically breed in the clearings, fire-breaks, glades and fringes of upland broadleaved woodland, and in lowlands in floodplain forest and *acacia* copses. In Hungary, as elsewhere in Europe, the species has adapted well to man-made habitats such as parks, gardens, cemeteries, vineyards, orchards, allotments and stockyards. In urban areas, the species has benefited from the provision of nestboxes.

STATUS IN HUNGARY: Common and widespread breeder. Population size unknown. Overall numbers have probably declined over the last 25 years. Migrant. Protected.

STATUS INTERNATIONALLY: Palearctic breeding range. European population declining.

DISTRIBUTION: Suitable woodland nationwide. Common in Transdanubian Uplands and Northern Hills. More scattered in lowlands.

TIMING: First birds arrive mid April. Return migration begins in August, though most leave in September. Birds seen in October are mainly through-migrants from northern Europe.

Red-breasted Flycatcher *Ficedula parva*
Kis légykapó

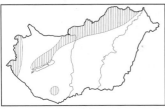

In Hungary the flycatcher species most tied to upland forest. In fact, Hungarian Red-breasted Flycatchers rarely breed away from mature beech woodland or mixed deciduous stands which include beech. Although an inhabitant of the high, closed canopy, males often sing from exposed perches in glades or open stream valleys. Nowhere common, the largest population, of around 100 pairs, is in the Bükk hills. Elsewhere, small localised populations of between ten and 25 pairs are the norm.

STATUS IN HUNGARY: Uncommon breeder. Population size and trends unknown. Probably between 1,000 and 2,000 pairs. Migrant. Protected.

STATUS INTERNATIONALLY: Palearctic breeding range. European population considered stable.

DISTRIBUTION: Scattered in woodland nationwide. Rather local in Northern Hills and Transdanubian hill ranges. As a breeding species absent from lowlands, though does occur here in copses, on tree-lined dykes and in wind-breaks during migration.

TIMING: Summer. First birds arrive in early May. Most leave in September.

Red-breasted Flycatcher

Collared Flycatcher *Ficedula albicollis*
Örvös légykapó

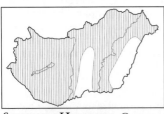

Collared Flycatchers are very much Central and Eastern European birds, and Hungary has its fair share of the population. The species is the most common and widespread *Ficedula* in the country, being locally common in mature broadleaved, mainly oak and beech woodland and parkland across much of the country. In some areas, such as the Pilis hills, long-running nestbox projects have aided the study of the species.

STATUS IN HUNGARY: Common to very common breeder. Although studied locally, population size and nationwide trends unknown. Migrant. Protected.

STATUS INTERNATIONALLY: Breeding range within Western Palearctic. European population considered stable.

DISTRIBUTION: Almost any broadleaved woodland in Transdanubia and the Northern Hills. Also Debrecen Great Forest and floodplain woodland. As a breeding species absent from most

of the Great Plain, though regular here, and in urban areas, on passage.
TIMING: First birds arrive in mid April. During incubation in late May and June keeps a very low profile and can be decidedly difficult to locate. Most leave in late August.

Pied Flycatcher *Ficedula hypoleuca*
Kormos légykapó

The rarest of Hungary's flycatchers, Pied may not breed every year. The very few breeding pairs represent some of the southernmost in the species' Eastern European range. Most confirmed records are from the west of the country in the broadleaved woodland of the Alp Foothills, especially oak, beech and ash woods bordering Austria around Sopron and Kőszeg. In Zala County, pairs have bred in nestboxes in some years. Singing males and occasional nesting records also from the Vértes, Pilis and Buda hills. There have also been reports of hybridisation with the more common Collared Flycatcher.

STATUS IN HUNGARY: Common on passage. Rare and irregular breeder, with 0-25 pairs annually. Protected.
STATUS INTERNATIONALLY: Breeding range within Palearctic. European population stable.
DISTRIBUTION: Woods, floodplain forest, gardens and parks nationwide on passage. Breeds sporadically, mainly in western Transdanubia.
TIMING: Singles and small parties pass through on spring migration, mainly mid April into May. In autumn, first through-migrants arrive in early August, with numbers peaking in early September.

TIMALIIDAE (Babblers)

Bearded Tit *Panurus biarmicus* (Bearded Reedling)
Barkóscinege

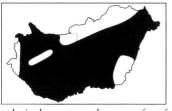

In Hungary, Bearded Tits are found not only in large *Phragmites* reedbeds around lakes and fishponds but also in rushes *Typha* and sometimes quite small isolated stands or strips of such vegetation in marshes and by backwaters, canals and rivers. Although resident, noisy parties of up to 100 birds disperse and wander from breeding areas in autumn and winter, sometimes flying large distances cross-country over open land. Being numerous locally, birds are relatively easy to observe, often feeding on open ground on the top of dykes. Bearded Tits are vulnerable to reed harvesting and burning in some areas of the country though this does not threaten the overall population. Birds are of the eastern *russicus* race, which are generally paler than the nominate birds of western Europe.

STATUS IN HUNGARY: Fairly common resident. Population size and trends unknown. Certainly many thousands of pairs. Protected.
STATUS INTERNATIONALLY: Breeding range within Palearctic. European population stable.
DISTRIBUTION: Wetlands nationwide. Particularly common in reed-fringed fishponds on the Great Plain. In Transdanubia very common at Lake Fertő, Lake Velence and Kis-Balaton.
TIMING: All year round.

Bearded Tits

AEGITHALIDAE (Long-tailed Tits)

Long-tailed Tit *Aegithalos caudatus*
Őszapó

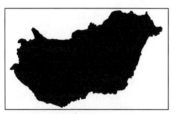

Another species which in Hungary is very much a woodland bird, seldom visiting urban gardens. Some do breed in parks, though more typical habitats are open broadleaved woods, floodplain forest and young conifer plantations. Both the nominate *caudatus* and *europaeus* races occur as well as intergrades between the two. It is not unusual to see mixed-race pairs, and indeed it is often impossible to state safely which race birds are as there is great individual variation in plumage.

STATUS IN HUNGARY: Fairly common resident. Population size and trends unknown. Thought to have declined in some areas in recent decades. Protected.

STATUS INTERNATIONALLY: Palearctic breeding range. European population considered stable.

DISTRIBUTION: With the exception of dense forest, woodland nationwide. Only an occasional visitor to open country.

TIMING: All year round. Family parties, often mixed with other passerines, are somewhat nomadic in autumn and winter.

PARIDAE (Tits)

Marsh Tit *Parus palustris*
Barátcinege

Although essentially a bird of Hungary's deciduous woods, especially oak and beech, Marsh Tits now increasingly occur in orchards, parks, allotments and other secondary habitats, particularly where feeders and nestboxes have been erected. Most Hungarian birds are of the

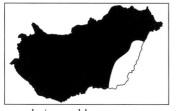

stagnatilis race, though the nominate *palustris* breeds in western Transdanubia. Intergrades between the two no doubt occur. The official Hungarian nomenclature regards the birds breeding in the west as another race, '*communis*', though this is not widely recognised.

STATUS IN HUNGARY: Fairly common and widespread resident. Population size and trends unknown. Protected.

STATUS INTERNATIONALLY: Palearctic species. European population stable.

DISTRIBUTION: Woodland nationwide, especially in Transdanubia and the Northern Hills. Mostly absent from the Great Plain.

TIMING: All year round. In winter, some move to open wooded country and urban areas where they do not necessarily breed.

Willow Tit *Parus montanus*
Kormosfejű cinege

The rarest of Hungary's breeding *Parus* species, with nesting first confirmed only in the early 1960s. Willow Tits have moved into Hungary from expanding populations in neighbouring Slovakia and Austria and mainly nest in mature spruce, of which the country has very little, and mixed conifer and beech forest. In winter, more occur, with small influxes, presumably from Austria, joining flocks of other *Parus* and *Regulus* species in forest and in floodplain alder, willow and oak woods. Two races are considered to occur in Hungary, the nominate *montanus* in western Transdanubia and *borealis* in the northeast of the country.

STATUS IN HUNGARY: Rare resident. National population size and trends unknown. Probably 200-250 pairs. May well be increasing in range. Protected.

STATUS INTERNATIONALLY: Palearctic species. European population stable.

DISTRIBUTION: Confined to the very west and northeast of the country. Breeding in the Sopron and Kőszeg hills along the Austrian border and the Mátra, Bükk, Zemplén, Aggtelek and probably other ranges in the north. Absent from lowlands.

TIMING: All year round. In autumn and winter possible along rivers and in woodland where it does not breed.

Crested Tit *Parus cristatus*
Búbos cinege

As with Willow Tit, this is another species more typical of the conifer forest of neighbouring countries and its Hungarian distribution reflects this. Confined to the very west and northeast, Crested Tits have, however, increased in recent years in both number and range, and though the species is still scarce overall it is more numerous than Willow Tit. Highest numbers are found in the Alp Foothills along the Austrian border and in southwest Transdanubia. Some also occur along the Slovakian border at Aggtelek, though fewer than 100 pairs are estimated here. Birds breed mainly in mature spruce though some occur in mixed conifer forest and in arboretums.

STATUS IN HUNGARY: Rare resident. Probably between 300 and 400 pairs. Seems to have increased slightly in range. Protected.

STATUS INTERNATIONALLY: Western Palearctic species. European population stable.

DISTRIBUTION: Mainly Transdanubia where fairly common locally in the Sopron and Kőszeg hills, scattered in the Bakony Hills, locally common in Zala County, with some pairs in Somogy County. Small populations in the northeast in the Aggtelek, Bükk and Zemplén hills.

Mainly sedentary but outside the breeding season joins mixed *Parus* flocks and occurs over a wider area.

TIMING: All year round.

Coal Tit *Parus ater*
Fenyves cinege

Coal Tits are much more common and widespread than their conifer-loving congeners Willow and Crested Tits. They occur in younger stands of spruce and pine, mixed woods, in parks and arboretums and even in some lowland conifer plantations. The species has readily taken to nestboxes. Most breeding birds disperse from nesting territories in autumn, and through the winter are more likely to occur in orchards, gardens and at urban feeders.

STATUS IN HUNGARY: Common resident. Population size and trends largely unknown, though numbers and range seem to have increased. Influxes from elsewhere in winter. Protected.

STATUS INTERNATIONALLY: Palearctic species. European population stable.

DISTRIBUTION: Breeding populations scattered nationwide. Widespread in Transdanubian and Northern Hills. Has colonised both upland and some lowland conifer plantations. In winter, occurs in lowland mixed woodland and urban parks and gardens where it does not breed.

TIMING: All year round.

Blue Tit *Parus caeruleus*
Kékcinege

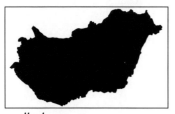

Blue Tits offer no surprises in Hungary, being familiar birds and occurring, as elsewhere in Europe, in all types of natural and man-managed deciduous woodland. They are, however, not as common in urban gardens, orchards and parks in Hungary as Great Tit and indeed overall are not as numerous as their congener. Although not migratory, many Hungarian Blue Tits disperse outside the breeding season and frequent more open country, often roosting in reedbeds.

STATUS IN HUNGARY: Very common and widespread resident. Population of around a million pairs estimated. National trends unknown. Protected.

STATUS INTERNATIONALLY: Range almost totally within Western Palearctic. European population stable if not increasing.

DISTRIBUTION: Deciduous woodland nationwide. Widespread in Transdanubia and the Northern Hills. As a breeding bird rather scattered on the Great Plain but common here in winter.

TIMING: All year round.

Great Tit *Parus major*
Széncinege

The most common *Parus* species and indeed one of the most common of all birds in Hungary. Originally a species of deciduous woodland proper, Great Tits are now common in all man-managed woods including parks, gardens, cemeteries, orchards, vineyards and allotments in both rural and urban areas. Some also nest in conifers. Most birds are sedentary though some wander outside the breeding season to more open country and urban areas, and occasionally to neighbouring countries and beyond. Readily takes to nestboxes and visits urban feeders in

winter. The old adage that an unfamiliar call in woodland more than likely belongs to a Great Tit is true in Hungary as those of Hungarian birds can vary considerably from those found in western Europe.

STATUS IN HUNGARY: Very common and widespread resident. Population size of over a million pairs estimated. National trends unknown. Protected.

STATUS INTERNATIONALLY: Palearctic range, extending into Indian subcontinent and the Indo-Pacific region. European population stable.

DISTRIBUTION: All kinds of woodland nationwide.

TIMING: All year round.

SITTIDAE (Nuthatches)

Nuthatch *Sitta europaea* (Common Nuthatch, Eurasian Nuthatch)
Csuszka

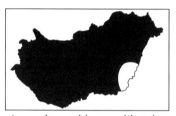

One of the most conspicuous woodland birds in Hungary, Nuthatches are widespread in both rural and urban areas where there are mature broadleaved trees. They are less common in mixed or pure coniferous woods and rarely occur in plantations. After Great Tit, the species most likely to be heard and encountered on a woodland or park walk. Has colonised many secondary habitats such as gardens, old orchards, cemeteries, allotments, arboretums, city parks, and has readily taken to nestboxes. Hungarian birds are of the *caesia* race.

STATUS IN HUNGARY: Very common and widespread resident. Population size and trends unknown. Protected.

STATUS INTERNATIONALLY: Palearctic species, extending into Indo-China. European population stable.

DISTRIBUTION: Deciduous woodland nationwide. Very common in the Northern Hills and most of Transdanubia; also Debrecen Great Forest. Rather scattered on the Great Plain, inhabiting some remnant woods and town parks but absent from most of Békés and perhaps other counties. Highly sedentary but some movement into urban areas, especially to feeders in winter. Some dispersal into lowlands also observed in winter.

TIMING: All year round.

TICHODROMADIDAE (Wallcreepers)

Wallcreeper *Tichodroma muraria*
Hajnalmadár

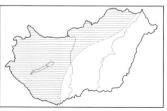

Although not reported every year, Wallcreepers almost certainly visit Hungary annually. The majority of records concern single birds in autumn and winter, though up to six in association have been reported. Most stay for only a few days at any one site. Up to the 1970s, the species regularly occurred on rock walls and crags in the Northern Hills, particularly in the Bükk range, and in Transdanubia, especially the Mecsek and Bakony ranges. Nowadays, records from these areas are rather sporadic. Perhaps not surprisingly, rarely observed on the Great Plain, though has occurred in towns there such as Debrecen and Szeged. It is not clear from where these visiting birds originate. The nearest breeding populations are to the east in the Romanian Carpathians, the north in Slovak mountain ranges and the west in the Austrian Alps.

STATUS IN HUNGARY: Rare but annual passage and winter visitor. Protected.

STATUS INTERNATIONALLY: Palearctic species. European range has contracted in recent decades.

DISTRIBUTION: Traditional sites are scattered nationwide at historical ruins, quarries, limestone walls and crags. Regular sites include Sümeg ruin and Badacsony Hill in Veszprém County, Kesztölc in Komárom-Esztergom County and Boldogkővár in the Zemplén hills. Records also from buildings such as Pécs cathedral, Pécs TV tower, Veszprém castle, Pannonhalma abbey and the palace and hotel walls in Lillafüred near Miskolc. Also records from buildings and Gellért Hill in Budapest.

TIMING: Recorded in every month except June and August. Most records from October to March, with majority in November.

CERTHIIDAE (Treecreepers)

Common Treecreeper *Certhia familiaris* (Eurasian Treecreeper)
Hegyi fakúsz

The Hungarian name of this species translates as 'Hill Treecreeper', which to a fair extent does reflect its distribution in the country. Although there is overlap, this species seems to occur mainly in upland forest, whilst the more numerous Short-toed Treecreeper is essentially found in foothills and lowlands. In Hungary, a *Certhia* species in conifers or dense woodland is invariably, but not always, Common Treecreeper. In winter, occurs in lowland woodland where it does not breed. Two races occur in Hungary, in Transdanubia mainly *macrodactyla,* and east of the Danube the nominate *familiaris*. Intergrades no doubt occur.

STATUS IN HUNGARY: Fairly common resident. Population size and trends unknown. Protected.

STATUS INTERNATIONALLY: Palearctic species. European population considered stable.

DISTRIBUTION: Most upland woodland. In winter, disperses to lower and more open woods, often with *Parus* and *Regulus* species.

TIMING: All year round.

Short-toed Treecreeper *Certhia brachydactyla*
Rövidkarmú fakúsz

The more common of the two *Certhia* species, Short-toed Treecreeper is found in lowlands and some upland areas, where it overlaps in range with its congener. At higher elevations, Short-toed Treecreepers occur in open broadleaved woodland and forest edges, especially oak. Rarely in conifers. In lowlands they are familiar birds of parks, gardens, orchards, poplar plantations and, particularly, floodplain willow, poplar and oak woods where they can be locally common.

STATUS IN HUNGARY: Common resident. Population size and trends unknown. Protected.

STATUS INTERNATIONALLY: Range confined to Western Palearctic. European population considered stable.

DISTRIBUTION: Mainly lowland woodland nationwide. Common in riparian woods. In

winter joins roving flocks of *Parus* and other species including its close relative, occurring where it does not necessarily breed.
TIMING: All year round.

Short-toed Treecreeper

REMIZIDAE (Penduline Tits)

Penduline Tit *Remiz pendulinus*
Függőcinege

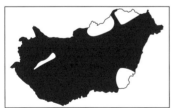

Penduline Tits are typical birds of fishponds and lakes with reedbeds lined by or dotted with willows, alders, tamarisks and poplars. Some also inhabit wet thickets, tree-lined ditches, riverbanks, canal banks and marshes where there is a combination of tree and reed vegetation. Their characteristic hanging nest can be at almost any height, usually over water or reeds but sometimes in trees several hundred yards from water. In autumn, birds flock up and roam through reedbeds across the country. Some overwinter and are possibly joined by birds from further north, whilst others migrate to the Mediterranean basin.
STATUS IN HUNGARY: Fairly common breeder. Some resident, some migratory. Population size and trends unknown. Protected.
STATUS INTERNATIONALLY: Palearctic species. European population considered to be increasing.
DISTRIBUTION: Suitable wetlands nationwide. Locally common around larger fishpond systems and lakes with adequate trees for nesting.
TIMING: All year round. Most birds are short-distant migrants, leaving mainly in October and returning in March.

Penduline Tit

ORIOLIDAE (Orioles)

Golden Oriole *Oriolus oriolus*
Sárgarigó

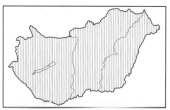

More than perhaps any other species, Golden Oriole seems to thrive in Hungary's many lowland poplar plantations. However, pairs also nest in other man-made and managed habitats such as parks, orchards, allotments, rural gardens and vineyards with trees. In open country, breeds in *acacia* copses, colonnades, wind-breaks and floodplain woods; in upland areas in open or fragmented woodland and forest edges being absent from closed forest or conifers. For a bird which is most common in and around settlements, Golden Orioles are rather secretive and shy of man and often difficult to observe. Their presence is, however, almost always betrayed by their characteristic song.

STATUS IN HUNGARY: Common and widespread breeder. Population size and trends unknown. Migrant. Protected.

STATUS INTERNATIONALLY: Breeding range almost totally within Palearctic. European population stable.

DISTRIBUTION: With exception of closed forest, woodland nationwide.

TIMING: First birds arrive at the end of April. Most in early May. Majority depart in late August and early September.

Golden Oriole

LANIIDAE (Shrikes)

Red-backed Shrike *Lanius collurio*
Tövisszúró gébics

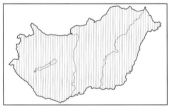

By far the most common of Hungary's shrikes. There has been much discussion in Britain about the reasons for the decline of Red-backed Shrike. Suitable habitat management has been discussed as a way to encourage the species. When one visits Hungary one may be forced to rethink. Hungarian Red-backed Shrikes breed in a very wide range of habitats: rural gardens, cemeteries, scrub and waste-land, farmland, grassland, vineyards, roadside verges, plantations, woodland edges and clearings, in both uplands and lowlands. Highest numbers are in sunny, dry areas with bushes for nesting and trees or wires for perches. Although the species is not threatened, Red-backed Shrike numbers in Hungary have declined slightly in recent decades.

STATUS IN HUNGARY: Common and widespread breeder. Population size unknown, proba-bly somewhere between 50,000 and 100,000 pairs. Migrant. Protected.
STATUS INTERNATIONALLY: Palearctic breeding range. European population declining.
DISTRIBUTION: Nationwide. Rare in urban areas and absent from closed forest.
TIMING: First birds arrive in late April, though most in early May. Return migration is more staggered, beginning in August, lasting through September into early October.

Lesser Grey Shrike *Lanius minor*
Kis őrgébics

Once a widespread species, Lesser Grey Shrike has declined steadily in Hungary in recent decades as in most of Europe. The reasons for this are not entirely clear, as although habitat has been lost and available prey undoubtedly reduced by agricultural intensification and the use of pesticides, much seemingly suitable habitat still exists. Today the species is very much a bird of dry *puszta* areas with copses and wind-breaks, and only here is it more common than

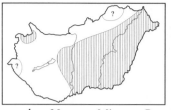

Red-backed Shrike. In some parts of the Kiskunság and Hortobágy, Lesser Grey Shrikes are still locally common and are typical birds of roadside wires and lines of *acacias*. In foothills and parts of Transdanubia, some birds breed in wooded pasture, orchards and vineyards but never in forest proper.

STATUS IN HUNGARY: Uncommon to fairly common breeder. Fewer than 10,000 pairs estimated. Has declined over last 30 years. Migrant. Protected.

STATUS INTERNATIONALLY: Breeding range within Palearctic. European population declining.

DISTRIBUTION: Mainly lowlands east of the Danube. In many areas of the country rather local. Now rare in most of Transdanubia. Locally common in parts of the Great Plain, especially the Kiskunság.

TIMING: Summer. Arrives rather late and leaves early. First birds arrive at the beginning of May, but most mid month. By the last week of August majority have left.

Lesser Grey Shrike

Great Grey Shrike *Lanius excubitor* (Northern Shrike)
Nagy őrgébics

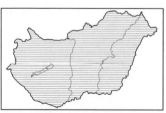

Single birds dot the Hungarian countryside throughout the winter, often staying in one regular spot for the whole season. Occasionally two birds, rarely more, are seen together. Interestingly, Great Grey Shrikes never arrive in Hungary's lowlands before Lesser Grey Shrikes have departed, and *vice versa* in spring, though occasionally some birds arrive before the last Red-backed Shrikes have left. Great Grey Shrikes winter in habitats where both these congeners breed in summer. Breeding has been suspected in the Northern Hills and the Hanság region but never confirmed. Certainly the species breeds close to Hungary's northern border in neighbouring Slovakia.

STATUS IN HUNGARY: Fairly common winter visitor. Protected.

STATUS INTERNATIONALLY: Old World species. European population declining.

DISTRIBUTION: Open country nationwide.

TIMING: From September to April. Majority arrive in mid October and leave in March.

CORVIDAE (Crows)

Jay *Garrulus glandarius* (Eurasian Jay)
Szajkó

With the exception of open treeless country, Jays occur nationwide, though the classic Hungarian nesting habitat is deciduous woodland, particularly hilly country with oaks, hornbeam and beech. Rarely found in coniferous forest. There has been some movement into floodplain parkland, plantations, orchards, urban parks and lowland copses, but in Hungary Jays are still essentially shy birds of extensive woodland. Mainly resident, though small parties wander somewhat outside the breeding season and occasionally flocks from elsewhere invade the country. In some years such invasion flocks number several hundred birds each. Jays remain unprotected in Hungary because of their alleged damage to crops and predation of songbirds, however, the traditional hatred of all corvids no doubt in part lies behind this regulation. Despite this, numbers have steadily increased over the last 20 years. The nominate race breeds, whilst the Adriatic *albipectus* race has been recorded in winter.

STATUS IN HUNGARY: Very common and widespread resident. Over 100,000 pairs estimated and increasing. Unprotected.
STATUS INTERNATIONALLY: Mainly Palearctic species. European population stable.
DISTRIBUTION: Woodland nationwide.
TIMING: All year round.

Magpie *Pica pica* (Black-billed Magpie)
Szarka

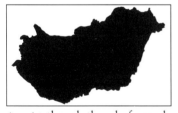

As elsewhere in Europe, Magpies are successful birds in Hungary and a species which is unfortunately generally derided and unprotected. It is, however, a bird which fulfils a very important role as a provider of nest sites for other species. Red-footed Falcon, Kestrel and Long-eared Owl often rely on Magpie nests for breeding sites. Birds breed in a wide range of both rural and urban habitats with trees but avoid closed upland forest and completely treeless *puszta,* though they do forage here. Some have even bred in fishpond reedbeds. In the 1970s and 1980s around 100,000 Magpies were estimated to be shot annually. Today rather fewer are killed, though this may well be owing to the current high cost of cartridges and hunting in Hungary rather than any change in attitude towards the species.

STATUS IN HUNGARY: Very common and widespread resident. Over 100,000 pairs estimated. Population stable if not increasing. Unprotected.
STATUS INTERNATIONALLY: Holarctic species. European population increasing.
DISTRIBUTION: Nationwide.
TIMING: All year round.

Nutcracker *Nucifraga caryocatactes* (Spotted Nutcracker)
Fenyőszajkó

Nutcrackers have been suspected of breeding in Hungary, mainly in the Zemplén hills, but this has never been confirmed. It is feasible that birds from the nearby and substantial Slovakian population occasionally extend south into the country but an overlooked Hungarian breeding population is very unlikely. A noted invasion species, the last large influx was in 1972. Single birds of the nominate *caryocatactes* race are regular in the forested hills bordering Slovakia and Austria each winter. The Siberian race *macrorhynchos* has also occurred, but the

last large scale invasion of this race was as long ago as 1911.

STATUS IN HUNGARY: Rare but regular winter visitor. Some years see small influxes, occasionally invasions. Protected.

STATUS INTERNATIONALLY: Palearctic species. European population stable.

DISTRIBUTION: Forested hills, especially the Börzsöny, Aggtelek and Zemplén ranges in the north, and the Sopron and Kőszeg ranges in western Transdanubia. In invasion years occurs nationwide.

TIMING: Has occurred in every month except July, but most likely from October to February.

Jackdaw *Corvus monedula* (Eurasian Jackdaw, Western Jackdaw)
Csóka

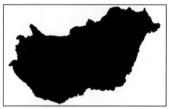

Essentially a lowland species, Jackdaws are common in some parts of Hungary, though nowhere abundant, whilst rare in others. They are absent from upland forest and overall have a rather scattered distribution. In rural areas, Jackdaws nest in the company of Rooks, in old Black Woodpecker holes, hollow trees, on cliffs, in quarries or around farms and villages; in urban areas on buildings, in chimneys, nestboxes and natural tree holes in town parks.

Pairs usually nest in loose colonies. Although mainly sedentary, some birds flock up and wander outside the breeding season, often in the company of Starlings, Rooks and Jackdaws from elsewhere. Jackdaw numbers fell in the 1970s and 1980s owing to loss of nesting sites, persecution, the use of poisoned baits and the general use of chemicals in agriculture. Although protected, Jackdaws nesting in rookeries were particularly affected by the poisoning and shooting intended for their unprotected congener. The species is now recovering. Breeding birds are regarded as of the '*turrium*' race by the Hungarian nomenclature, though most authorities do not separate these birds from the nominate race. The eastern race *soemmerringii* invades in winter and there are at least three collected records of the western European *spermologus*. A Balkan race '*collaris*' is also mentioned in the Hungarian nomenclature as having occurred.

STATUS IN HUNGARY: Fairly common resident. Between 10,000 and 15,000 pairs estimated. Recent increase after decades of decline. Protected.

STATUS INTERNATIONALLY: Palearctic species. European population increasing.

DISTRIBUTION: Rather scattered in open country with trees. Also urban areas nationwide.

TIMING: All year round.

Rook *Corvus frugilegus*
Vetési varjú

The Hungarian Rook population steadily increased up to the 1980s. Since then, there has been a large decline in the number of pairs owing to changes in farming, use of pesticides, culling by poisoning eggs and, to a certain extent, shooting. A reduction in both the number and size of rookeries has also had an adverse effect on Red-footed Falcons as they are also the main nesting sites for this species. In some areas corvid nests are still shot-through without regard for the occupants whether Rooks, Long-eared Owls or falcons. Most Hungarian rookeries comprise hundreds of pairs though a few with over a thousand pairs exist. Rooks breed almost entirely in lowlands, in floodplain woods, farmland copses and parkland. Since the Second World War, the species has gradually moved into urban areas.

STATUS IN HUNGARY: Common and widespread resident. 100,000-200,000 pairs. Has declined. More in winter. Unprotected.

STATUS INTERNATIONALLY: Palearctic species. European population increasing.

DISTRIBUTION: Lowlands nationwide, predominantly agricultural land, wooded *puszta*, floodplains and habitats in and around settlements. In winter, large numbers congregate in railway sidings, parks and urban areas.

TIMING: All year round. Huge influxes in autumn and winter from the north and east.

Hooded Crow *Corvus corone cornix*
Dolmányos varjú

Although widely distributed, Hooded Crows mainly occur in lowland farmland and around wetlands. The species is essentially sedentary though small flocks disperse short distances outside the breeding season. Hooded Crows can be shot all year round in Hungary and, as with other corvids, the 'tradition' of shooting-through nests no doubt claims Long-eared Owls and other species which use old Hooded Crow nests. As with its congeners, numbers fell in the 1970s and 1980s (50,000 pairs estimated in 1984) but are now recovering with up to 70,000 pairs in 1994. Carrion Crow C. *c. corone* (Hungarian Kormos varjú) is a regular visitor to the west of the country though some have been recorded further east, even beyond the Tisza. A few Carrion pairs (0-20 annually) usually breed in Vas County and the Sopron area. The suddenness with which Austria's Carrions become Hungary's Hoodeds is often visibly remarkable. Intergrades between Hooded and Carrion are frequent as are mixed nesting pairs. There are also two records of the Hooded '*sardonius*' cline from the Mediterranean and Balkans. Perhaps strangely, Hooded Crow is unprotected, whilst Carrion Crow is protected. From 50-60,000 Hoodeds are shot each year.

STATUS IN HUNGARY: Common and widespread resident. Only absent from closed forest. Around 70,000 pairs estimated. Increasing.

STATUS INTERNATIONALLY: Palearctic species. European population increasing.

DISTRIBUTION: Nationwide, though rarely in upland closed forest. Mainly open farmland and *puszta*, open woodland and around fish-farms. Over the last 20 years has gradually moved into urban parks.

TIMING: All year round.

Raven *Corvus corax* (Common Raven, Northern Raven)
Holló

As recently as the 1970s, Ravens were almost eradicated in Hungary owing to direct and indirect poisoning and general persecution. Since becoming protected and the banning of certain pesticides and poison baits, the species has recovered from a low of around ten pairs to currently around 500. In many areas a visible increase in numbers can be seen as having occurred in the last decade. One of the earliest breeding birds in Hungary, often laying in February, Ravens nest in lowland areas on electricity pylons and trees, and in uplands mainly on cliffs and in quarries. Essentially sedentary, though in autumn and winter some birds, mainly juveniles, move to lowland farmland and fishponds. One of the few corvids that cannot be legally shot.

STATUS IN HUNGARY: Uncommon to fairly common resident. Around 500 pairs. Increasing. Protected.

STATUS INTERNATIONALLY: Holarctic species. European population increasing.

DISTRIBUTION: Rather scattered. Present in most hill ranges and foothills. Some in floodplain forest and farmland, but still rather uncommon in most lowland areas.

TIMING: All year round. Birds occupy nesting sites as early as February.

Ravens

STURNIDAE (Starlings)

Starling *Sturnus vulgaris* (European Starling)
Seregély

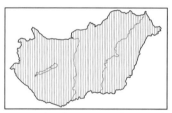

Starlings are essentially still a rural species in Hungary, breeding in both lowlands and uplands in open woodland, forest edges, riverine woods, copses, orchards, allotments, vineyards and around farms. Pairs are invariably isolated in woodland owing to their reliance on natural or woodpecker nest holes, but the species will form colonies, especially in farm buildings. Readily takes to nestboxes. Has colonised urban areas breeding in parks and buildings, but not to the degree seen in western Europe. In autumn, large passage flocks invade cultivated areas, especially vineyards and orchards, and are regarded as pests and thus remain unprotected. In some areas flocks roost in reedbeds.

STATUS IN HUNGARY: Very common and widespread breeder. Population size and trends unknown. Migratory. A few overwinter. Unprotected.

STATUS INTERNATIONALLY: Palearctic species. Introduced elsewhere. European population probably stable.

DISTRIBUTION: Nationwide.

TIMING: Possible all year round, though breeding birds occur mainly from February to October. In autumn, large flocks from the north and east invade. Some in urban areas in winter.

Rose-coloured Starling *Sturnus roseus* (Rosy Starling)
Pásztormadár

Most summers see a few nomadic Rose-coloured Starlings on the Great Plain. Very occasionally in invasion years, which invariably coincide with explosions in the grasshopper population, small colonies are established. After a gap of 33 years (previous confirmed breeding was in 1961) nesting occurred again in 1994 during a classic invasion of between 1,500 and 2,000 birds. Seven colonies were found in all: five in farmsteads and a deserted Soviet barracks on

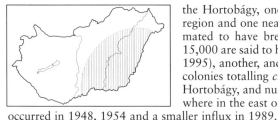

the Hortobágy, one at Nagyecsér in the Borsod-Mezőség region and one near Tokaj. A total of 600 pairs were estimated to have bred, which compares to 1925, when *c.* 15,000 are said to have nested. At the time of writing (June 1995), another, and larger, invasion is underway with five colonies totalling *c.* 1,500 pairs already established on the Hortobágy, and numerous flocks being reported from elsewhere in the east of the country. Other post-war invasions occurred in 1948, 1954 and a smaller influx in 1989.

STATUS IN HUNGARY: Irregular summer visitor. Periodical invasions. Protected.

STATUS INTERNATIONALLY: Palearctic species. European populations irregular. Overall population probably stable.

DISTRIBUTION: In invasion years settles on *pusztas* across the Great Plain. Traditional areas being Bihar, Békés and Csongrád Counties and particularly the Hortobágy. Uncommon west of the Tisza and rare in Transdanubia.

TIMING: Summer. May to August.

Rose-coloured Starlings

PASSERIDAE (Sparrows)

House Sparrow *Passer domesticus*
Házi veréb

As elsewhere in Europe, House Sparrows in Hungary are birds of urban and semi-urban areas, rural farms and human settlements generally. In rural areas the species often breeds in mixed colonies with Tree Sparrows in the sides of White Stork nests. Sand Martin and Bee-eater burrows, particularly those in quarries, are also used. Mainly sedentary but at the end of summer large flocks wander to cultivated areas.

STATUS IN HUNGARY: Very common and widespread resident. Population size and trends unknown; certainly large and probably stable. Unprotected.

STATUS INTERNATIONALLY: Holarctic and Oriental range. Elsewhere introduced. European population stable.

DISTRIBUTION: Nationwide. Absent only from dense forest and the heart of extensive wetlands.

TIMING: All year round. Large flocks invade farmland in autumn. In winter, birds congregate in urban areas.

Tree Sparrow *Passer montanus*
Mezei veréb

In contrast to House Sparrow, essentially a bird of rural areas, especially cultivated land, though some do occur around settlements and in parkland. The two species often overlap in habitat use in parks, farmyards, vineyards, allotments and fish-farms, where they feed on spillage from food-hoppers, but Tree Sparrows rarely venture as far into towns as their congener. Flocks also occur more often in and around reedbeds, on dykes and in open land. Breeds in trees, buildings and, where available, in Sand Martin and Bee-eater holes. Not so sedentary as House Sparrow, sometimes moving hundreds of miles after the breeding season, though not a true migrant.

STATUS IN HUNGARY: Very common and widespread resident. Population size and trends unknown. Unprotected.

STATUS INTERNATIONALLY: Palearctic and Oriental. Elsewhere introduced. Overall European population stable.

DISTRIBUTION: Mainly farmland and open country nationwide.

TIMING: All year round.

Tree Sparrows

FRINGILLIDAE (Finches)

Chaffinch *Fringilla coelebs*
Erdei pinty

One of Hungary's most common birds, found almost everywhere with trees, from forest and floodplain woodland to gardens and parks. Occurs in both rural and urban habitats in

lowlands and uplands. Some breeding birds are migratory, moving to the Mediterranean basin in autumn. These are replaced by birds from further north and east in winter. Following Brehm, the official Hungarian nomenclature treats Hungary's breeding birds as of a separate central European race '*hortensis*', whilst other authorities regard these as the nominate.

STATUS IN HUNGARY: Very common and widespread breeder. Partial migrant though many resident. Influxes in winter. Population size and trends unknown. Protected.

STATUS INTERNATIONALLY: Palearctic species. European population stable.

DISTRIBUTION: Wooded habitats nationwide. In winter, large flocks in open country.

TIMING: All year round.

Brambling *Fringilla montifringilla*
Fenyőpinty

Varying numbers of Brambling move through Hungary each autumn whilst others overwinter on farmland and *puszta*, often in mixed flocks of sparrows, buntings and other finches. Occasionally in autonomous flocks of from 20-50 birds. Invasions have occurred in the forests of the Northern Hills and the Sopron area in years when beechmast has been plentiful. Some flocks of several thousand each were observed in the Sopron hills in December 1990.

STATUS IN HUNGARY: Fairly common winter visitor. Protected.

STATUS INTERNATIONALLY: Palearctic species. European population stable.

DISTRIBUTION: Lowlands nationwide. Occasionally suitable forested areas.

TIMING: Winter. October to March.

Serin *Serinus serinus* (European Serin)
Csicsörke

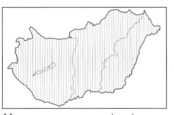

Serins first colonised Hungary around 100 years ago. They are now familiar birds in and around settlements in both lowlands and foothills, particularly in parks, school-yards, wasteland, allotments and gardens. In Budapest and other cities, birds sing from TV aerials and telegraph wires, from where they launch into their bat-like display flights. Some breed in orchards, vineyards and open woodland, never in closed forest, but above all, Serins are urban birds in Hungary even occurring in areas with high-rise blocks and only limited greenery. Although essentially a migrant, some, possibly birds from further north, occasionally overwinter in cultivated land in small mixed flocks with Goldfinches, Greenfinches and other passerine species.

STATUS IN HUNGARY: Fairly common breeder. Population size and trends unknown. Probably increasing in both number and range. Migrant. Protected.

STATUS INTERNATIONALLY: Western Palearctic species. European population increasing and expanding in range.

DISTRIBUTION: With exception of forest and open *puszta*, breeds nationwide. Common in Transdanubia. Rather scattered on Great Plain.

TIMING: First birds arrive in March, though most in April. At the end of summer, flocks up with other finches and moves to open country. Most leave for the Mediterranean basin in October.

Serin

Greenfinch *Carduelis chloris* (European Greenfinch)
Zöldike

With the exception of closed forest, Greenfinches breed in woodland of all kinds across the country. Most typical habitats are secondary ones such as gardens, orchards, parks, plantations, scrubby or weedy allotments and farmland copses. Although not a true migrant, most Hungarian Greenfinches move from breeding areas at the end of summer and form winter flocks with other Fringillidae and ground-foraging species in lowland cultivated areas, especially stubble fields. Some birds move further south towards the Mediterranean and Balkans but are replaced by others from further north. Most breeding birds are of the nominate race, though the Mediterranean *aurantiiventris* race may occur in the south of the country.

STATUS IN HUNGARY: Common and widespread. Some resident, some partially migratory. Others nomadic. Population size and trends unknown. Influxes in winter. Protected.

STATUS INTERNATIONALLY: Palearctic species. Introductions elsewhere. European population probably increasing.

DISTRIBUTION: Suitable habitats nationwide.

TIMING: All year round.

Goldfinch *Carduelis carduelis*
Tengelic

Goldfinches are widespread in Hungary, occurring in both urban and rural areas in most kinds of man-made and natural woodland, though never in dense plantations or forest proper. Typical habitats are parks, cemeteries, scrubby open country, weedy allotments and orchards, wasteland, open young plantations and farmland. Mainly resident but, as with Greenfinch, some birds move south in autumn, whilst birds from populations further north invade Hungary. Often wanders in charms after the breeding season. In winter, when in mixed finch flocks in open country, particularly weedy *puszta* and stubble fields, Goldfinches are invariably more numerous than their congeners. Hungarian birds are of the nominate race.

STATUS IN HUNGARY: Very common and widespread resident. Population size and trends unknown. Certainly tens of thousands of pairs. Protected.

STATUS INTERNATIONALLY: Palearctic and Oriental species. Elsewhere introduced. European population stable.

DISTRIBUTION: Nationwide. Widespread in lowlands.

TIMING: All year round.

Siskin *Carduelis spinus* (Eurasian Siskin)
Csíz

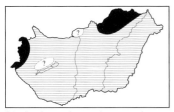

In summer, a few Siskins are usually observed in upland coniferous and mixed forest around the country, though to date there seems to be only one confirmed breeding record, from the Bükk hills in 1959. The species is certainly irregular in summer and may not breed every year. Siskins are, however, common visitors to Hungary on passage and in winter. In some years, large numbers move through, particularly in autumn, occurring in woodland with alder and birch, but also urban parks, gardens, orchards, arboretums, plantations and weedy open country. Most years see small numbers overwintering, especially in alder thickets and secondary habitats where there are suitable trees. Also frequents urban feeders.

STATUS IN HUNGARY: Common passage and winter visitor. Very rare and irregular breeder. Protected.

STATUS INTERNATIONALLY: Palearctic and Oriental species. European population stable.

DISTRIBUTION: Besides the Bükk, may well have bred in the Alp Foothills, Sopron area, Bakony, Börzsöny, Zemplén and other hill ranges. Most widespread on passage and in winter.

TIMING: Possible all year round. Autumn passage mainly in September and October. Spring peak in March and April.

Linnet *Carduelis cannabina* (Common Linnet, Eurasian Linnet)
Kenderike

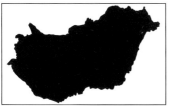

In Hungary, Linnets breed in rural areas in farmland, scrubby woodland, clearings and young plantations, and in and around settlements in orchards, vineyards, allotments, gardens and parkland. In winter, birds flock up with other species, particularly Goldfinches, Twites and Tree Sparrows, and roam over open weedy *puszta* and stubble fields in areas where they do not necessarily breed. There is a fluctuating population of resident birds, nomads, some which migrate to the Mediterranean, and others which move in from the north and east in winter.

STATUS IN HUNGARY: Fairly common and widespread breeder. Population size and trends unknown. Mainly resident, though rather nomadic. Some partially migratory. Protected.

STATUS INTERNATIONALLY: Palearctic species. European population probably declining slightly.

DISTRIBUTION: Lowlands, foothills and cultivated country. Occurs in more open country on passage and in winter.

TIMING: All year round.

Twite *Carduelis flavirostris*
Téli kenderike

It is not unusual to see flocks of several hundred Twite in midwinter in eastern Hungary, but smaller flocks of between ten and 50 birds are the norm. Birds feed on weedy *puszta*, occasionally fallow and stubble fields and in areas such as the Hortobágy often on *puszta* where

sea-lavender bloomed the previous summer. Most often seen in swirling flocks with other finch species, particularly Linnets and Goldfinches. Birds which visit Hungary are of the nominate Fenno-Scandic race.

STATUS IN HUNGARY: Fairly common winter visitor. Protected.

STATUS INTERNATIONALLY: Palearctic species. European population stable.

DISTRIBUTION: Predominantly saline *puszta* and fallow land on the Great Plain. Kiskunság salt lakes, Pusztaszer, Szeged Fehér-tó and the Hortobágy are regular areas. Not as widespread in Transdanubia though may be overlooked here.

TIMING: Mid October to early March. In January, larger flocks often formed.

Redpoll *Carduelis flammea* (Common Redpoll, Mealy Redpoll)
Zsezse

A rather irregular and often elusive species in Hungary, with wintering numbers varying greatly from year to year. Small numbers occur every winter and no doubt some birds join the mixed passerine flocks which roam Hungary's lowlands in this season. But more likely to be found in the company of Siskins in lightly wooded habitats such as arboretums, parks and gardens with alder and other preferred tree species. Very occasionally large numbers invade, the last notable occasion being the winter of 1985-86. The nominate race *flammea* (Mealy Redpoll) mainly occurs, though the montane *cabaret* race (Lesser Redpoll) has been recorded. The Hungarian nomenclature also mentions the occurrence of *'holboelli'*, which is now generally regarded as a variant of the nominate, but which some observers have even considered a separate species.

STATUS IN HUNGARY: Uncommon winter visitor. Protected.

STATUS INTERNATIONALLY: Holarctic species. European population considered stable.

DISTRIBUTION: Most observations from Great Plain though this may reflect the number of observers rather than the true distribution of the species. Also urban habitats, even city parks. Fewer records from Transdanubia where probably overlooked.

TIMING: Possible from September to April. December and January are usually peak months in invasion years.

Common Crossbill *Loxia curvirostra* (Common Crossbill, Red Crossbill)
Keresztcsőrű

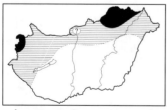

Hungary's relative lack of coniferous, particularly mature spruce, larch and pine forest, has meant that Crossbills have always been somewhat irregular as breeding birds. But, with the species common in neighbouring Austria to the west and in the Slovakian and Romanian Carpathians to the north and east, post-breeding influxes are regular. Hungarian breeding birds also disperse after the breeding period, often to the Balaton area, Budapest and other urban areas. Some are occasionally reported from lowland areas lacking conifers. In some years invasions occur, with numerous flocks of several hundred birds reported from around the country.

STATUS IN HUNGARY: Rare and irregular breeder. 0-100 pairs. Influxes in summer and autumn. Periodical large invasions. Protected.

STATUS INTERNATIONALLY: Holarctic and Oriental, extending into Neotropics. European population considered stable.

DISTRIBUTION: Breeds irregularly in the Sopron, Kőszeg, Bükk, Zemplén and probably other

hill ranges. Also occasionally breeds in arboretums, plantations and parkland. In invasion years almost anywhere with conifers.
TIMING: Possible all year round but most likely in autumn and winter.

Bullfinch *Pyrrhula pyrrhula* (Common Bullfinch, Eurasian Bullfinch)
Süvöltő

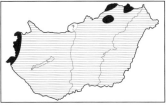

Visiting birdwatchers are often surprised to find a lack of Bullfinches in Hungary in summer. Quite simply, the regular European breeding range of the species encircles the Carpathian basin in which the country is situated. The species is common in all neighbouring countries and the few Hungarian breeding birds can be regarded as extensions of those populations. The species is more common as a passage and winter visitor to Hungary from northern and eastern Europe.

STATUS IN HUNGARY: Common winter visitor. Rare and somewhat irregular breeder. Fewer than 50 pairs. Protected.
STATUS INTERNATIONALLY: Palearctic species. European population stable.
DISTRIBUTION: In winter, nationwide. As a breeder, scattered in the Sopron, Kőszeg and Őrség hills bordering Austria, with a few in the Northern Hills.
TIMING: Possible all year round. Through-passage birds arrive in October and November. Some remain all winter to March.

Hawfinch

Hawfinch *(Coccothraustes coccothraustes)*
Meggyvágó

Hawfinches are widespread in Hungary, though in some regions they have a somewhat irregular distribution. In some areas they are abundant, whilst in other similar habitat rather scattered. Prime habitat is broadleaved woodland, particularly beech and hornbeam, but also oakwoods, orchards and in urban areas parks, avenues and gardens, especially those with wild or cultivated cherry trees. Some also breed in mixed open woods and isolated remnant woodland on the Great Plain. In winter, regularly visits feeders in suburban and inner-city gardens. After the breeding season, some are nomadic, forming small parties but seldom flocking up in as large numbers as other finches and rarely visiting open country. Mainly sedentary, though some birds leave for the Mediterranean area whilst others move in from northern Europe. Contrary to some described behaviour, Hawfinches in Hungary are often confiding and regularly seen by pools, puddles and in busy parks in Budapest and other cities.

STATUS IN HUNGARY: Fairly common resident. Mostly resident though some migratory. Population size and trends unknown. Certainly many thousands of pairs. Protected.

STATUS INTERNATIONALLY: Palearctic species. European population stable.

DISTRIBUTION: Mainly deciduous woods nationwide.

TIMING: All year round.

EMBERIZIDAE (Buntings)

Lapland Bunting *Calcarius lapponicus* (Lapland Longspur)
Sarkantyús sármány

Whether it was previously overlooked or simply did not occur, Lapland Bunting was first recorded in Hungary only in 1960 when 50 birds were observed in Hortobágy National Park. Gradually records increased, and today, though certainly nowhere abundant, the species is a regular winter visitor to a few saline *puszta* regions on the Great Plain. Single birds to flocks of around 100 occur. Occasionally flocks of over 400 have been recorded on the Hortobágy. It is not clear whether the birds which arrive in late autumn stay throughout the winter or move on to be replaced by new flocks, but the winter occurrence of the species fluctuates considerably. Birds may disappear for several weeks in harsh weather before being observed anew.

STATUS IN HUNGARY: Rare to locally common passage and winter visitor. Protected.

STATUS INTERNATIONALLY: Holarctic species. European population stable.

DISTRIBUTION: Occurs regularly but very locally on Great Plain, elsewhere only sporadically. Very rare in Transdanubia where may be overlooked.

TIMING: First birds arrive in mid September. Most in October and November. Numbers peak again in March. Late birds occasionally in April.

Lapland Bunting

Snow Bunting *Plectrophenax nivalis*
Hósármány

Snow Buntings visit Hungary every winter but in unpredictable numbers. Flocks of up to 500 birds are not unknown on the Hortobágy, though smaller parties are the norm. There are occasional records of invasions of thousands of birds though these are rather exceptional. Most occurring birds are of the nominate *nivalis* race. Birds of the Siberian race *vlasowae* (also called '*pallidior*') have been recorded.

STATUS IN HUNGARY: Uncommon to locally common winter visitor. Protected.
STATUS INTERNATIONALLY: Holarctic species. European population considered stable.
DISTRIBUTION: Mainly saline *puszta* on the Great Plain such as at Hortobágy, Kiskunság, Kardoskút and the Pusztaszer region. Scattered records from Transdanubia and along the Danube.
TIMING: Has occurred from October to March. Classic months are November, December and January.

Yellowhammer *Emberiza citrinella*
Citromsármány

By far the most common *Emberiza* species in Hungary, found in all open and hilly country and most upland woodland. Typical breeding habitats are oakwoods, mixed forest edges and clearings, young plantations, fire-breaks, karst scrub, copses, parkland, orchards, vineyards and wooded farmland. Forms large flocks, often with other buntings, finches and larks, in cultivated areas in winter. Birds from further north move in to winter. The majority of breeding birds are of the nominate race, though the Hungarian nomenclature regards these as a separate central European race '*sylvestris*'. East of the River Tisza the *erythogenys* race occurs. Overlap no doubt occurs.

STATUS IN HUNGARY: Very common and widespread breeder. Population size and trends unknown. Mainly resident, some may migrate. Nomadic in winter. Protected.
STATUS INTERNATIONALLY: Palearctic species. European population stable.
DISTRIBUTION: Nationwide.
TIMING: All year round.

Cirl Bunting *Emberiza cirlus*
Sövénysármány

The rarest and most local breeding *Emberiza* in Hungary, though this status may soon be claimed by the declining Ortolan Bunting. The first confirmed breeding record was in 1975 when two pairs were found in the Villány hills, though the species was no doubt breeding here and perhaps elsewhere previously. In 1981, seven pairs were located and, in 1982, just four. More recently a maximum ten pairs are thought to have bred in 1994. The tiny Hungarian population typically breeds on open, rocky, sunny slopes of rolling limestone hills, covered in vineyards, allotments and orchards. With this kind of habitat quite widespread, a colonisation of Hungary from the Mediterranean area has been envisaged, but has yet to materialise.

STATUS IN HUNGARY: Very rare resident. 5-10 pairs. Protected.
STATUS INTERNATIONALLY: Western Palearctic species. European population stable.

DISTRIBUTION: Very local in the Villány and Mecsek hills in southern Transdanubia. Sedentary, though may move short distances in winter. Breeding suspected in the past at Budaörs in Pest County.
TIMING: All year round.

Rock Bunting *Emberiza cia*
Bajszos sármány

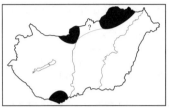

Besides holding one of the most northerly populations of Rock Bunting, Hungary is unusual in being just about the only country in Europe where the species has recently increased and expanded its range. Breeding was first confirmed in 1955 near Jósvafó in the Aggtelek hills, and since then pairs have been found in most suitable habitats around the country. The limestone karst at Aggtelek supports the core Hungarian population of several hundred pairs. Recent surveys here have shown that 10-hectare plots in typical habitat hold 6-9 pairs. Elsewhere, scattered populations of tens of birds breed in rocky limestone areas and quarries. Birds typically prefer warmer, south-facing rocky slopes or ridges covered in scrub, bushes and young trees, particularly oak. Most birds disperse in autumn moving short distances or joining roving flocks of other buntings and finches. Some may be migratory.

STATUS IN HUNGARY: Rare to locally common breeder. National population size unknown. Estimates range from 300 to 1,000 pairs. Probably increasing. Resident, though in winter rather nomadic, some possibly migratory. Protected.

STATUS INTERNATIONALLY: Palearctic species. Considered vulnerable in Europe.

DISTRIBUTION: Scattered in Transdanubia and Northern Hills. Known areas are the Buda, Pilis, Börzsöny, Gerecse, Bükk, Torna, Mecsek and Villány hill ranges.

TIMING: Possible all year round, but in breeding areas mainly February to October.

Rock Bunting

Ortolan Bunting *Emberiza hortulana*
Kerti sármány

Ortolan Bunting has never been common or widespread in Hungary, but today numbers have reached an all time low. In the 1960s numbers peaked at several hundred breeding pairs, but then began to decline to the present figure of fewer than 20 pairs. In Hungary, as elsewhere, intensive agricultural and vinicultural methods are regarded as being responsible. Historically the species bred around Budapest, above Lake Balaton and in other parts of the country where

its seemingly favoured habitats of lightly wooded vine-yards, orchards and allotments with grassy areas, often on south-facing hillsides, are found. Some pairs are also occasionally found by lowland copses and plantations with adjacent rough grassland. From time to time isolated pairs or small populations occur around the country only to disappear after a few years.

STATUS IN HUNGARY: Very rare breeder. From 0-20 pairs. Declining. Migrant. Strictly protected.

STATUS INTERNATIONALLY: Palearctic breeding species. European population considered vulnerable and declining.

DISTRIBUTION: Very local and irregular. In recent years breeding populations found only in four isolated areas: lowland woods in Békés County, the southern slopes of the Mátra Hills near Gyöngyös in Heves County, the south of Tolna County, and the Villány hills in Baranya County.

TIMING: Summer. Birds arrive in Hungary at the end of April and depart in late August into September.

Reed Bunting *Emberiza schoeniclus*
Nádi sármány

Reed Buntings are common birds of marshes, reservoirs, lakes, fishponds and canal and river banks where there is adequate vegetation such as reed, rush, sedge with willow or alder bushes. Birds are mainly resident, though some migrate to the Mediterranean in late autumn, whilst birds from elsewhere in Europe move in to winter. Large winter flocks, often with other buntings and finches, occur not only on wetlands but in drier areas such as grassland, fallowland and cultivated areas. The Hungarian nomenclature regards most breeding birds as of the *ukrainae* race whereas other authorities consider them to be *stresemanni*. A further three races have occurred: the nominate *schoeniclus* is a common winter visitor, *intermedia* from the eastern Mediterranean also occurs in winter, mainly in Transdanubia, and there are some records of the Black Sea race *tschusii*.

STATUS IN HUNGARY: Common and widespread breeder. Population size and trends unknown. Mainly resident. Some migratory. Influxes in winter. Protected.

STATUS INTERNATIONALLY: Palearctic species. European population stable.

DISTRIBUTION: Breeds in and around wetlands nationwide. Open country in winter.

TIMING: All year round.

Corn Bunting *Miliaria calandra*
Sordély

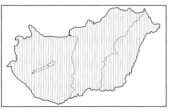

Although numbers have fallen in recent decades, Corn Buntings are still widespread in farmland, *puszta*, meadows, pastures and open country with trees, telegraph poles and wires which are used as perches and songposts. Some also occur in open areas in foothills. The decline in Hungary is probably not as marked as in most of Europe, but the reasons are almost certainly the same: agricultural change, intensification and the use of chemicals being suspected. Most migrate short distances, some are resident. In late autumn, resident birds join mixed flocks of other buntings, sparrows and finches in open farmland. In harsh winters most of these birds leave Hungary.

STATUS IN HUNGARY: Fairly common breeder. Around 10,000 pairs estimated. Has declined. Most birds migratory. Some occasionally winter. Protected.

STATUS INTERNATIONALLY: Palearctic species. European population declining.
DISTRIBUTION: Lowlands nationwide. Locally common on Great Plain. More scattered in Transdanubia.
TIMING: Except for very hard winters, all year round. Migratory birds present from March to November.

RARE VISITORS AND VAGRANTS

Presenting a comprehensive review of the occurrences of rare visitors and vagrants to Hungary has proved far from straightforward. The Hungarian Rarities Committee was established in 1987 and since then has sought to examine and scrutinise submitted records of rarities. Up to 1975, rare bird reports were accepted on the basis of the knowledge and judgements of the eminent ornithologists of the day. Between 1975 and 1987 a limbo period prevailed when records were not regularly screened. In the strictest sense the only reliable records on the present day Hungarian list are those which have been verified by collected specimens (Hungarian hunter-ornithologists were particularly diligent in collecting skins) and those which have been accepted since the establishment of the Rarities Committee in 1987. *Only those species which are recognised by the Rarities Committee (as of 1 January, 1995) have been included in the following section.* I have also endeavoured to mention only those individual records of each species which are generally considered reliable. However, documenting these records has proved a mine-field. Many reports published in the ornithological literature, which subsequently became accepted as *bona fide* records, were in the past not adequately scrutinised or even examined at all. For example, Three-toed Woodpecker *Picoides tridactylus* is confidently included in one Hungarian publication as a visitor despite there being not one single verified record. The Rarities Committee is currently reviewing many historical records in an attempt to finally clarify the situation. There are already some 'victims' of the clean-up. Bar-headed Goose *Anser indicus* now languishes in the recently introduced category D, as there is 'reasonable doubt that it has ever occurred in a wild state'. Will Hungary's Pallas's Rosefinch *Carpodacus roseus* go the same way? The only Azure Tit *Parus cyanus* on the Hungarian list is also currently under strong pressure. Thus, for some of the species that follow, the figures for the number of occurrences are approximations.

Great Northern Diver *Gavia immer* (Common Loon)
Jeges búvár

Seven records, all of single birds. With Hungary land-locked and almost surrounded by the high mountains of the Carpathians, the fact that the species has been recorded at all perhaps indicates the importance of the Danube as a migration flyway. With the exception of a May record from the turn of the century all have been in winter.
STATUS IN HUNGARY: Very rare vagrant. Protected.
STATUS INTERNATIONALLY: Arctic and Nearctic breeding species. European populations considered stable.
DISTRIBUTION AND TIMING: Seven records: Makád, Csepel Island, Danube, 24 May, 1904. Balatonkenese, Lake Balaton, 15 December, 1929. Dinnyés, Transdanubia, 9 December, 1930. Budapest, Danube, 11 January, 1935. Balatonalmádi, Lake Balaton, 30 November, 1982. Szeged Fertő, 2 December, 1984. Dead specimen, brought to Budapest Museum, 1 December, 1985.

White Pelican *Pelecanus onocrotalus* (Great White Pelican, Rosy Pelican)
Rózsás gödény

Bred in Hungary in the last century before most of the country's large wetlands were drained. Although there are nesting colonies in the nearby Balkans, the likelihood of a return to breed-

ing is remote. The 20 or so records from the last 50 years concern both juveniles and adults, often solitary, though six were at Tiszafüred in 1981. Most are considered true vagrants, though the possibility of some zoo escapes cannot be ruled out.

STATUS IN HUNGARY: Rare vagrant. Strictly protected.
STATUS INTERNATIONALLY: Palearctic and African breeding species. Rare in Europe but population considered stable.

DISTRIBUTION AND TIMING: Most records from large fishponds on the Great Plain (Hortobágy, Biharugra) and Lake Velence, Hanság and Kis-Balaton in Transdanubia. Records from April to November.

Dalmatian Pelican *Pelecanus crispus*
Borzas gödény

Bred in Hungary's then extensive marshes until the early 19th century. Occurs less frequently than White Pelican, with probably only six reliable post-war records, all from wetlands east of the Danube.

STATUS IN HUNGARY: Very rare vagrant. Strictly protected.
STATUS INTERNATIONALLY: Palearctic breeding species. Rare in Europe and classified as globally threatened.

DISTRIBUTION AND TIMING: Six post-war records: Two, Zabszék, Kiskunság salt lakes, 2 May, 1972. One, Csaj-tó, 18 May, 1975. One, Hortobágy, 22 June, 1988. Two, Szeged Fehértó, 18 May, 1989. One, Hortobágy, 15-16 July, 1989. Five (three adults, two immatures), Lake Tisza and Hortobágy-halastó, 22 May-1 June, 1990.

Cattle Egret *Bubulcus ibis*
Pásztorgém

Around ten post-war records. With populations not far away in the Mediterranean, and the species generally expanding its overall global range, it is perhaps strange that it remains only a rare vagrant to Hungary. Some birds are thought to have originated from collections in Austria.

STATUS IN HUNGARY: Vagrant. Protected.
STATUS INTERNATIONALLY: Almost global distribution. Expanding European range.

DISTRIBUTION AND TIMING: All observations of single birds: Szeged Fehér-tó, Sasér (twice), Csaj-tó and Hortobágy. In Transdanubia, Dinnyés, Hanság and Lake Fertő (twice). Spring to autumn.

Greater Flamingo *Phoenicopterus ruber*
Nagy flamingó

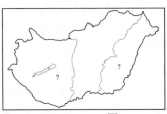

Fewer than 20 post-war reports. The origin of some birds remains in doubt. As one would expect, reported birds were of the Old World *roseus* race. None accepted since 1988.

STATUS IN HUNGARY: Accidental. Protected.
STATUS INTERNATIONALLY: Scattered world range including southern Europe, Africa and South-East Asia. Also separate race in Central America. Very local and fluctuating populations in Europe.

DISTRIBUTION AND TIMING: Around 11 records east of the Danube, six from Transdanubia and the Danube. Mostly single birds from spring to autumn.

Bewick's Swan *Cygnus columbianus*
Kis hattyú

Just 11 accepted records, though more have certainly occurred. Reports of this rare visitor began to increase in the 1970s, but only three submitted since 1988, one of which was accepted. May occur every year but reports not quite annual.
STATUS IN HUNGARY: Rare winter visitor. Protected.
STATUS INTERNATIONALLY: Breeding range confined to Palearctic tundra. Has increased in European wintering areas.
DISTRIBUTION AND TIMING: Possible on wetlands nationwide from October to April.

Pink-footed Goose *Anser brachyrhynchus*
Rövidcsőrű lúd

A few may occur annually among flocks of passage and wintering geese, especially Bean Goose, but are not observed or reported every year. Numbers recorded vary from one to 81 seen at Kunmadaras, Hortobágy, 18 April, 1982, 12 of which remained until 11 May.
STATUS IN HUNGARY: Rare vagrant. Protected.
STATUS INTERNATIONALLY: Breeding areas confined to North Atlantic. Population increasing.
DISTRIBUTION AND TIMING: Has occurred from October to February at regular goose sites, mainly in Transdanubia. Two accepted records since 1988: 22, Nyírőlapos, Hortobágy, 22 February, 1992. 1-6, Kis-Balaton, 8-11 February, 1993.

Brent Goose *Branta bernicla*
Örvös lúd

Around 30 reports, all apparently of the dark-bellied nominate race. Usually one, occasionally two birds, in the company of other geese, mainly from October to March at regular goose sites. One summer record of one bird from Köröstarcsa, 10-20 August, 1983.
STATUS IN HUNGARY: Rare vagrant. Protected.
STATUS INTERNATIONALLY: Circumpolar arctic breeding species. Very localised breeder and considered vulnerable.
DISTRIBUTION AND TIMING: Three accepted records since 1988: One 2nd-year, Mexikópuszta, 22 March, 1992. One adult, Mexikópuszta, 5 May, 1992. One, Máta, Hortobágy, 11 December, 1992.

Ruddy Shelduck *Tadorna ferruginea*
Vörös ásólúd

Fewer than 30 records. Some may refer to escapes. Usually from one to four birds on salt lakes or fishponds.
STATUS IN HUNGARY: Rare vagrant. Protected.
STATUS INTERNATIONALLY: Palearctic and African breeding species. Considered vulnerable in Europe.
DISTRIBUTION AND TIMING: Possible all year round. Periodical influxes, most recently in July 1994 when up to 13 were reported nationwide, including eight at Sárkeresztúr, Transdanubia, though this record was not submitted to the Rarities Committee!

Marbled Duck *Marmaronetta angustirostris* (Marbled Teal)
Márványos réce

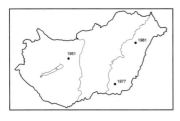

Three post-war records. Said to have bred in the last century.
STATUS IN HUNGARY: Accidental. Strictly protected.
STATUS INTERNATIONALLY: Palearctic breeding species. Globally threatened and endangered in Europe.
DISTRIBUTION AND TIMING: Three post-war records: Four, Lake Velence, January-March, 1951. One, Kardoskút, 22 November, 1977. One, Hortobágy-halastó, 4 May, 1981.

Common Eider *Somateria mollissima* (Eider)
Pehelyréce

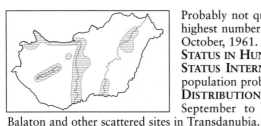

Probably not quite annual. Mostly one or two birds, the highest number being seven at Fonyód, Lake Balaton, 10 October, 1961.
STATUS IN HUNGARY: Rare winter visitor. Protected.
STATUS INTERNATIONALLY: Holarctic species. European population probably stable.
DISTRIBUTION AND TIMING: Most records from September to November. Mainly the Danube, Lake Balaton and other scattered sites in Transdanubia.

King Eider *Somateria spectabilis*
Cifra pehelyréce

Four records. One from 1875 and three this century, two of which were shot birds and, most recently, a 1st-spring male which stayed on the Danube for four days in April, 1986.
STATUS IN HUNGARY: Accidental. Protected.
STATUS INTERNATIONALLY: Circumpolar arctic species. Population probably stable.
DISTRIBUTION AND TIMING: Three post-war records: One shot bird, Hódmezővásárhely, Csongrád County, 1957. One juvenile female, shot, Békés, 7-18 January, 1973. 1st-spring male, Danube, Visegrád, 3-6 April, 1986.

White-headed Duck *Oxyura leucocephala*
Kékcsőrű réce

Although never common, bred on salt lakes in the Kiskunság region up to 1960. Until 1949, also sporadically in Transdanubia. Last pair bred at Fülöpháza, Kiskunság National Park, which became the site of a reintroduction project started in 1983. The project was unsuccessful for various reasons and was discontinued in 1994. Recent records may well relate to birds released from the project during the late 1980s.
STATUS IN HUNGARY: Extinct breeding species. Very rare vagrant. Strictly protected.
STATUS INTERNATIONALLY: Scattered within Palearctic. Globally threatened and endangered in Europe.
DISTRIBUTION AND TIMING: Most records from Great Plain in spring and autumn.

Egyptian Vulture *Neophron percnopterus*
Dögkeselyű

Just four post-war records of single birds, all from the Great Plain.
STATUS IN HUNGARY: Accidental. Strictly protected.
STATUS INTERNATIONALLY: Range within Palearctic, India and Africa. Endangered in Europe.
DISTRIBUTION AND TIMING: Four records: Bélmegyer, Békés County, November, 1963. Shot specimen, Kiskunmajsa, Kiskunság, June, 1970. Injured adult collected, Dévaványa, Békés, May, 1972. Adult, Hortobágy, 10 July, 1985.

Griffon Vulture *Gyps fulvus* (Eurasian Griffon Vulture)
Fakókeselyű

The most frequently reported vulture species, but not annual. Most records from the east and south of the country. Has occurred in almost every month.
STATUS IN HUNGARY: Vagrant. Protected.
STATUS INTERNATIONALLY: Range within Western Palearctic, southwest Asia and Middle East. European population recovering from a decline.
DISTRIBUTION AND TIMING: Only two confirmed records since 1988: Dead juvenile, Bölcske, Tolna County, 22 September, 1991. Adult, Fertőbőz, Lake Fertő, 26 August, 1994.

Black Vulture *Aegypius monachus* (Cinereous Vulture)
Barátkeselyű

Only four records, two from the last century, two pre-war; all of single birds, three of the four in May. Category B.
STATUS IN HUNGARY: Accidental. Strictly protected.
STATUS INTERNATIONALLY: Palearctic species. Rare and considered vulnerable in Europe.
DISTRIBUTION AND TIMING: Four records: Hortobágy, June, 1871. Fejér County, Transdanubia, 4 May, 1882. Császárszállás, Szabolcs-Szatmár-Bereg, 14 May, 1923. Heves County, 20 May, 1932.

Steppe Eagle *Aquila nipalensis*
Pusztai sas

Once very scarce or perhaps overlooked, but now reported almost annually from *puszta* areas east of the Tisza, usually in summer. Probably fewer than ten reliable records in all. Only four accepted since 1988.
STATUS IN HUNGARY: Vagrant. Protected.
STATUS INTERNATIONALLY: Range mainly in Eastern Palearctic and India. Rare, and considered vulnerable in Europe.
DISTRIBUTION AND TIMING: Four records: One, Szolnok, 5 November, 1992. One 2nd-year, Darassa, Hortobágy, 7-8 May, 1993. One, Darassa, Hortobágy, 29 June-14 September, 1993. One, Hortobágy, 9-11 August, 1994.

Bonelli's Eagle *Hieraaetus fasciatus*
Héjasas

Two post-war records. Both from the Tisza floodplain. Most recent report from 1993 not submitted to Rarities Committee.
STATUS IN HUNGARY: Accidental. Protected.
STATUS INTERNATIONALLY: Palearctic, African and Oriental species. Declining and endangered in Europe.
DISTRIBUTION AND TIMING: Two post-war records: Szeged Fehér-tó, 9 June, 1949. Tőserdő, 7 February, 1960.

Eleonora's Falcon *Falco eleonorae*
Eleonóra-sólyom

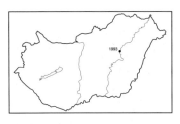

Several post-war reports, but only one accepted record.
STATUS IN HUNGARY: Accidental. Strictly protected.
STATUS INTERNATIONALLY: Breeding range almost totally confined to Mediterranean. Population probably stable.
DISTRIBUTION AND TIMING: One accepted record: One dark-phase adult, Tiszasüly, 9 May, 1993.

Black Grouse *Tetrao tetrix*
Nyírfajd

No records in the last 50 years. Category B. With populations in neighbouring Slovenia, Austria, Slovakia, Ukraine and Romania all in decline, and the species being rather sedentary, renewed occurrence in Hungary seems unlikely.
STATUS IN HUNGARY: Accidental. Protected.
STATUS INTERNATIONALLY: Palearctic species. European population in decline and vulnerable.
DISTRIBUTION AND TIMING: Bred in northeast of the country in the last century in the Nyírség region. These birds were at the very edge of the then large Carpathian population.

Capercaillie *Tetrao urogallus*
Siketfajd

Occurred and bred in the Őrség, Kőszeg and Sopron areas on the Austrian border (Alp Foothills) until the 1960s. These birds were considered to belong to a central European race '*major*', but are generally regarded as a variant within the nominate race. Birds from Austria very occasionally seen in above areas.
STATUS IN HUNGARY: Vagrant. Protected.
STATUS INTERNATIONALLY: Palearctic species. European population in decline.
DISTRIBUTION AND TIMING: No confirmed records since 1988. Last report was an unconfirmed observation by foresters of a male and a female in the Őrség region in 1985.

Purple Gallinule *Porphyrio porphyrio* (Purple Swamphen)
Kék-fú

One confirmed record. A single bird which stayed for a week at Lake Velence in October 1967 and was photographed.
STATUS IN HUNGARY: Accidental. Protected.
STATUS INTERNATIONALLY: Mainly African, Oriental and Australasian species, with isolated populations in Western Palearctic. Recovering in Europe after a sharp decline.
DISTRIBUTION AND TIMING: One record: Agárd, Lake Velence, 15-22 October, 1967.

Demoiselle Crane *Anthropoides virgo*
Pártásdaru

Reports of this species have increased in recent decades. Single birds reported almost annually on the Great Plain. Most recent record was a bird which moved around eastern Hungary for three months from mid July to late October, 1994.
STATUS IN HUNGARY: Rare vagrant. Protected.
STATUS INTERNATIONALLY: Breeding range within Palearctic. Small Western Palearctic populations in decline.
DISTRIBUTION AND TIMING: Most records from Hortobágy, Kardoskút and other sites east of the Tisza where Common Cranes gather. Majority from August-November.

Little Bustard *Tetrax tetrax*
Reznek

Bred until early this century in the Kiskunság, Hortobágy and elsewhere. Last confirmed breeding in 1918 at Bagotapuszta, Hortobágy. Suspected nesting in 1952 and 1973 but not confirmed. Nowadays single birds are occasionally reported from the Great Plain. The Hungarian nomenclature regards former breeding birds as of the 'orientalis' race. The species is now regarded as monotypic.
STATUS IN HUNGARY: Vagrant. Strictly protected.
STATUS INTERNATIONALLY: Palearctic species. European populations in decline and considered vulnerable.
DISTRIBUTION AND TIMING: No records since 1988.

Black-winged Pratincole *Glareola nordmanni*
Feketeszárnyú székicsér

Essentially a rare vagrant though has bred periodically, the last time in 1980. Four confirmed post-war breeding records concerning a maximum 5-6 pairs. Three times on the Hortobágy, once in the Kiskunság, and always with Collared Pratincoles. Attempted to breed, Karcag area, in 1995.
STATUS IN HUNGARY: Rare vagrant. Strictly protected.
STATUS INTERNATIONALLY: Breeding range confined to the Palearctic. Rare and considered vulnerable in Europe.
DISTRIBUTION AND TIMING: Four post-war breeding records: One pair, Kunmadaras, Hortobágy, 1973. One pair, Fülöpszállás, Kiskunság, 1975. One pair, Nyírő-lapos,

Hortobágy, 1979. 2-3 pairs, Nyírő-lapos, Hortobágy, 1980. Accepted records since 1988: Szarvas, 14 September, 1992. Hortobágy, 1 June, 1994. Two, Hortobágy, June-July, 1995.

Killdeer *Charadrius vociferus*
Ékfarkú lile

Two records of single birds. The first Hungarian record was a long-staying bird found on a gravel bank by the Danube in 1986. The second, as with so many Hungarian wader rarities, was seen on a drained fishpond on the Hortobágy in 1992.
STATUS IN HUNGARY: Accidental. Protected.
STATUS INTERNATIONALLY: Nearctic and tropical American range. Common and widespread.
DISTRIBUTION AND TIMING: Two records: Almásfüzitő, Danube, 1 November-30 December, 1986. Hortobágy-halastó, 10 August, 1992.

Greater Sand Plover *Charadrius leschenaultii*
Sivatagi lile

One record. A bird among Lapwings and Little Ringed Plovers, which stayed for a week in July 1992 in Lake Fertő National Park. Race not noted.
STATUS IN HUNGARY: Accidental. Protected.
STATUS INTERNATIONALLY: Breeding range within Palearctic. Small European population (Turkey) considered endangered.
DISTRIBUTION AND TIMING: One record: Adult male, Mexikópuszta, Lake Fertő, 7-14 July, 1992.

Spur-winged Plover *Hoplopterus spinosus* (Spur-winged Lapwing)
Tüskés bíbic

One record. A bird associating with Lapwings on drained fishponds at Csaj-tó in autumn 1993. The bird stayed for a week and was one of the first rarities to attract birders from all over Hungary.
STATUS IN HUNGARY: Accidental. Protected.
STATUS INTERNATIONALLY: Western Palearctic and African breeding species. European populations declining and endangered.
DISTRIBUTION AND TIMING: One record: Csaj-tó, Csongrád County, 17-24 October, 1993.

Sociable Plover *Chettusia gregaria* (Sociable Lapwing)
Lilebíbic

Probably a total of five records, all of single birds, the first from 1900. More recently, three records from the Hortobágy and one from the Kiskunság.
STATUS IN HUNGARY: Accidental. Strictly protected.
STATUS INTERNATIONALLY: Breeding range in central Palearctic. European population (Russia) endangered.
DISTRIBUTION AND TIMING: Five records: Tata, Transdanubia, 29 September, 1900. Hortobágy, 6 August, 1972. Juvenile, Hortobágy, 5 October, 1985. Adult, Fülöpszállás, Kiskunság, 24-26 April,

1992. Adult, Kunmadaras, Hortobágy, 9 October, 1992.

White-tailed Plover *Chettusia leucura* (White-tailed Lapwing)
Fehérfarkú lilebíbic

Two records of single birds. The first, a long-staying bird at Lake Velence, in 1975; the second, a winter-plumaged bird on drained fishponds in the northeast Hortobágy in 1987. STATUS IN HUNGARY: Accidental. Protected. STATUS INTERNATIONALLY: Breeding range in central Palearctic. Small Western Palearctic population stable. DISTRIBUTION AND TIMING- Two records: Agárd, Lake Velence, 23 May, 1975. Adult, Virágoskút ponds, Balmazújváros, 15 November, 1987.

Pectoral Sandpiper *Calidris melanotos*
Vándor partfutó

All six records have occurred since 1987. This is no doubt owing in part to the new breed of Hungarian wader enthusiast who scours dried fishpond systems in search of rarities. A particularly interesting record was three juveniles at Naszály-Ferencmajor fishponds in Transdanubia in September 1993. A total of seven birds, all juveniles. STATUS IN HUNGARY: Rare vagrant. Protected. STATUS INTERNATIONALLY: Eastern Palearctic and Nearctic breeding species. Population probably stable. DISTRIBUTION AND TIMING: Six records: Juvenile, Kisrét, Kiskunság, 27 September-1 October, 1987. Juvenile, Fényes fishponds, Hortobágy, 5 September, 1988. Juvenile, Elep fishponds, Hortobágy, 6-7 October, 1991. Adult, Csécsi fishponds, 17-21 July, 1993. Three juveniles, Naszály-Ferencmajor fishponds, 12 September, 1993. Juvenile, Szarvas, 11 September, 1994.

Purple Sandpiper *Calidris maritima*
Tengeri partfutó

Two records, both birds collected in the last century. Recent reports not confirmed. Category B. STATUS IN HUNGARY: Accidental. Protected. STATUS INTERNATIONALLY: Circumpolar arctic breeding species. European population stable. DISTRIBUTION AND TIMING: Two records: Pest County, 1820. Lake Fertő, 1857.

Buff-breasted Sandpiper *Tryngites subruficollis*
Cankő-partfutó

Hungary's only record was a bird associating with Dotterels on a saline *puszta* in Hortobágy National Park in 1993.
STATUS IN HUNGARY: Accidental. Protected.
STATUS INTERNATIONALLY: Nearctic breeding species. Population probably stable.
DISTRIBUTION AND TIMING: One record: Szelencés-Angyalháza, Hortobágy, 10-22 October, 1993.

Slender-billed Curlew *Numenius tenuirostris*
Vékonycsőrű póling

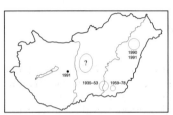

This rare species has been reported in Hungary around 85 times this century. The majority of records are from two sites on the Great Plain: Kardoskút (up to 1978) and Hortobágy, especially drained fishponds at Hortobágy-halastó. Birds have been seen in every month except February and June, with most observations in September-October.
STATUS IN HUNGARY: Very rare visitor. Strictly protected.
STATUS INTERNATIONALLY: Breeding confined to Eastern Palearctic. Globally threatened. Considered to be on the verge of extinction.
DISTRIBUTION AND TIMING: There have been around 16 reports since 1980, not all confirmed. The majority have come from one well watched site, Hortobágy-halastó. Accepted records since 1988: One bird, Hortobágy-halastó, 1 October, 1990. Six birds, Nagyiván Puszta, 1-2 December, 1990. One bird, Sárkány-tó, Transdanubia, 19 May, 1991. One bird, Kondás, Hortobágy-halastó, 27 October, 1991. Three birds, Virágoskúti fishponds, Balmazújváros, 31 October-1 November, 1991.

Lesser Yellowlegs *Tringa flavipes*
Sárgalábú cankó

Two Hungarian records of this regular vagrant to Europe from North America. The first, a bird found dead on a salt lake in the Kiskunság in 1959.
STATUS IN HUNGARY: Accidental. Protected.
STATUS INTERNATIONALLY: Nearctic breeding species. Population probably stable.
DISTRIBUTION AND TIMING: Two records: One dead specimen, Fülöpháza, Kiskunság, 12 September, 1959.
One adult, Szeged Fertő, 26 June, 1990.

Grey Phalarope *Phalaropus fulicarius* (Red Phalarope)
Laposcsőrű víztaposó

Around 15 largely unconfirmed records this century, all single birds. Just one since 1988.
STATUS IN HUNGARY: Very rare vagrant. Protected.
STATUS INTERNATIONALLY: Circumpolar arctic breeding species. Small European populations probably stable.
DISTRIBUTION AND TIMING: One record since 1988: One adult, Sárkeresztúr, Transdanubia, 21 May, 1989.

Pomarine Skua *Stercorarius pomarinus* (Pomarine Jaeger)
Szélesfarkú halfarkas

Probably not quite annual, or at least not reported every year. Singles, occasionally two birds, are the norm in autumn. A few summer and winter records.
STATUS IN HUNGARY: Rare autumn visitor. Protected.
STATUS INTERNATIONALLY: Circumpolar arctic breeding range.
DISTRIBUTION AND TIMING: Records from around the country: noted sites are Lake Fertő, Danube, Csaj-tó, Szeged Fehér-tó, Hortobágy. The classic month for the species is October.

Long-tailed Skua *Stercorarius longicaudus* (Long-tailed Jaeger)
Nyílfarkú halfarkas

Identification pitfalls may in part be responsible for the fact that this species is not reported every year. Single birds are the norm and records are divided almost evenly between adult and juvenile birds.
STATUS IN HUNGARY: Rare vagrant. Protected.
STATUS INTERNATIONALLY: Circumpolar arctic breeding range. European population stable.
DISTRIBUTION AND TIMING: With the exception of two in March, June to October is the usual period of occurrence. Half of all records have been between 22 August and 9 September. Most observations from fishponds on the Hortobágy, Szeged Fehér-tó, Lake Balaton and Lake Velence.

Great Skua *Stercorarius skua*
Nagy halfarkas, Szkua

Probably four records. All single birds, initially or subsequently found dead. The third record was a specimen which spent most of August 1989 on Lake Balaton, and when later picked up dead was found to be carrying an Icelandic ring. The fourth record, again found dead at Balaton, carried a Moscow ring.
STATUS IN HUNGARY: Very rare vagrant. Protected.
STATUS INTERNATIONALLY: European (North Atlantic) breeding range. Population increasing.
DISTRIBUTION AND TIMING: Four records: Balatonfüred, Lake Balaton, 17 August, 1959. Mórichely, Zala County, 29 September, 1963. Lake Balaton, 7-30 August, 1988. Keszthely, Lake Balaton, May, 1993.

Great Black-headed Gull *Larus ichthyaetus*
Halászsirály

The occurrence of this species in Hungary is another case where several records quickly followed the first. Since the first confirmed observation in 1992, several birds have been sighted, with some staying all summer. Just how many different individuals have occurred is unclear, though it seems that at least four different birds were on the Hortobágy in 1994.
STATUS IN HUNGARY: Rare vagrant. Protected.

STATUS INTERNATIONALLY: Palearctic breeding species. European population stable.
DISTRIBUTION AND TIMING: Around six records: 1st-summer, Hortobágy, 1 June-16 August, 1992. Two (one adult and one 2nd-year), Hortobágy-halastó, 1993. Adult, Danube Bend, 6-7 March, 1993. Adult, Szentes, 11 August, 1993. Two (one adult, one 2nd-year), Hortobágy, from 1 March, 1994. Four, Hortobágy, 12 September, 1994.

Franklin's Gull *Larus pipixcan*
Prérisirály

The discovery of an adult bird in winter plumage at the heart of the Great Plain in 1992 was another occasion that roused normally local-patch loyal Hungarian birders to travel.
STATUS IN HUNGARY: Accidental. Protected.
STATUS INTERNATIONALLY: North American breeding species. Thought to be in decline.
DISTRIBUTION AND TIMING: One record: Adult winter, Kőrősladány, 19-22 September, 1992.

Sabine's Gull *Larus sabini*
Fecskesirály

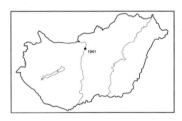

Just one record from the River Danube in 1941. Category B.
STATUS IN HUNGARY: Accidental. Protected.
STATUS INTERNATIONALLY: Circumpolar arctic breeding range. Very rare breeder in Western Palearctic.
DISTRIBUTION AND TIMING: One record: Juvenile, Káposztásmegyer, Budapest, 17 December, 1941.

Slender-billed Gull *Larus genei*
Vékonycsórú sirály

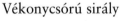
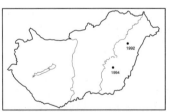

Just two records, both concerning adult birds at sites east of the Tisza. The first was on fishponds at Hortobágy, the second, two years later, on paddyfields near Szarvas.
STATUS IN HUNGARY: Accidental. Protected.
STATUS INTERNATIONALLY: Breeding range extends from Mediterranean and Black Sea basins through Middle East into Asia. Population probably stable.
DISTRIBUTION AND TIMING: Two records: Adult, Hortobágy-halastó, 3-7 May, 1992. Adult, Szarvas, Békés County, 22 June, 1994.

Ring-billed Gull *Larus delawarensis*
Gyűrűscsőrű sirály

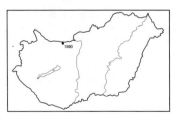

The one accepted record for Hungary of this regular visitor to Europe is a single bird seen on the Danube among other gulls in 1990.
STATUS IN HUNGARY: Accidental. Protected.
STATUS INTERNATIONALLY: North American breeding species. Population increasing.
DISTRIBUTION AND TIMING: One record: 1st-winter, River Danube at Süttő, Komárom County, 21 December, 1990.

Iceland Gull *Larus glaucoides*
Sarki sirály

Just one record of a single bird at Lake Balaton in 1934.
Category B.
STATUS IN HUNGARY: Accidental. Protected.
STATUS INTERNATIONALLY: North Atlantic (Nearctic)
breeding range. Population probably stable.
DISTRIBUTION AND TIMING: One record: Balatonszemes,
Lake Balaton, 10 December, 1934.

Glaucous Gull *Larus hyperboreus*
Jeges sirály

Probably five records this century, all of single birds from
November to January.
STATUS IN HUNGARY: Rare vagrant. Protected.
STATUS INTERNATIONALLY: Circumpolar arctic breeding
range. Western Palearctic population has declined.
DISTRIBUTION AND TIMING: Three post-war records:
Szeged Fehér-tó, 19 December, 1976. Danube, Almásfüzitő.
9-24 November, 1985. Hortobágy, 25 March, 1994.

Great Black-backed Gull *Larus marinus*
Dolmányos sirály

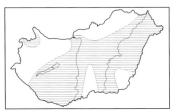

Between 40 and 50 reports since the first confirmed bird in
1930. Mostly single birds, though up to three have been
seen together. Majority from fishponds, occasionally the
Danube and Tisza, from October-December.
STATUS IN HUNGARY: Vagrant. Protected.
STATUS INTERNATIONALLY: North Atlantic breeding
range. European population has increased.
DISTRIBUTION AND TIMING: Three accepted records
since 1988: One, Elep fishponds, 16 April, 1989. One immature, Hortobágy-halastó, 13
August, 1991. One, Elep fishponds, Hortobágy, 16 November, 1993.

Gull-billed Tern *Gelochelidon nilotica*
Kacagócsér

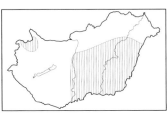

Not quite annual. Majority of reports from east of the
Danube, particularly fishponds and salt lakes in the
Kiskunság. Usually single birds seen. Has bred, last occa-
sion at Kelemen-szék, Kiskunság, in 1967.
STATUS IN HUNGARY: Vagrant. Protected.
STATUS INTERNATIONALLY: Almost cosmopolitan range.
Endangered in Europe where population has declined
sharply.
DISTRIBUTION AND TIMING: Only five accepted records since 1988, mainly from July. Many
records probably not submitted.

Sandwich Tern *Sterna sandvicensis*
Kenti csér

Probably around six reliable records, all in the last 30 years. The first was a bird shot in the Kiskunság in May, 1967.
STATUS IN HUNGARY: Accidental. Protected.
STATUS INTERNATIONALLY: Breeds in parts of North and Central America and Eurasia. European population in decline.
DISTRIBUTION AND TIMING: One confirmed record since 1988: One, Irmapuszta, Somogy County, 3 December, 1994.

Arctic Tern *Sterna paradisea*
Sarki csér

There have been numerous claims of observations of this species in Hungary, but at present only three accepted records, all of single birds from widely scattered sites, and all in the last four years.
STATUS IN HUNGARY: Accidental. Protected.
STATUS INTERNATIONALLY: Holarctic breeding species. European population stable.
DISTRIBUTION AND TIMING: Three records: Szeged Fertő, 12-14 October, 1991. Hortobágy, 8 November, 1991. Lake Fertő, 29 July, 1993.

Little Tern *Sterna albifrons*
Kis csér

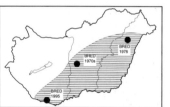

Hungary is one of the very few totally land-locked countries where this species has bred. Nesting sites have been on gravel islets in the Danube, on fishponds and salt lakes.
STATUS IN HUNGARY: Vagrant. Irregular breeder. Strictly protected.
STATUS INTERNATIONALLY: Cosmopolitan species. Declining in Europe.
DISTRIBUTION AND TIMING: Has bred along the Danube, Dráva, in the Kiskunság, Csaj-tó fishponds and unsuccessfully at Nagyszik, Hortobágy. Outside breeding season, vagrants occur at wetlands on the Great Plain. From the end of April to September. Last confirmed breeding at Kelemen-szék, Kiskunság, in the 1970s.

Razorbill *Alca torda*
Alka

A remarkable record from 1935 of a bird killed by flying into a church tower in thick fog is the only one for Hungary. Category B.
STATUS IN HUNGARY: Accidental. Protected.
STATUS INTERNATIONALLY: North Atlantic breeding range. European population probably stable.
DISTRIBUTION AND TIMING: One record: Hajdúböszörmény, Hajdú-Bihar County, winter, 1935.

Puffin *Fratercula arctica* (Atlantic Puffin)
Lunda

Both Hungarian records relate to juveniles, and although 87 years apart, occurred within 20 km of each other. Both birds were of the *grabae* race. Category B.
STATUS IN HUNGARY: Accidental. Protected.
STATUS INTERNATIONALLY: North Atlantic and Arctic breeding range. Locally common, but European population in decline and considered vulnerable.
DISTRIBUTION AND TIMING: Two records: Hódmező-vásárhely, Csongrád County, 13 December, 1862. Szeged Fehér-tó, 25 July, 1949.

Chestnut-bellied Sandgrouse *Pterocles exustus*
Pusztaityúk

The only Hungarian record is also the only one for Europe: a female with a flock of Pallas's Sandgrouse shot in 1863. The verifying skin was apparently destroyed during the Second World War. Category B.
STATUS IN HUNGARY: Accidental. Protected.
STATUS INTERNATIONALLY: Africa, Arabian and Indian range. Population status unknown.
DISTRIBUTION AND TIMING: One record: Adult female, Szany, Győr-Sopron County, August, 1863.

Pallas's Sandgrouse *Syrrhaptes paradoxus*
Talpastyúk

As elsewhere in Europe, major invasions occurred in the last century in 1859, 1863 (see above species), 1864, 1888, 1891 and 1892. No records in the last 50 years. Category B.
STATUS IN HUNGARY: Rare vagrant. Protected.
STATUS INTERNATIONALLY: Normal range Eastern Palearctic. Invasion species. Population size unknown.
DISTRIBUTION AND TIMING: Reported to have bred in 1864 and 1988 in the Lake Fertő area. Invasions this century: 1905, 1906, 1908, 1913, 1917, 1921, 1922, 1944.

Rufous Turtle Dove *Streptopelia orientalis* (Oriental Turtle Dove)
Keleti gerle

One record: a juvenile bird associating with Collared Doves in a garden in Szeged in the southeast of the country. The bird stayed only a few hours but was photographed. Race not noted.
STATUS IN HUNGARY: Accidental. Protected.
STATUS INTERNATIONALLY: Asian and Oriental species. Population size unknown.
DISTRIBUTION AND TIMING: One record: Juvenile, Szeged, Csongrád County, 18 December, 1985.

Snowy Owl *Nyctea scandiaca*
Hóbagoly

Around ten records, all from winter (November-March), all single birds except for two at Kapuvár, Transdanubia, in January 1934.
STATUS IN HUNGARY: Very rare vagrant. Strictly protected.
STATUS INTERNATIONALLY: Circumpolar arctic breeding range. Rare and considered vulnerable in Europe.
DISTRIBUTION AND TIMING: Post-war records: Szeged Fehér-tó, November, 1970. Budapest, 1 March, 1971. Sárrét, Székesfehérvár, 13-14 December, 1972. Karcag, Jász-Nagykun-Szolnok County, 29 December, 1984. Nyírmada, Szabolcs-Szatmár-Bereg County, 19 February, 1985.

Hawk Owl *Surnia ulula*
Karvalybagoly

Just one record from 1937. Category B.
STATUS IN HUNGARY: Accidental. Protected.
STATUS INTERNATIONALLY: Holarctic species. Breeding population fluctuates. Overall, probably stable.
DISTRIBUTION AND TIMING: One record: Pusztaszer, Csongrád County, 7 November, 1937.

Pygmy Owl *Glaucidium passerinum* (Eurasian Pygmy Owl)
Törpekuvik

Four records. Last two birds both found dead in January 1994. Given that the species breeds very close to the Hungarian border in Austria and Slovakia, its rarity is perhaps surprising. However, the species is a forest bird, rather sedentary and the areas where it may occur large and rather thinly watched.
STATUS IN HUNGARY: Rare vagrant. Protected.
STATUS INTERNATIONALLY: Palearctic species. Numbers fluctuate. Overall, European population has declined.
DISTRIBUTION AND TIMING: Four records: Sopron hills, Transdanubia, 20 November, 1977. Aggtelek National Park, 25 February, 1992. Dead specimen, Sopron, 14 January, 1994. Dead specimen, Hatvan, Heves County, 19 January, 1994.

Tengmalm's Owl *Aegolius funereus* (Boreal Owl)
Gatyáskuvik

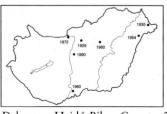

Probably seven records, all of single birds. Five in the last 50 years, with two from April 1960 (possibly same bird?). Only one confirmed since 1988.
STATUS IN HUNGARY: Accidental. Protected.
STATUS INTERNATIONALLY: Holarctic species. Populations fluctuates. European population probably stable.
DISTRIBUTION AND TIMING: Probably seven records: Fót, Pest County, 19 March, 1929. Tarpa, Nyírség, 1935. Debrecen, Hajdú-Bihar County, 28 October, 1954. Baja, Bács-Kiskun County, 2 April, 1960.

Heves, Heves County, 5 April, 1960. Esztergom, Komáron-Esztergom County, 20 June, 1972. Adult male, trapped Ócsa, Pest County, 18 November, 1990.

Calandra Lark *Melanocorypha calandra*
Kalandrapacsirta

Considering the species breeds in four neighbouring counties and its nomadic tendency in winter, a perhaps surprisingly low total of five records ever involving just six birds, all in the last 50 years and all from September-February east of the Danube.
STATUS IN HUNGARY: Rare vagrant. Protected.
STATUS INTERNATIONALLY: Palearctic species. Declining in Europe.

DISTRIBUTION AND TIMING: Five records: Albertfalva, 29 November, 1947. Two, Nagyiván Puszta, Hortobágy, 4 January, 1974. Hódmezővásárhely, Csongrád County, 21 January, 1978. Nagyiván Puszta, Hortobágy, 17 February, 1979. Hajdúböszörmény, Hajdú-Bihar, 14-15 December, 1980.

Citrine Wagtail *Montacilla citreola*
Citrombillegető

In line with the recent increase across Europe, all five Hungarian records have occurred in the last six years. Interestingly, the first two records were on the 6th of the month in 1989 and then 1992, at sites only a few miles apart, with another on the 7th at one of the sites in 1993. Races not noted.
STATUS IN HUNGARY: Rare vagrant. Protected.
STATUS INTERNATIONALLY: Palearctic breeding range. Population perhaps expanding westwards in range.

DISTRIBUTION AND TIMING: Five records: Adult male, Fertőrákos, Transdanubia, 6 May, 1989. Adult male, Fertőújlak, Transdanubia, 6 May, 1992. Adult male, Hortobágy-halastó, 14 May, 1992. 2nd-year male, Hortobágy, Derzsi fishpond, 22 April, 1993. Adult male, Fertőújlak, 7 May, 1993.

Pied Wheatear *Oenanthe pleschanka*
Balkáni hantmadár

Around eight records, all in the last 40 years. All records involve adult males. A pair is thought to have bred near Szeged in 1976. Three out of the first four records were from the same limestone hills near Budapest.
STATUS IN HUNGARY: Very rare vagrant. Protected.
STATUS INTERNATIONALLY: Palearctic breeding species. Population size and trends unknown.
DISTRIBUTION AND TIMING: Eight records: Budaörs, Budapest, 15 May-15 June, 1955. Budaörs, Budapest, 2-3 September, 1956. Dunabogdány, Pest County, July, 1964. Budaörs, Budapest, 13-15 June, 1965. Pair, Szeged, Csongrád, 24-26 June, 1976. *May have bred.* Tokaj Hill, 4 April, 1979. Tokod, Komárom-Esztergom County, 17 August, 1979. Kesztölc, Komárom-Esztergom County, 6 June, 1982.

Black-eared Wheatear *Oenanthe hispanica*
Déli hantmadár

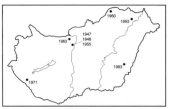

Probably eight records. First recorded at Budaörs (see above species) when a male stayed through the summer of 1947. All birds were of the *melanoleuca* race.
STATUS IN HUNGARY: Rare vagrant. Protected.
STATUS INTERNATIONALLY: Most of breeding range within Western Palearctic. European populations have declined and considered vulnerable.
DISTRIBUTION AND TIMING: Probably eight records: Budaörs, Budapest, summer, 1947. Budaörs, Budapest, 6 May, 1948. Budaörs, Budapest, 12-15 June, 1955. Aggtelek, 11 April, 1960. Pilisvörösvár, Pest County, 10 June, 1963. Shot bird, Nagykanizsa, Zala County, April, 1971. Köröstarcsa, Békés County, 16-23 June, 1983. Zemplén hills, May-June, 1994.

Desert Wheatear *Oenanthe deserti*
Sivatagi hantmadár

The only record a female at the Nagyszik salt lake, Balmazújváros, in November 1991. Race not noted.
STATUS IN HUNGARY: Accidental. Protected.
STATUS INTERNATIONALLY: Mainly Palearctic breeding range. Population size and trends unknown.
DISTRIBUTION AND TIMING: One record: Female, Balmazújváros, Hortobágy, 17-21 November, 1991.

Naumann's Thrush *Turdus naumanni*
Rőtfarkú rigó

Another quite remarkable record. A live bird was noticed among Fieldfares in a Budapest food market in 1820, all had been caught by liming. The bird was taken to Budapest museum and identified as the nominate *naumanni* race. Category B.
STATUS IN HUNGARY: Accidental. Protected.
STATUS INTERNATIONALLY: Siberian breeding species. Population size and trends unknown.
DISTRIBUTION AND TIMING: One record: Budapest, winter, 1820.

Paddyfield Warbler *Acrocephalus agricola*
Rozsdás nádiposzáta

Two records of trapped birds. The first, a juvenile male of race *capistrata* caught in a ringing camp in Kiskunság National Park in 1978. Balkan birds (of which this was presumably one) sometimes regarded as race '*septima*'.
STATUS IN HUNGARY: Accidental. Protected.
STATUS INTERNATIONALLY: Breeds within Palearctic. Small European population probably stable.
DISTRIBUTION AND TIMING: Two records: Juvenile, Fülöpháza, Kiskunság, 11 August, 1978. Fenékpuszta, Balaton, 23 September, 1992.

Sardinian Warbler *Sylvia melanocephala*
Kucsmás poszáta

An adult male caught during ringing in vineyards above Lake Balaton in 1979 is the only Hungarian record. Race not noted but almost certainly the nominate.

STATUS IN HUNGARY: Accidental. Protected.

STATUS INTERNATIONALLY: Breeding range within Western Palearctic. Common and widespread in Mediterranean.

DISTRIBUTION AND TIMING: One record: Adult male, Szentgyörgy Hill, Tapolca, Veszprém County, 29 July, 1979.

Yellow-browed Warbler *Phylloscopus inornatus*
Vándor füzike

Just two records. The first, a bird caught at a ringing camp in the Bükk hills in 1989. The second, a bird seen just one month later in willows along the Danube north of Budapest.

STATUS IN HUNGARY: Rare vagrant. Protected.

STATUS INTERNATIONALLY: Breeding range almost totally within Eastern Palearctic. Common in breeding areas.

DISTRIBUTION AND TIMING: Two records: Juvenile, (race not noted) Egerszalók, Bükk hills, 8 October, 1989. Adult *humei,* Surány, Szentendre Island, Pest County, 9 November, 1989.

Bonelli's Warbler *Phylloscopus bonelli*
Bonelli-füzike

With a large breeding population in neighbouring Austria, it is perhaps rather surprising that there is only one Hungarian record, a bird caught at the Fenékpuszta ringing camp, at the southwest end of Lake Balaton, in 1989. Race not noted.

STATUS IN HUNGARY: Accidental. Protected.

STATUS INTERNATIONALLY: Western Palearctic breeding species. Common in breeding areas and population stable.

DISTRIBUTION AND TIMING: One record: 1st-year, Fenékpuszta, Lake Balaton, 28 August, 1989.

Azure Tit *Parus cyanus*
Lazúrcinege

The one currently accepted record was a bird trapped at the Ócsa ringing camp, southeast of Budapest, in 1989. A record of another trapped bird from Gyula the previous year was removed from the Hungarian list when it was subsequently considered to be a Blue Tit x Azure Tit hybrid, the so-called 'Pleske's Tit' *Parus pleskii*. The present record is under renewed scrutiny and may also be removed.

STATUS IN HUNGARY: Accidental. Protected.

STATUS INTERNATIONALLY: Palearctic species. Common in most of breeding range.

DISTRIBUTION AND TIMING: One record (under review): Ócsa, Pest County, 28 October, 1989.

Long-tailed Shrike *Lanius schach* (Rufous-backed Shrike)
Hosszúfarkú gébics

The one Hungarian record is also the only one for Europe and was the first for the Western Palearctic. The *erythronotus* race occurred. However, this record is under review
STATUS IN HUNGARY: Accidental. Protected.
STATUS INTERNATIONALLY: Eastern Palearctic and Oriental species. Population size unknown.
DISTRIBUTION AND TIMING: One record: Fehértó, Hanság, Transdanubia, 21 April, 1979.

Woodchat Shrike *Lanius senator*
Vörösfejú gébics

As in most neighbouring countries, Woodchat Shrikes have all but disappeared from Hungary in the last 25 years. As I write, the species is probably extinct as a breeding bird. The reasons for this are not entirely clear. Never very common and always somewhat scattered in Hungary, the species bred regularly in western Transdanubia until the 1970s, with some pairs occasionally on the south-facing slopes of the Bükk and Aggtelek hills and in the Debrecen area. Although some habitat has undoubtedly been lost or degraded, it is unlikely that this is the sole cause of the species' decline in Hungary.
STATUS IN HUNGARY: Probably extinct as a breeding species. Otherwise vagrant. Protected.
STATUS INTERNATIONALLY: Breeding range almost totally confined to Western Palearctic. Vulnerable in Europe and declining.
DISTRIBUTION AND TIMING: Most regular areas early in the century were Sopron, Vas, Fejér, Zala and Somogy Counties in Transdanubia. Some pairs bred on warmer slopes of Northern Hills. One record since 1988: Székes Fehérvár, 7 September, 1990.

Alpine Chough *Pyrrhocorax graculus* (Yellow-billed Chough)
Havasi csóka

Probably four records. One confirmed since 1988. Each of single birds, the first shot. With the nearest population being in the Austrian Alps, it is perhaps not surprising that all were in Transdanubia.
STATUS IN HUNGARY: Very rare vagrant. Protected.
STATUS INTERNATIONALLY: Palearctic species. European population probably stable.
DISTRIBUTION AND TIMING: Four records: Döröske, Vas County, 24 January, 1933. Egervár, Zala County, 17 November, 1935. Velem, Kőszeg hills, Vas County, 11 February, 1985. Nyergesújfalu, Komárom County, 16 September, 1990.

Chough *Pyrrhocorax pyrrhocorax* (Red-billed Chough)
Havasi varjú

Only one confirmed record. A bird of the continental *erythropthalmus* race shot on Christmas Day 1928. Category B. As the range of the species has contracted in Central Europe, away from Hungary, renewed occurrence seems increasingly less likely.
STATUS IN HUNGARY: Accidental. Protected.
STATUS INTERNATIONALLY: Mainly Palearctic species. European population in decline and considered vulnerable.

DISTRIBUTION AND TIMING: One record: Salgótarján, Nógrád County, 25 December, 1928.

Arctic Redpoll *Carduelis hornemanni* (Hoary Redpoll)
Szürke zsezse

Although there have been some reports, no accepted records in the last 50 years. Two records from the last century, both of the *exilipes* race. Category B.
STATUS IN HUNGARY: Accidental. Protected.
STATUS INTERNATIONALLY: Circumpolar arctic species. Population size and trends unknown.
DISTRIBUTION AND TIMING: Two records: Gubacsipuszta, Budapest, 3 December, 1880. Kőszeg, Vas County, January, 1894.

Two-barred Crossbill *Loxia leucoptera* (White-winged Crossbill)
Szalagos keresztcsőrű

The first Hungarian record of this species was a bird carried home by a cat in Abaúj-Zemplén County. The second, a bird found dead two months later in a conifer forest in Transdanubia. Both Hungarian records relate to dead juvenile females found in 1990, the year of a major European invasion. Race not noted, but presumably the Eurasian *bifasciata*.
STATUS IN HUNGARY: Accidental. Protected.
STATUS INTERNATIONALLY: Holarctic species. Population size and trends unknown.
DISTRIBUTION AND TIMING: Two records: Juvenile female, Sátoraljaújhely, 12 September, 1990. Juvenile female, Biatorbágy, Pest County, 16 December, 1990.

Common Rosefinch *Carpodacus erythrinus* (Scarlet Rosefinch)
Karmazsinpirók

With records on the increase and the species breeding tantalisingly close in neighbouring Slovakia, a confirmed Hungarian breeding is eagerly awaited. All 8 accepted records since 1988.
STATUS IN HUNGARY: Vagrant. Protected.
STATUS INTERNATIONALLY: Palearctic species. European population may be increasing.
DISTRIBUTION AND TIMING: 8 records: . Adult female, Fertőrákos, Transdanubia, 24 July, 1990. Adult male, Hortobágy, 20 May, 1992. Two, male and female, Fenékpuszta, Transdanubia, 30 May, 1992. Singing male, Hortobágy, 31 May 1992. Juvenile, Hanság, Transdanubia, 8 August, 1992. Female, Rétszilas, Transdanubia, 22 April, 1994. Adult male, caught, Karcag, 22 May, 1991. Ist-summer male, Egyek, 22 May, 1994.

Pallas's Rosefinch *Carpodacus roseus*
Rózsás pirók

Perhaps not surprisingly, some doubt hangs over the origin of a bird caught in a residential part of Buda in 1850 and which constitutes Hungary's only record. Category B.
STATUS IN HUNGARY: Accidental. Protected.
STATUS INTERNATIONALLY: Siberian breeding species. Population size and trends unknown.
DISTRIBUTION AND TIMING: One record: Istenhegy, Budapest, 1 December, 1850.

Pine Grosbeak *Pinicola enucleator*
Nagy pirók

The only confirmed Hungarian record was a bird shot in the very west of the country in 1928. In 1978, two males and one female were reported, but not confirmed, near Budapest. There is also a report of birds being released after a cagebird event.
STATUS IN HUNGARY: Accidental. Protected.
STATUS INTERNATIONALLY: Holarctic species. European population considered stable.
DISTRIBUTION AND TIMING: One record: Molnaszecsőd, Vas County, Transdanubia, 17 January, 1928.

Pine Bunting *Emberiza leucocephala*
Fenyősármány

The only Hungarian record is of a male caught at a ringing camp in 1986.
STATUS IN HUNGARY: Accidental. Protected.
STATUS INTERNATIONALLY: Breeding range almost totally within Eastern Palearctic. Small Western Palearctic population probably stable.
DISTRIBUTION AND TIMING: One record: Male, Barlahida, Zala County, 1 January, 1986.

Little Bunting *Emberiza pusilla*
Törpesármány

Both records of this quite recent addition to Hungary's list concern single birds in the autumn. The first was a juvenile and once again a bird caught at a ringing camp.
STATUS IN HUNGARY: Accidental. Protected.
STATUS INTERNATIONALLY: Palearctic species. European population stable.
DISTRIBUTION AND TIMING: Two records: Juvenile, Ócsa, Pest County, 7 November, 1988. Adult, Kunkápolnás marsh, Hortobágy, 22 October, 1990.

BIBLIOGRAPHY

Agárdi, E. (1952-1955) A hajnalmadár Magyarországon. *Aquila* 59-62: 287-294.
Agárdi, E. (1958) Megfigyeléseim a balkáni gerés a balkáni fakopáncs délkelet-dunántúli és észak-őkelet-magyarországi előfordulásáról. *Aquila* 65:286-287.
Andrési, P. (1989) Az örvös rigó (*Turdus torquatus*) előfordulása Magyarországon 1975 és 1984 között. *Madártani tájékoztató 1989*: január-június: 80.

Bankovics, A. (1974) Újabb adatok a halvány gezéről: *Hippolais pallida*. *Aquila* 80-81: 293.
Bankovics, A. (1976) Megfigyeléseim a hajnalmadárról. *Aquila* 83: 143-149.
Bankovics, A. (1991) Szalagos keresztcsörű Magyarországon. *Aquila* 98: 184.
Bankovics, A. *Magyarország madarainak névjegyzéke*. (In prep.).
Bársony, G. (1958) Balkáni fakopáncs előfordulása Miskolcon. *Aquila* 65: 290.
Birding World Complete List of the Birds of the Western Palearctic. (1995).

Clement, P., Harris, A., and Davis, J. (1993) *Finches & Sparrows: An Identification Guide*. Helm. London.
Cramp, S., Simmons, K. E. L., and Perrins, C. M.(eds) (1977-94) *The Birds of the Western Palearctic*. Vol.I-IX. OUP, Oxford.
Csaba, J. (1955) A balkáni fakopáncs terjeszkedése Vas megyében. *Aquila* 59-62: 388.

Danko, S. (1994) Occurance and Nesting of Pygmy Cormorant (*Phalacrocorax pygmeus*) in the Slovak Republic and in Neighbouring Countries. *Aquila* 101: 53-64.
Dorning, H. (1944) A balkáni fakopáncs Csömörön. *A Természet* 40: 68.
Dudás, M., and Sándor, I. (1993) A pusztai ölyv (*Buteo rufinus*) fészkelése a Hortobágyon. *Aquila* 100: 272-273.

Faragó, S. (1994) Az ugartyúk (*Burhinus oedicnemus*) fészkelése a Moson-síkon. *Aquila* 101: 216-218.
Fatér, I. (1994) Túzokvédelem az élőhelyeken. *Madártávlat* 1. 2.
Fenyvesi, L. (1992) Szürke gém (*Ardea cinerea*) és vörösgém (*Ardea purpurea*) hibridizációk Dinnyésen. *Aquila* 99: 170-171.
Firmánszky, G. (1989) Az uhu Magyarországon (Unpublished report)
Fenyvesi, L. (1995) 1994-es költési eredmények Dinnyésről. *Madártani Tájékoztató 1995*. Január-június: 14-15.

Gorman, G. (1990) A dictionary of bird names in three languages. *Aquila* 96-97: 139-147.
Gorman, G. (1994) The Rose-coloured Starling invasion, and breeding in Hungary. *Birding World* Vol.7. No. 8: 316-318.
Gorman, G. (1991) *A Guide To Birdwatching In Hungary*. Corvina, Budapest.
Gorman, G. (1994) *Where To Watch Birds In Eastern Europe*. Hamlyn, London.
Gorman, G. (1995) Display of Great Bittern. *British Birds* Vol.88, No.1: 47.
Greschik, J. (1938) A balkáni fakopáncs előőfordulása és fészkelése a Magyar Alföldőn. *Kócsag* 9-11: 84-93.
Gretton, A. (1991) The ecology and conservation of the Slender-billed Curlew (*Numenius tenuirostris*). Cambridge, UK. ICBP (Monogr.6).
Győry, J., and Schmidt, E. (1960-1961) A balkáni halvány geze terjeszkedése és megjelenése Magyarországon. *Aquila* 67-68: 17-25.

Hadarics, T. (1993) A sivatagi lile (*Charadrius leschenaultii*) első megfigyelése Magyarországon. *Aquila* 100: 274-276.
Hadarics, T., Mogyorósi, S., and Pellinger, A. (1993) Vöröscsillagos kékbegy (*Luscinia s. svecica*) első bizonyított előfordulása Magyarországon. *Madártani Tájékoztató 1993*: január-június: 26.
Hadarics, T., Mogyorósi, S., and Pellinger, A. (1993) Réti fülesbagoly (*Asio flammeus*) költése a Fertő-tó vidékén. *Aquila* 100: 277-278.
Haraszthy, L. (ed.) (1984) *Magyarország fészkelő madarai*. Natura, Budapest.
Haraszthy, L. (ed.) (1988) *Magyarország madár-vendégei*. Natura, Budapest.
Harrison, P. (1985) *Seabirds: An Identification Guide*. Helm, London.

Kalotás, Z. (1985) A vetési varjú (*Corvus frugilegus*) táplálkozása és gazdasági jelentösége Magyarországon. *Aquila* 92: 175-237.
Kalotás, Z., and Pintér, A. (1984) A gyöngybagoly fehér mellü alfajának (*Tyto alba alba*) fészkelése Tolna megyében. *Aquila* 91: 17-18.
Kasza, F. (1994) Üstökös réce (*Netta rufina*) fészkelése a szegedi Fehér-tón. *Madártani Tájékoztató 1994*: január-június: 20.
Keve, A. (1948-1951) A balkáni fakopáncs terjeszkedése a Dunántúlon. *Aquila* 55-58: 246.
Keve, A. (1952-1955) A balkáni fakopáncs terjeszkedése Európában. *Aquila* 59-62: 299-305.
Keve, A. (1984) *Magyarország madarainak névjegyzéke*. Akadémia, Budapest.
Király, A. (1991) *Stork Protection on Electric Works*. Budapest.

Kovács, G. (1991) Migration of Dotterels in the Hortobágy. *Aquila* 98: 83-94.

Kovács, G. (1991) Törpe sármány (*Emberiza pusilla*) megfigyelése a Hortobágyon. *Madártani Tájékoztató 1991*: július-december: 31.

Kovács, G. (1994) Ritka partimadárfajok növekvő előfordulása a Hortobágyon. *Aquila* 101: 218-220.

Kovács, G. (1994) Population Increase and Expansion of the Aquatic Warbler (*Acrocephalus paludicola*) on the Hortobágy between 1977 and 1994. *Aquila* 101: 133-139.

Madge, S., and Burn, H. (1992) *Wildfowl: An Identification Guide to the Ducks, Geese and Swans of the World*. Helm, London.

Madge, S., and Burn, H. (1993) *Crows and Jays*. Helm, London.

Magyar, G.(1988) Az ékfarkú lile (*Charadrius vociferus*) első megfigyelése Magyarországon. *Aquila* 95: 182-184.

Magyar, G. (1992) *A Birder's Field Checklist of the Birds of Hungary*. Lake Helen.

Magyar, G. (1995) Adatok az északi búvár és a sarki búvár egymáshoz viszonyított előfordulási gyakoriságához. *Füzike* 8: 6-8, május, 1995.

Márkus, F. (1994) in *The Nature of Farming*: 26-27. IEEP, London.

Mikkola, H. (1983) *Owls of Europe*. Poyser, Calton.

Müller, I., and Fenyvesi, L. (1991) Az üstökös réce (*Netta rufina*) megtelepedése Dinnyésen. *Madártani Tájékoztató 1991*. Január-június: 12.

Pátkai, I. (1948-1951) Balkáni fakopáncs a Mátrában. *Aquila* 55-58: 245.

Pellinger, A., and Mogyorósi, S. (1994) Mesterséges szigetek küszvágó csérek (*Sterna hirundo*) számára. *Aquila* 101: 220-221.

Peterson, R.T. *et al*. (1986) *Európa Madarai*. Gondolat, Budapest.

Radetzky, J. (1977) A kék-fú (*Porphyrio porphyrio*) magyarországi megfigyelése. *Aquila* 83: 183-185.

Rékási, J., and Kerényi, Z. (1992) Hajnalmadár (*Tichodroma muraria*) Pannonhalmán. *Madártani Tájékoztató 1992*. Július-december: 25.

Rose, Paul M. (ed.) 1995, *Western Palearctic and South West Asia Waterfowl Census 1994*. IWRB Publ.35.

Schmidt, A. (1986-1987) Cifra pehelyréce (*Somateria spectabilis*) a visegrádi Dunán. *Aquila* 93-94: 309.

Schmidt, A. (1990) Keresztcsőrű (*Loxia curvirostra*) adatok az Alföldröl.*Madártani tájékoztató 1990*: július-december: 47.

Schmidt, E. (1992) Áttelelö barátkák (*Sylvia atricapilla*). *Madártani Tájékoztató 1992*. Január-június: 13.

Sterbetz, I. (1974) Dögkeselyű Békés megyében. *Aquila* 78-79: 226.

Streit, B., and Kalotás, Z. (1987) Adatok a füleskuvik (*Otus scops*) fészkelésbiológiájához. *Aquila* 93-94: 279-286.

Szabó, L., and Győry, J. (1962) Csíz fészkelése a Bükk hegységben. *Aquila* 67-68: 141-146.

Szimuly, G. (1994) Vándor partfutók (*Calidris melanotos*) Naszály-Ferencmajorban. *Aquila* 101: 212-213.

Székely, T. (1991) Status and breeding biology of Kentish Plovers in Hungary: a progress report. *Wader Study Group Bull*. 62: 17-23.

Székely, T. (1992) Reproduction of Kentish Plovers *Charadrius alexandrinus* in grasslands and fishponds: the habitat mal-assessment hypothesis. *Aquila* 99: 59-68.

Székely, T., and Lessells, C.M. (1993) Mate change by Kentish Plovers *Charadrius alexandrinus*. *Ornis Scand*. 24: 317-322.

Szép, T. (1991) A Tisza magyarországi szakaszán fészkelő partifecske (*Riparia riparia*) állomány eloszlása és egyedszáma. *Aquila* 98: 111-124.

Szép, T., and Barta, Z. (1991) The threat to Bank Swallows from the Hobby at a large colony. *The Condor* 94: 1022-1025.

Szép, T. (1991) The Present and Historical Situation of the Corncrake in Hungary. *Die Vogelwelt*, Heft/1-2.

Tömösváry, T. (ed.) (1995) *Boronkai Füzetek*: II.1995 1.szám. Magyarországi rétisasvédelmi konferencia.

Tardy, J. (1994) *Természetvédelem 1994*. KTMTvH. Budapest.

Tóth, A. (ed.) (1988) *Tudományos kutatások a Hortobágyi Nemzeti Parkban 1976-1985*. OKTH, Budapest.

Tucker, G.M., and Heath, M.F. (1994) *Birds in Europe: their conservation status*. BirdLife, Cambridge.

Varga, F. (1994) *Cuckoo Observations Around The Source Of the River Zagyva*. Salgótarján.

Varga, F. (1995) Magányosan fészkelő gyurgyalagok (*Merops apiaster*). *Madártani Tájékoztató*, 1995, január-június: 30-31.

Varga, Z. (1991) Az Aggteleki Nemzeti Park császármadár állománya. *Aquila* 98: 57-70.

Vasvári, M. (1930) Új harkály a magyar faunában. *Állattani Közlemények* XXVII: 93-96.

Vizslán, T. (1989) Fenyőrigó (*Turdus pilaris*) fészkelések 1987-ben Sajóecsegén és Boldván. *Madártani Tájékoztató 1989*: január-június: 77.

Voous, K.H. (1991) *List of Recent Holarctic Bird Species*. BOU, London.

Waliczky, Z., Magyar, G., and Hraskó, G. (1983) A sövénysármány (*Emberiza cirlus*) újabb előfordulása Magyarországon. *Aquila* 90: 73-79.

Waliczky, Z. (1991) *Európai jelentőségű madárélöhelyek Magyarországon*. Budapest.

Zsoldos, Á. (1987) Kucsmás poszáta (*Sylvia melanocephala*) első megkerülése Magyarországon. *Aquila* 93-94: 313.

INDEX

ENGLISH NAMES

SCIENTIFIC NAMES